W9-BCB-901

The American
Immigration Collection

I am a Woman —and a Jew

ELISABETH G. STERN

(pseud., Leah Morton)

Arno Press and The New York Times

NEW YORK 1969

*

Library of Congress Catalog Card No. 69-18791

*

Reprinted from a copy in the
Columbia University Libraries

*

Manufactured in the United States of America

I AM A WOMAN —AND A JEW

I AM A WOMAN —AND A JEW

by Leah Morton

"With the wind of God in her vesture, proclaiming the deathless, ever-soaring spirit of man."—Locke

NEW YORK

MANUFACTURED COMPLETE BY THE
KINGSPORT PRESS
KINGSPORT, TENNESSEE
United States of America

TO

KARL EDWIN HARRIMAN

I AM A WOMAN —AND A JEW

I

I REMEMBER looking down at the face of my father, beautiful and still in death, and for a brief, terrible moment feeling my heart rise up —surely it was in a strange, suffocating relief?—as the realization came to me: "Now I am free!" All my life, for twenty-nine years, he had stood like an image of fine-carved stone, immovable, unbending, demanding that I submit my will and my thought, my every act in life, to the creed he represented. His creed was that of Judaism, brought to the twentieth century from the fifteenth, and held with an intensity and a passionate faith that would destroy everything in his life, the very happiness of his children, that it might not be, in one small observance, unhonored.

I looked from his features, at peace at last, to those of the man near me, my husband, whose tender eyes met mine with the love that he has given me abundantly, and with the sacrifice of everything else in his life to it. My husband's eyes were tender, but they were not sad, not brimming with the bitter loss that lay in my mother's glance, nor even with the deep sorrow that shone in the tears of the bearded rabbis and of the pious merchants about the bier. He could not feel near, nor even really unhappy over the passing of the man who, though he had been father to his wife, had lived in a world utterly removed from his own. My husband's people have been Christians for many generations: his grandmother, though born a Jewess, became a Christian when she married. His associations and memories are built on repression in human intercourse, on a tolerant acceptance of dogma in others, even Jews, but with no deathless need for it. To him the passion of my father, as well as the somber exaltation of my father's friends now about his lifeless body, were alike incomprehensible, despite his gentle acknowledgment of the right each has to build his creed, and to believe in it and practice it. He was a stranger in that room of death, that stranger I had brought into my father's life, when I had joined his life with mine.

I had thought that, by marrying a Christian, I, who was in my heart no longer a Jew, would be free. I was to find not only that on that day of my father's death, but twice again, how mistaken I had been.

The first clear impression of my childhood is that of a warm day in summer. My mother, in her puffed sleeves and tight-fitting dress, walked near my father, in his long coat and high hat; for he was assistant to the rabbi in our city. We children—there were five of us—trudged behind our parents, looking neither to right nor left, but plodding steadily ahead. We dared not stop, for that would annoy father.

Presently mother looked around, and with her sweet, rosy face crinkling into her little smile that we children loved, she said staidly, to father, "I shall have to wipe Simeon's nose; the little scamp has a cold." Father stopped, quietly, not turning around. We children relaxed, halted in our tracks and waited while she administered to dimpled roly-poly Simeon. Simeon did not look then like the highly aggressive young business man he now is! Mother patted each of us—Etta, with her golden hair and Spanish skin (inherited from mother's own grandmother); Hannah, with her brown curls and sleepy hazel eyes (exactly like our father's); Robert, all dark splendor (like our father's father); and I, very tall for my age, very thin, with enormous brown eyes, an excessively high forehead that we all thought the acme of homeliness, and a funny nose that had neither the exquisite delicate curve of Hannah's, nor the round impudence of Simeon's, but was only a sort of parody of the Polish noses servants had. They called me the "Polak," because I was quick and vivid, dreamy and intense, and sometimes obstinate as a stupid Polish servant who will not see what her betters tell her. When my father said quietly, "Do thus," and I asked, "Why?" he would look at me with his deep glance and reply, conclusively, "Do not be a little Polak." I would meekly submit, realizing that I, alone, of all the children resisted him. When I did not, however, his eyes would grow cold as two amber stones, and he would wait, without speaking, until his will had conquered mine.

To-day I was so tired! I was so thin that sometimes mother said she felt a wind would blow me away. I was too eager for books, to eat. And we were so poor that sometimes there was actually not enough to eat for the five of us. I looked piteously at mother, and she put her hand in her pocket, drew out a sweetmeat and, quietly, with her little dimpling smile, gave us each one. She put her finger on her lip, and went back to father. It was a sin to eat the sweetmeats. We were fasting that day and were not to eat, not even to wet our mouths with so much as a sip of water, until sundown. I, who was thirteen, was particularly responsible for keeping the rule. I looked at my candy. My mother glanced back. Her face was mischievous and yet curiously sober under her "sheitel," prescribed for pious Jewish women. It was as if she asked God to take lightly the sin we committed.

"Let us walk on, Isaiah," she said to father, and we went on quietly. We were going to the river on the city's outskirts. (On holidays we were, of course, not allowed to ride, and therefore trudged the five miles.) We came at last to the river's edge. There our father stood, and waited a moment. His face, as always when he prayed, became exalted, unbelievably beautiful, its paleness glowing with a sort of still fire of white, his very lips losing color in his religious ecstasy. My grandfather had been, in Poland, one of the group of religious dreamers—Chassidim—who lived in trances, forewent food, and lived (scantily enough) on what pious neighbors gave them. He had been a "holy man," so holy that his touch and prayer were said to have the power of healing.

Our father prayed now. It was, surely, a strange sight. The river along which we stood was the Ohio. Great boats were steaming up its waters; giant loads of steel and iron to build the railroads and the shops and factories of the twentieth century were passing us. Opposite our shore, far in the distance on the other side, burned furnaces of steel. The life of a new world was created here. And my father spoke in a tongue written more than five thousand years ago, prayed as his forefathers on an ancient river, the

Jordan, had prayed, with the same simplicity and unaltered faith. He prayed that his sins should be washed away by the waters before us.

For it was this reason that had taken us all to the river, through the hot, long day. I looked into the muddy waters below us, and at my father. And I felt oddly numb. All my life I had so believed that, even when I resisted him, he was right. But to-day it seemed to me childish and perhaps even silly to stand there, chanting that beautiful old tongue, the Hebrew, that I, too, had been taught, and asking that our sins be washed away.

My mother did not permit the Gentile children in our little street to come into our home. It was not that their parents were working people (they were almost all mill workers) and our father a scholar. He had a real sympathy for and understanding of the honor of labor, which we children have inherited from him for all our lives. Mother did not wish Gentile children in the house because we could not afford to have them. Every time a Gentile child touched a dish, it was, in my father's eyes, defiled, and had to be thrown out. It was simpler and wiser to forbid them the house, mother found. She herself, was conscientiously pious, and though she did not understand much Hebrew (as her daughters did), she religiously used it in daily prayer, and obeyed every one of the precepts a good housewife ought, as set down in the books.

But, though the Gentile children were not permitted in our home, I heard from them some of the things in which they believed. Most of the people near us were Catholics or Presbyterians, for we lived in a small Scotch-Irish city. The Irish believed that if you told the priest what you had done, you would not be punished for your misdeeds. The Presbyterians were so religious that, when they went to church on Sunday, they walked there and back, not using the street car. These Presbyterians my father grudgingly approved: we Jews, also, did not ride on our Sabbath or our holy days; the Presbyterians had only copied us. But when I told him one day of the Catholics, he looked down at me from his tall height, and said, "You can see how foolish and childish ignorant people are. A priest tells them that if they go to him and confess, he can forgive them. Can a sin be undone by a confession or even the wish to undo it?"

And yet here was my father, grave and pleading, sending our sins down the waters of the Ohio.

I looked at him, opened my mouth, but did not speak. I knew he would be angry if I said what I wished to ask. From that day, however, I did not accept anything he told me about our faith until I had analyzed it myself. What I wanted was to practice it as I believed it. But that was, I soon discovered, impossible.

At school with me was one young girl whom I loved most dearly. It was not only that her eyes were clear and blue, beautiful as flowers, and all the eyes I knew among my folks were brown or black or golden. It was not because her skin, fine and white, colored like roses blowing, and all the girls I knew had cheeks of pale olive or white with brilliant scarlet. It was because of her spirit that was as fine as clear water, and her quiet voice, grave and slow, even though she was so young. Because she was a Gentile, a Presbyterian, and I a Jewess, we never saw each other in our homes, but we walked together after school, talking of books, and of the heroes in them, of friends and their doings, and a great deal of religion. Her folks were "blue" Presbyterians, so rigid in their faith that they did not even cook their meals on Sunday, preparing them on Saturday, just as my own mother prepared our meals for our Sabbath on Friday.

My friend's name was Rose, and she spoke of her Lord Jesus as if he were near her, as perhaps he was. "I feel as if he were right with me sometimes," she said once, pausing as if she had just then, indeed, seen him.

We were both approaching fourteen years of age; we were adolescent girls, full of a new life. I did not understand how anyone could believe in Jesus; I had been told how much my people in Galicia and Russia had suffered in his gentle name. But my imagination was captured by Rose's faith and passionate belief.

I told her a story my father had once told me, of a day in which he, a little boy of twelve, had been sent forth, to walk alone the twenty miles to a neighboring town where there was a Rabbinical seminary. His people sent him to live as a "Yeshiva Bochur," a youth studying at the "Yeshiva" and fed, day by day, by kind people, who pledged themselves to give him food. It was a bitter thing for a little boy to do, but my grandfather was too great a scholar to have money, nor would he have had any, indeed, without shame. My father walked quickly and forlornly, and on the way he met a stupid, coarse man who had left the Polish village some time before. There was a story about this man: he was an informant who stole his people's children for Alexander's army. Alexander of Russia decided to press the unwilling Jews into his army, to Christianize them when possible. He did it in a simple way: he razed a Jewish village, stole its youth, sent it off to the camps, and did not let the boys return home until they were of age—and no longer Jews. Hundreds of these children (most of them between twelve and fourteen years of age) never saw their parents again.

My father spoke to the man he met, answering his questions. But his questioner was tipsy. He talked, and he talked much, himself. He was going back, he said, the way father had come, and it was lucky for father he was away—for many of the boys there would make another sort of journey! Father looked at the burly man. He understood, of course, for did not children of his time grow up to fear the man and the dreadful tragedy for which he stood? He bade his companion farewell and walked on. And in the woods he turned back, ran the long miles home, raced into the little synagogue to his uncle who was mystically praying there, warned him that the procuror was on his way to take all the sons in the village. The man came as he was speaking. The crying of little boys could be heard, the terrible cries of their mothers. From the rotting floor of the old synagogue, father ripped some boards. He pushed his brother and two other boys down first, then he, too, crept into the space beneath and replaced the boards over them.

Above their heads they heard the anguish of the town lifted to the ears of God. But it was not until late at night that they crept out, to streets deserted of playmates, to mothers mourning as for the dead.

"I lay in the earth, as if I were buried, a whole day, that I might not become a Gentile," said my father, ending his story.

He went to the Yeshivah, and at seventeen was a teacher there. The intense distrust, the hatred and indignation he felt for that other Jew, Jesus, who had caused so much suffering to his people, were part of my being. The very word "Jesus" was not permitted in our house.

At fourteen I found myself becoming a woman, nervous, high-strung, full of visions. Soon I was to grow broader, to add gentle curves to my gangling girl figure, but I was then emaciated as a young tree in winter. One day I was alone in the house. Every morning, at dawn, my father rose to "read the Torah" in his great books, and all through my girlhood I lived with the sound of his chanting voice, at night the last sound, in the morning the first, as background. My father had finished, and was off to synagogue. My mother was away, with a sick relative, the children with her. I was alone. I stood in front of father's bookcase, lined with Hebrew books, and seemed to feel a presence speak to me. The room grew full with that Presence; it took me and dissolved me, and made me part of it. I fainted. I had seen God. But before I quite lost consciousness, I heard Rose's voice say, as clearly as if she were speaking to me, "Jesus will come to you some day."

I was simply an overwrought little girl, expressing a nervous physical crisis in a not unusual way. But a quarter of a century ago people did not think so of natural occurrences. My father stepped into the room and found me lying unconscious. He picked me up, brought me to.

And, as I realized my surroundings again, I sobbed out, "Jesus! Oh, father, I felt a divine presence and I saw Jesus!"

I have never seen a face more stern, more austere and terrible than his then. He wept.

The old women came in to see me. One old woman

whispered to me a story of a girl she had known in Lithuania who had been possessed of a devil that entered her body, swelled her like a "great balloon," and finally reached her heart, which it bit, and killed her.

Every one in the house knew I had said I saw Jesus. It was not that they believed I had seen Jesus; but I had spoken as if I believed in Him.

It was a long time before my father's eyes lost their hard questioning look, cold and questioning together. We never spoke of it again. I never saw Rose again. At the close of the school year she moved, and thereafter attended another school. Years later, I heard she had become a missionary in China, that she was fanatically religious, devoting her life to her work with the single mindedness of a nun, and with a nun's austerity.

But from that day, I was no longer really a Jewess. I had seen a vision of God, and He had been awful. So awful had He been that my heart had lost life as I beheld Him.

II

I MEANT to make my life beautiful. I did not quite know how, but I meant to make it rich and —free.

I used to tell myself that, when I was a big girl, sixteen perhaps, I would be free. I would do as I believed I ought then, and not as I was told.

I religiously observed all the rules of religious life, though they no longer meant anything to me. It was not necessary for me to observe them, for my father never supervised me. But it would have seemed to me I was untrue to the thing *he* believed if I failed to do as he believed. I prayed three times a day (even taking my Hebrew book to high school, though I was terrified lest some fellow student should find what the book was through the words which my lips moved in study period). I tied my handkerchief about my wrist on Saturdays, rather than put it in my pocket; for the Law says one may not carry a handkerchief, even in a pocket, but clothing one may wear. I did not eat meat on bread spread with butter, for milk and meat together are forbidden. I did not speak to the Gentile boys at high school.

I thought of myself as very homely, as indeed I was. Hannah and Etta had grown to be lovely, in prescribed Semitic fashions, one plump and fair, the other like a languorous rose of Sharon. I looked like a studious boy who did not have enough to eat, and happened to be masquerading in pigtails.

In my day the flapper had not arrived. Sex was not a newspaper word. Love meant marriage. Liquor meant damnation. Divorce meant disgrace. Young girls did not hear any of these words spoken by their elders in their presence.

For all that, we knew just as much of life as the girl of to-day, though perhaps not so truthfully. We were entering life, and were curious about it. In our biology class, our teacher, fair and plump and always slightly moist, spoke to us of animals, plants, amœba, worms, and even the bony structure of a cat—and then closed the semester. But some of the girls told one another what they knew. In the skating parties, girls and boys met, and if they kissed, the rest did not tell. There was never a party held without the "kissing games" of all kinds.

I was not permitted to go to the parties. They were in Gentile homes, and I would not be permitted to so much as drink from a cup they had defiled. On Friday evenings the rest of the class went to a weekly party, but I was not permitted even to see them dance. However, I did not really care. Though I no longer believed in my father's faith, it was beautiful to me. Friday evening was an evening of glamor and loveliness.

We were poor, so poor that sometimes, to go to high school, I had to get up in the morning, wash my blouse and iron it; for I had no other. After school I sewed for a neighbor, or taught Hebrew to a slow boy who was preparing to "enter the Covenant"—which I, a mere female, had never been asked to do. For lunch at high school I used to take bread and nothing else, and drink water. I used to pretend that I would not eat ice cream or candy as did the other girls, because they were not made by Hebraic laws regulating food; but I did not tell that I might have brought with me sweets so made by manufacturers of my own faith.

On Friday nights, however, I sat at the white tablecloth (the rest of the week it was checked) with my father sitting near the six glowing candles in the brilliantly polished brass candlesticks which my great-grandmother had lighted in her day, too. My mother wore the pretty close-fitting dress that was her "holiday dress," and a frilled apron over it, with hand-made embroidery bordering its hem. We all sat in spotless Sabbath cleanliness, and waited until the prayer over the homemade wine, and homemade bread, had been made by father and by each of the beggars he had collected after synagogue had closed. Then we ate—gefüllte fish, chicken soup, chicken boiled to the consistency of cheesecloth, sweets and nuts with raisins for dessert. Sometimes the beggars were very hungry. Once a wanderer from Rumania ate my portion, Etta's, and would have eaten Simeon's, too, but Simeon stopped him by a piteous wail. When the strangers ate my sisters' food and mine, mother would look at us, twinkle her dark eyes, and we would shrug resignedly, and eat white bread and wine, pretending we were not interested in food. But there was no need to pretend; the guests did not so much as notice us, who were only girls.

Then, after the meal, came the time we loved. The strangers told tales of strange lands—Rumania, Hungary, Austria, Galicia, Turkey and that one place of which father spoke with a throb in his voice, Palestine.

Then we would have the Sabbath songs, "Zmirras"—sweet and old, some as old as the memory of the modern Jew, brought from far, far lands, to our table—sung in Hebrew. Presently my father would take his huge books down, and, though I was only a girl and knew better than to ask questions or even to speak, I would listen to old tales, hear the old men arguing over the interpretations of a word or a commentary in the Talmud, and sit as if at a play long told, and told for me again. Mother would sit, too, her eyes full of wonder, of love, never leaving my father's face, for she adored him and thought him the greatest of all humankind.

But one day, one Friday in winter, as I came into my classroom, some one stopped me at the door and blocked my way. I looked up into a pair of cheerful blue eyes and I saw a handsome, boyish face with a friendly smile. That was a Christian boy in my class, a very nice boy, whose name was not Irish, like the names of many others, but was taken out of American history. Let us say it was Wayne, for it is as historic.

He flushed as he stopped me, and said, "Look here, say—would you like to come to—I mean, won't you come to the Friday dance with me, Leah?"

He might have shot me and given me less of a shock. The party Friday night, with a Gentile boy! He added that he would come for me whenever I wished, and we could take the car from near my house.

A Gentile Boy! "I—I don't ride on Friday. It's my—our Sabbath, you know," I stammered. "I'm—you know I'm a Jewess, don't you?"

His blue eyes danced. "Oh, well, your last name isn't Irish, you know!"

I had not ever thought it was funny to talk about being Jewish; one took it very seriously indeed. One set one's self apart. But I could not resist smiling with him.

"I don't dance," I added then.

His face clouded. "You mean you don't want to go with me?" he asked.

I knew very little, indeed, about men then, for I answered, with wonder, "Why, you're the most—the most popular boy in the class—and I'm the homeliest girl—"

Perhaps he, too, did not know the rules by which he, as a man, was to be ruled later, for he blushed deeply, and said, "Oh, rot!"

We both seemed to find nothing further to add to that. But he looked down at me, and said quickly, "I think you're—sweet. I like you a lot. That's the truth, and you don't mush, either."

It was the first time I had ever thought of myself as interesting to a man. It was more thrilling than being asked to a dance, for dances are crowds, and "You are sweet" was *myself*. At a dance, even if some one took you, he might go to another girl for all the dances, but who could take from me the discovery: "You are sweet"?

"I'll—I'll ask my mother!" I whispered, running off with my pigtails flying.

My mother would not hear of it.

"What? Go out Sabbath evening? They play music, even if they don't dance. The men who play music break the Sabbath. You would be a party to their breaking the Sabbath. And what would I say to your father about your being away on Friday night?

Who ever heard of any one being away Friday night?"

It seemed unanswerable.

I did not go to the dance, nor to any dance on Friday night all through high school.

But twice a month was held a "chapel dance," on Monday afternoons. Something I had not wanted before seemed suddenly valuable, indispensable to me. I wanted fun, pleasure, young friends.

I had been working hard. I was doing my school work, helping at home, working to earn money for my expenditures, and teaching sometimes. Play had never occurred to me. When I was small, oh, up to eight or nine, I had played when mother did not need me. But since I was twelve I had been like a little woman in the house. I lived only for books. I read, and read, without stopping, all through the library, shelf after shelf, and then back again, in the Juvenile room, and then began on the Adult room as soon as the kind librarian would let me. My father did not approve of my going to high school. It was time for me to think of marrying a pious man. He and mother disagreed about it—their one quarrel—but I was going to high school.

It was, perhaps, due to my going to high school, mother said, gently and dubiously, that I wanted something new. I wanted to dance, to play, to have fun just like the other girls in my classes. I didn't mean to go to work at fourteen or fifteen, marry at sixteen, be a mother at eighten and an old woman at thirty. I wanted a new thing—happiness. I was different from my sisters, who thought of marrying as soon as possible.

My mother drew fine dark brows together. There is no need to say in words how dear she had always been, how understanding, how much a friend. She had the rare quality of understanding childhood, even in her own children. And she had not forgotten her own girlhood. She smiled at me, her quick, characteristic smile, that lifted the corners of her mouth into dimples.

"I remember," she said, "what happened when I tried to dance! Grandfather, you know, was rabbi in a little town. There was a wedding, and, after he had gone, the young people gathered and began to dance, not the sensible square dances, but a polka. My cousin from Königsburg had brought it over, the scamp!

"I stood looking—I was only sixteen or so—my feet itching. Suddenly, I jumped into the middle of the room, let some one clasp me, and began to dance! It was—well, it was wonderful! And then, as suddenly, the room seemed to grow dead still, so still! I felt something hot and stinging on my cheek, and something hot and wet follow it. Grandfather had come back and found me dancing the polka with a man's arms around me, me a girl old enough to marry! He slapped me smartly, and I wept, and went home. That was the only time I ever danced!"

She laughed, her lips crinkling as she stopped.

She took my face in her little hands, round and soft, in spite of her constant work.

"You shall learn to dance," she said, "my daughter!"

And dance I did. I learned to dance in what, I suppose, was a dreadful public dance hall, for I paid a quarter a lesson there, once every Wednesday night, and I danced with the lady instructor when she thought of me; but I faithfully put my foot out—one, two, three, and turn—as the long line of men and women learned the steps of the waltz. I learned to two-step, and to schottische, and even—wild days, those—to do the barn dance. Mother took me to the hall, and came to take me back home at eleven.

Then I went to a dance. I went with the blue-eyed boy, and wore a dress of mother's cut down and made to fit me. I did not tell her I was going with a Gentile. I simply told her I was going to a dance at school.

My swain met me after school, and we walked up together to the chapel, there to talk until the pianist arrived, for we had no brass bands then. The room became crowded. He put out his arms, and said, "Shall we dance?"

Before me came my father's face, still and austere. I felt something chill me.

"Oh, Jack," I said, "I—I don't feel well. I'm going home."

And home I went. I could not dance with a Gentile.

III

I THOUGHT Jack would never see me again, but he sent me a book instead, a book called "Elsie Venner," which I thought highbrow of him. I felt unhappy, though; surely one returned another book, and we could not afford such an expenditure. I apologized to Jack, to his wonder, I think.

Then, one day, the school was electrified. In the school was one girl more vivid, not more beautiful but more alive, than the rest, Ethel Carter. Her hair was like a dense, dark velvet cap, her eyes brilliant dark birds in her face. She let the boys kiss her when she danced with them. Her father was divorced from her mother. One morning, early, the chapel was electrified by a policeman coming into the room, calling out Ethel's name, and taking her away. That was before the day of juvenile courts. Ethel had stolen from one of the stores.

The newspapers were full of it. And something dreadful came out, that Ethel's name had been "Cantor," before it was changed by her father to "Carter"; they were Jews with "changed names." The Yiddish papers mentioned them with regret.

My father put down his paper, and spoke with scorn: "This is the sort of Jew they say is American, who changes his face, changes his name; and he changes, too, the honor standards of Jewish womanhood for his daughter." My own father had not changed his name, nor his face by shaving off the beard required by Mosaic law. Only *I* had almost disgraced the honor of Jewish womanhood, by dancing with a Gentile!

Young people learn only from those who are their teachers, their parents included. I thought then that to loosen the lines that set me apart as a Jewess would be only to dishonor. The story of Ethel had implications which the newspapers hinted at—another person, a man, was one of them.

But the story of Ethel had hardly been forgotten when another burst into print. A teacher in one of the schools where the principal was thought the most honorable man in the school, gave birth to his child. She killed herself and the child, and in her desk was found a letter addressed to him, pleading with him to help her, to let her go to his wife for aid.

The newspapers filled columns with the story. Here was a girl not a Jewess, and her shame was not less than Ethel's. Could it be, I wondered, that dishonor and shame came from one's self, and had nothing at all to do with religious divisions kept or broken? This second girl had been a Gentile, and the man was Gentile, too.

I did not know of love, or the meaning of passion. I had never even danced with a man, and I was almost eighteen. My heroes were in Tennyson's poems, in the novels of Thackeray and George Eliot and Zangwill. I could not understand what would be enough to sweep a girl to her shame.

I was working in the evening at a settlement in our city, in charge of one of the clubs. My girls were nearly of my age, and many of them lived in the streets near my home, for we did not move from the

Ghetto of our city to which my father had come when first he arrived as an immigrant.

In the settlement were other workers, too, some of them at college and one other, like myself, at high school. This one was much older than the rest of the club leaders, for he had come to America as an adult, had worked in a factory, and was now, belatedly, obtaining an education. One of the young men was big and burly, with hair in fair curls around his head and keen, cruel gray eyes. He was brilliant, a remarkable student, and a great career was predicted for him. He enjoyed bringing groups of young men together, drawing them into a discussion, and then, mercilessly, stripping the words of one after the other to their absurd beginnings. "You ought to be a lawyer," the victims often would say feebly. He was to be a surgeon, however.

One evening there was a festival at the settlement house, and the club leaders held a sort of party after it. The young medical student, Myer, was organizing it with zest, with the compelling power he imposed on every one he met. Suddenly he came into my clubroom, where I was speaking to a last girl who lingered.

"Will you come to our 'spread'?" he asked. "It's to to be in the upstairs office."

He went out before I could answer, and I could hear him repeat the same words in the clubroom next to mine.

I came in a little late. The room was crowded, the young club leaders laughing and dancing with abandon there. I had before arranged dances for my club girls, where we danced decorously together. But this was a party, and the first party of which I had ever felt part. These were all young Jewish people, my own people. But, amazingly, they were reacting precisely as did other young people I saw in the chapel. In corners men whispered to girls, and the girls giggled and blushed, protested and leaned forward again. The Jewish girls did not seem different as girls because of their Jewishness. Dancing, the boys strutted and whirled just as the Gentile boys did. On a chair in the corner sat a big young man, drawing a fair, pretty girl to his knee.

She leaped up, sprang away, and her hair fell in a heavy cascade of pale gold, strange among all those dark heads, to her knees.

"Oh, you shiska!" some one cried. She laughed, and put it up again. This girl was Helen Cohen. Her father had married a Gentile. I was forbidden to speak to her.

The young man from whom she had fled strolled over to me and stood a moment, then said, shortly, "Want to dance?" He was the student Myer, who had invited me to this celebration.

I grew red and moved away, but at that he turned, laughed and said, apologetically, "I didn't mean it that way! Please don't be the average young lady! I meant, did you want to dance, too—I do! Please!"

It had not occurred to me to be "the average young lady." But I said I would be glad to dance, and I moved forward with him. It was the first time a man had danced with me. The dance of romance then was the waltz of the "Blue Danube," and we moved to that. Again and again we danced, I did not know how many times. Above me smiled the small quick gray eyes, the full handsome mouth; his yellow head shone in the light each time we passed under the chandelier. When it was time to go home, it seemed to me that I had been in a strange dream, full of movement, of shining gold and gray.

My mother was waiting for me when I came home, and she greeted my new friend. She knew his mother, and his aunts, and all his cousins, it developed. She smiled, her little crinkling smile, as he told her, eagerly, he meant to come again: "I'm going to camp on your front stoop!"

She answered, "Well, if that's as far as you want to go, Myer!"

But he wanted to go much further, into my heart, into my life. He took possession of every hour I had free from school. He opened a world to me. He quoted Bernard Shaw with the strange passion young men used to have for that oracle; he read "The Master Builder" and "Peer Gynt" to me. He discovered for me my mind, and let me see his own.

One day we walked through the park outside the city, into the sunset, it seemed, and his hand went out and took mine, and I let it stay there. It seemed a solemn and a great moment to me. We walked all the way home without a word.

In the evening I looked toward the door of my clubroom, and there he stood, his gray eyes masterful and dominating. I went out into the little hall and pressed my face against the window opening into the pitch-dark courtyard. The world seemed so beautiful, so rich, that my very body seemed to me to be lifted out, into that dark, mysterious space. I felt my face turned and looked up into Myer's gray eyes.

"Will you kiss me?" he asked.

My nose was smudged with the dust on the window, and he brushed the dust away, smiling down at me, while I submitted quietly.

"Will you, now?" he asked.

But I felt my eyes fill with tears, as if he had asked me to desecrate a holy moment, and I could just whisper: "Not now—not until some day, Myer."

His face darkened, and he took my hands in his. He looked at me with the same possessiveness that my father held in his glance, as if I must obey. I remember that my lips trembled, and I said, "Don't ask me now, Myer, I don't feel—I don't feel that I can—kiss yet."

My mother heard of my engagement with concern. The family had been thinking of a husband for me, and there was one already all but chosen, a young student, the son of a rabbi, and to be a rabbi himself. Myer's father was only a merchant. Myer was not religious.

But I would not promise "to break with him."

It seemed to me that by choosing Myer I was, vaguely, finding a way to myself. The "little Polak" in me came out. I stood obstinately, hearing of no one but Myer. I would not listen to recriminations, scoldings, warnings.

We went for a walk one day, a long spring day, hand in hand, to read and lunch and talk. We took "Paracelsus" with us, for I had entered college now, and felt I understood the world's riddle. We sat on the green grass, Myer lying flat, I sitting with my book in my hand, reading the limpid lines of the poem. But suddenly Myer's hand went out, and he closed the book. He looked at me and said, quietly, "Will you kiss me to-day, Leah?" He took a blade of grass and touched my sunburned young arm with it, lightly, and a flush passed over my whole face and neck, a hot burn.

"Don't!" I whispered.

He grew red, too. I got up, and walked quickly away.

I could not explain it to him, but when he touched my arm so, as if it were his right to touch me so, I felt as if something sacred were violated—myself. I could not give myself so, even to him to touch.

It was my mother who ended the story. She told me that Myer was an atheist. She had asked him, and he had answered he did not believe in God.

"Would you marry such a man?" she asked.

For a moment I wanted to say, yes, I would. Then I would be free to find out whether I believed in God, or whether I were an atheist, too. But I thought of his hand and the green blade of grass touching my arm. A wave of repulsion passed over me. Was that love, and marriage, too? I did not know then more than the romantic descriptions of love I had read in poems and novels.

"I'll not marry him, mother," I said, and added, "not because he's an atheist, mother, no. But because I think I'm not capable of loving anyone enough to give up—anything I want for him."

It was not atheism I wanted. I would not, however, give myself, even to a Jew and one who was an atheist beside, if love did not seem beautiful to me. I must find what I believed. But when I found love, too, it must be beautiful, not afraid, shrinking, as with Myer. Some day it would come. If not, I told myself, there were other things great, beside love. There was fame, a great world outside to discover!

IV

I HAD planned to be a doctor, because that was what Myer wished, but as soon as I was free of my engagement I realized what I really wanted—to be a writer. My teacher at school was a young Princeton man, only recently out of college himself. He had lived through four very bitter years at college. He had been a proud young Jew among people whom he felt to be his inferiors, and who yet had the power to scorn and wound him. He was handsome in a magnificent way, like my own young brother Robert, dark and splendid, the Hebraic features adapted to the American background, as so often happens in the young American Jew. He was gifted, not with the irony of the Jew, as was Myer, but with the whimsical humor that created the poems of Rosenfeld. If he had been a poet in the Ghetto, he would have been supremely happy, expressing himself with genius. But he had the pride of a young prince, and the appearance of one, and lived the humiliation of the outcast.

His classmates had not been amused by him, as by others of the young Jews seeking favor and ingratiating themselves. He had walked like Absalom among them. He would not accept the ordinary honors—scholastic. He won his way to the rowing team, on the track team. He'd show these Gentiles he could do the things they did, and were proud of—even if he had to destroy himself to do so.

But though he left with a letter on his jersey, to be worn on his breast, he left without a real friend, except in one instance, when a young New Englander told him he was the "finest fellow he had met, even if he was a Jew."

He had not meant to teach. But he had been told it was hard to get a place as a college instructor, if one was a Jew. So he put aside the book he had planned, and taught English in our college to show *he* could teach if he wished. He was a strange figure of fire and passion and pride, repressing itself, hiding every feeling. "Jews are so emotional." He would not be emotional.

He stood for a new Judaism that demanded honor for its past, and yet at the same time the absolute right to freedom in its thinking. I was carried away by him and his faith in me. He saw us as two young Jews who would re-create the world, he with his power, I with my "poetry."

One other teacher I came to know as well as him, a tall young Scotchman, Professor McArthur, with tanned face and strong, unbendable shoulders. He taught in the engineering school, and we met at a class dance to which he had come. He was perhaps thirty to my twenty; I thought him unutterably mature. He had never seen a Jewess until he met me. In his Middle Western town, where his father was the country doctor, there was only one other Jewish family, the "store" family, whom he thought rather funny, much like the vaudeville Jew. At college he had no Jewish classmates—nor Catholic either, for that matter.

I was strange to him. After the first dance at college—for I had been dancing since I broke my engagement with Myer—he took me home. I did not go to my home, but my sister's. Hannah had married, a very excellent Jewish dentist. He spoke to me of his mother, whom he adored, and of his young brother. His father was recently dead, and his voice broke as he spoke of him. His father had been his chum.

"You loved him like that?" I asked.

"I couldn't talk of it," he answered quietly.

It seemed strange to me. Here was a son whose father had been not a priest to him and an austere teacher, but a friend, almost an older brother. He told me stories that illustrated the lightness of their feeling on the surface, its depth beneath. "He taught me to swim when I was four—threw me into the lake near the house, then when I howled, there he was, ready to grab me. He carried me home on all fours across the lawn to reward me." I could not think of my father so.

In our home the father was the head, revered and honored. One did not speak to him nor of him, lightly. He represented an ancient civilization. Even in my sister Hannah's house, though her husband was young—he shaved, of course, and even treated patients on Sunday—there was the understanding that her Isidore was a being a bit apart, the "father of the baby," above the mere mother.

When Professor McArthur spoke of his mother, his whole tone changed, its lightness went; it was of her that he spoke with that seriousness and careful respect we knew for our father. Ours was for the man in the home; his—the American—for the woman.

Even in the house of my uncle Simeon—where Aunt Sonia ruled with a rod of iron, a terrible old lady whom children and servants feared—even there, the mild voice of uncle could, by a low murmur, assert supreme authority. He might be the king only in name, and she his parliament, but his kingship was always given immediate recognition when he asked it.

Professor McArthur spoke as if his mother had decided their home life, the ideals of the children, his very profession. "Mother understood us, each; dad never interfered."

He himself planned to marry late, he said. He was not poor. He meant to do some research and then to write a book, and marry.

But before the semester was over, he had stopped talking of not marrying.

When the "Colonial Dance" of my class was given, he was my escort. He came in costume, a handsome figure, right out of a book. I looked like a fragile shadow of Colonial girlhood in my sprigged gown. We danced the square dances, drank the weak lemonade, joined in the college yells that my school, like most small colleges, thought indispensable.

He took me home, and on the way home he asked me to marry him. He told me I might remain a Jewess if I wished, that it meant nothing to him, as he knew it did not to me. He told me he would make me happy.

"Don't," I said. "I couldn't marry—a Gentile—ever." I forgot him before an hour had passed, I was thinking of one thing. I was to see my English teacher the following day.

My English teacher and I were to go to a Jewish wedding of a mutual friend, together. He was superior to the wedding, the "Jewishness" of it, but my father was to act as rabbi there; I was glad to go. I was glad to go because I was to go with Raphael.

I was teaching at night, coaching students in the afternoons—I was earning what seemed to me a great deal of money. I bought myself a pretty dress, and put my hair into the big fashionable pompadour of the day. When Professor Raphael came, I wished for a moment that I lived in a handsomer street, not in the Ghetto, but I was not ashamed of my father who came to greet him, nor of my mother. And my brother Robert was as handsome almost as he. My uncle Jacob, wealthy merchant and affable relative, sent me flowers to wear. Hannah lent me her new pumps.

Mother helped me into her heavy winter coat, for, of course, we were too poor to think of spending money for an evening wrap for me.

"Come home early," said mother, kissing me. "Be happy, my daughter."

From the upper window my sisters blew me each a kiss.

I felt very proud, because I was riding in a hack. Our neighbors never went in a hack except to a wedding or a funeral—and this was neither my wedding nor my funeral. I was riding with a man of the world, a Princeton graduate.

I sat very straight in the cab, trying to forget that my heart was pounding. Professor Raphael began to speak to me of the writing I was doing for him. He planned that I should do a whole series of themes on related subjects, which he would oversee. He thought I had the makings of a poet, but I must cultivate my prose style, and forget the rabbinical turn of my thought, inherited from my father.

Then he leaned forward and said, very quietly, "You know I want you to do beautiful things—because I like you so well."

My hands pressed closer together, tight, against one another, but I know I couldn't have answered.

I did not move, even when his hands came on mine and he said, in the same quiet voice, "I wanted to tell you, first of all, that I am going to get married. I am marrying a young lady I met at college. She is the sister of a friend of mine. You will like her—and she will love you." I think that, even to-day, I can feel the strange coldness that came to my hands that evening. "Her name is Florence T——," he ended. That was the name of his New England classmate.

I tried to look at him, but I was only just reaching out to twenty. I could not. I looked out of the window. He went on speaking: "I want you to know that I shall never forget our walks, nor the long talks we had. I will remember every time we danced. I—I think you know what I mean."

But I could not open my cold lips. I felt that I was being hurt in some way that I could not name, some way that hurt most because it degraded this man, who was not *love*, but *ideal* unattainable, to my young girlhood. I was only nineteen, I could not put it into phrases.

He leaned back, and away from me then, and said, "I think it would be a good thing if you married McArthur; he's in love with you. Don't marry a Jew, though, for God's sake."

I turned to him, then, and somehow I managed to say, "I don't think I'll ever—ever marry anyone at all. I'm not the kind."

Inside, we watched my father perform the ceremony of marriage that united a plump young Jewish lawyer, blond and good-natured and fat, to a pert little girl whose father had given her ten thousand dollars dowry on the consummation of this desirable match with a professional man who would give the whole family free legal advice for life.

My father leaned forward and blessed the bride. He called to the father, a portly real estate man, who made his money by extorting enormous rents from poor tenement dwellers. "Bless your daughter," he said, and waited while the awkward blessing was made. My father was as unaware of the story told in the fat face of the greedy little groom, as of the self-satisfaction in the bride's, or the relief in the countenance of her father. Only, when I was leaving, and bade the young wife good-by, she looked at me, held my hand a minute and, all the pertness going out of her face, she whispered, terrified, "I'm afraid. Just think, all my life's closed now!"

Professor Raphael was speaking to my father, and there seemed a kinship between them, despite their evident antagonism, the distrust of two generations of Jews, worlds apart, but together in America. My father seemed less of the world, but the younger man was no less beautiful than he, no less the expression of a race that will sacrifice everything to that which it believes.

When I came home mother was waiting for me, and she said, quickly, "You came right in?"

"And I'm going right to bed!" I answered, laughing.

V

I SHOULD have pined away after that, and lived a dead life. The truth is that I went to work at school with renewed zeal. But one thing I determined: to forget that I had ever wanted to write. I decided to become a social worker. I had found from Myer the key to my mind; from Raphael the gift of my imagination. But now I must find my work, my career.

I had heard that there was a school for social work, and that it was in New York. That was all I knew about it. Social work is to-day a profession, with rigid standards. There are some admirable schools to prepare one for the work. When I left college I knew that if one had a high school education, a hundred dollars for tuition and a letter vouching for one's good character, one could learn to be a social worker.

During college I had saved a little money, enough barely to put me through school for a year. I wrote to the school, and was enrolled.

I did not even know what the term "social work" meant. At college, the small college to which I went, the subject of social work had not even been named, and my professors were vague or frankly ignorant of anything about it when I asked them what one must do to prepare to be a social worker. From a chance sentence spoken by a friend of Professor Raphael's, however, I heard of a school where social work was taught.

It was a school where one would be taught how to do work for the oppressed, the poor, the hunted, he said. Settlement work, child-caring work, work with orphans and the aged, one could learn there, or how to be a visitor for the charity organization societies.

Here was a place where one could go to learn how to dedicate one's self to something beautiful, something as beautiful as charity; that was where I might go, then. I decided in that instant on my career, as a young missionary of another faith might have chosen to give her life to work among the poor and unenlightened in a distant land.

My fitness for this work, and what the future would hold for me in it, did not so much as occur to me to consider. To-day, with our painstaking attempts to study the mind of the child and of the older boy and girl, to choose that one path in which he or she may go with greatest happiness—vocational guidance—even the child whose parents are not familiar with the practical considerations of human life may be protected against mistakes. The round peg is put in the round hole; yet the tragedy of the misplaced life occurs, for all our expert knowledge, even to this wise day. I chose a profession because my ardent desire, the desire of youth to give itself to an ideal, showed this one way to me. That was all I knew of it.

I did not know any of the leaders in the profession; its very terms were new to me, utterly new. The charity organization methods, now understood by the layman reading his newspaper, were to me technical names as strange as medical terms might be to a new student. A "case" did not mean to me a human tragedy or a family complication. To inquire into the heart of a man or a woman, to seek out the hidden causes that made dark the life of a neglected child, was not to me "an investigation." It was giving myself, my intense interest and even my intimate affection, to the child or the adult. Years were to pass before I found that social work did not need—nor want to have—intensity of feeling, a burning desire to help one's neighbors, a great love for humankind, sympathy and unquestioning faith. It needed a cool mind to analyze causes of poverty and of sickness and even of crime, that they might be cured; it needed skepticism, that judgments might be formed justly; it required, by no longest odds, the heart of the worker, but his calm mind.

That was not ever mine to give. It was not in me to do work of the mind, without personal interest and affection. Social work was not my work. It took me twelve years to discover this, however.

The other day my little daughter asked me if she might have a new frock which she wished to wear at a school party. She was going with "Colin." My daughter is approaching fifteen; Colin, I know, is sixteen. "Colin" takes her out all the time. My friends are troubled because their daughters have beaus, but "Little Maid" told me frankly, oh, very candidly! that she had every intention of marrying Colin some day, though now she beats him at soccer, as he excels her in basketball. She is much the brighter in school, however. She is troubled because they must, she is certain, wait until she may be all of nineteen before it will be possible for them to marry. And she added, "I suppose that seems dreadful to you, Momsie; in your day they didn't think of girls of my age as mature at all, did they?" I did not tell her that long before I had even dreamed of the wonder of possessing her, long before I was myself born, my grandmother had been, at fifteen, mature enough to marry and to have a son; that my own mother had been a mother at eighteen.

What I thought of was that I must be truly old. "In your day." My day is so long ago! Just the other day I felt that I looked back so far when I said, "ten years ago I remember," but now I say "twenty-five years ago, when I was at school—" That is a quarter of a century!

I, like my husband, entered social work in its beginnings, when those who have made it first found its scope. We have seen its mistakes and its achievements. We know its limitations and its grandeurs. If at any time I speak with a bitter taste on my lips, it is not because I do not honor this profession and its workers, who are my friends. I speak with bitterness because of the mistakes of all beginners, in any endeavor. I am not concerned with the troubled question of whether social work is a profession, or just a job like secretarial work, or selling. I am not even concerned with the standards that are beginning to be set more and more rigidly for entrance into it.

I only know that when I entered it, as now, the beginner had a college education, that a number of years of preparation were required in the work to "gain experience"—apprenticeship—and then the real job began.

I did not know—and it would, in fact, have meant nothing to me—that social workers received less in salary than clerks, and that they had less chance for advancement; I did not know that they gave as much time in preparation to their work as did a minister, a lawyer (for twelve years ago the preparatory Arts degree was not required, generally, in these professions);—and yet, in this profession, the worker had the standing of a servant, owned, controlled and to be engaged and dismissed by a group of people who had no training for *his* work, who did not understand it and who yet were his employers, "the board." I have known some of the finest people in the world who have been behind great movements they began, and which they set going through "boards of directors" they formed—I have been on three or four boards myself. But the social worker generally, now as in the beginning, has a situation no other worker faces. He does work requiring the most highly skilled training, long training; he does it as a professional worker with honor from the community—but his job is never his own, as is the doctor's, the lawyer's, the minister's. He is the employee of his board, to be engaged or dismissed at their pleasure, to have the work he created with human beings and lives (about which his own life is twined in the doing) cut off, without choice on his part, by the pleasure of his board. And, all the time, if he or she has a will, it must be torn, wounded, as is his pride and his self-respect, by the men and women employing him, pulling at him, diminishing him. Sometimes it may be just one member of the board who is the "bitter pill." But in social work the situation is this: the controlling group, the group that pays, giving money because it wishes to give that money is a "group of volunteers," to use the professional parlance; the social worker is, however, "the paid worker." The group of board members, as volunteers, do not feel, however high their sense of civic or community duty may be, the need to fight for their "worker" against a fellow board member who is, after all, a friend and an influential fellow citizen. One unfriendly board member, standing alone, may block the whole work of the "paid worker."

Of course, the minister, too, may have one parishioner who is not a friend; the teacher may have one trustee who is disagreeable. But both teacher and minister have two advantages. The first is that the work of each is his own: his community or school cannot take that from him. And, though one man or woman may be unfriendly, he has the friendly publicity that his work receives as a right. The social worker works best when his work is not *his* accomplishment, but when he makes his board feel, each one, that it is their work he is doing. He must do his job, and "jolly" the board at the same time.

It makes me smile to read the diatribes of critics of social work; their wails at overhead expenses. The annual salary of social workers is, perhaps, $3,000 a year. No wonder they have families of one, and their wives look old at forty! Occasionally a man earns $5,000 a year, and even $7,000. These salaries are for administrative jobs, held by men who are more business men than social workers. The man working out a community problem is there because he feels there is something fine to be done; and he does it—at a double sacrifice, of himself and of his income.

Attend a national conference of social workers. Thousands of men and women meet from all over the United States to discuss a thousand human problems and how to meet them. And not once is there a meeting to discuss the increase of salaries. What other wage-earning body could offer that omission?

Oh, I have had heartaches, regrets, since I chose this

profession; but not for one day, nor for one hour, have I done anything but give it honor, honor due it in measure beyond my small giving.

There is nothing, surely, more disastrous than to choose the wrong profession. The misfit has always been a figure of tragedy. But I had done more than choose a wrong profession when I went to New York. I broke every tie at home to do it.

My father insisted that it was time for me to marry. My aunts said the same. My sister Hannah and her husband were shocked that a girl of twenty-one planned to spend more time, wasting money, on just educating herself. My sister Etta, teaching school, felt that I might be doing the same. Only mother said nothing. She just listened. But I knew she did not disapprove.

My father called me into his study to see him one day. "What is it you want?" he asked me. "You have a good home, and I think your mother and I have been kind to you in it. What are you seeking? Were you in love with young Raphael?"

I felt I would sink through the floor, but he said kindly, "I wonder if you know what you are doing, my daughter. I came to a new land for the sake of my children. I left my father, my own mother, to give a new life and religious freedom to my sons and daughters. I have left those who know me and honor me to live through contumely and misery here. And you are breaking away, destroying that for which I sacrificed everything."

I was to hear in my classrooms many lectures on the "problem of the immigrant," on "Americanization;" but none were to speak for that which my father represented, the old immigrant whose dream it was, as it was the Quaker's and the Puritan's, to find a new home of religious freedom in the new land, and who was, instead, to lose his children to that new land. My father's story was never considered in the classes I attended.

I could not tell him that I wanted the same thing for which he had come to America. I wanted to live and to act according to the faith I had, just as he wished it for himself. I wanted to be free to live as I believed, in every way. I wanted, first, the right to find out what I believed, what my faith was.

"If you go to New York," he said, "you will lose your Jewish spirit. What is this work for the poor? Is it work for their soul? Is it work for their religion? The synagogue will take care of its poor, and the rabbi. What sort of humanitarianism is it that does not see the need of each one's religion first of all?"

I waited, and then I answered, "I shall not lose my religion, father. I haven't had any for over two years."

He turned toward me, his face without color, his beard like gold brown flame. "You're a—you don't—you're not a Jewish woman?"

I answered, "I'm not anything you think, father. I've not been branded with a flaming iron. But I don't believe the way I used to any more."

"I warned your mother," he said then, quietly, "you would become lost to us if we let you have the education you wanted." He left the room. He did not even bid me good-by when I left for New York. All the time I was there, I received not a word from him, nor was his name mentioned to me in my mother's letters. I took summer courses, and worked in the winter between my classes. The second year I did not return home before school.

I felt lonely enough. I had thought that when I entered this new work I would discover a new world, a world where human beings were brothers in one grand, overwhelming faith. I was mistaken.

Our teachers were men and women doing various kinds of work in settlements, in housing organizations, in colleges. They preached to us the broad humanity of a new service. They spoke to us of giving the poor better houses, of fighting for better health for them, of discovering the secret causes that blighted their lives, that these might be wiped out. They preached a new religion, in which all of us were to serve before a great god of Love.

In the classrooms came middle-aged women, mostly unmarried, from little towns in the East and Middle West. They took notes of the lectures, of the mechanics of this new way of living and thinking:—how to "investigate a family," how to form a club, how to organize a board of directors for a new organization or institution. They learned how to compile statistics and how to write reports. They listened intently to data on racial relations, and how to "Americanize the immigrant"—then one of the new phrases appearing on the social work horizon where phrases come and go with such intensity.

But all the time they never moved a millimeter out of the little groove in which each had been born and in which each lived. They were not men and women learning a new gospel in which all men and all creeds were united for one cause, to make humankind happier and perhaps a little better; they were Baptists and Presbyterians and Catholics, each working for Christian America. They were as close inside their doors of dogma and sect as had been the Jewish home from which I came.

They had neither the fire nor the beauty of an old

tradition to bring to their tight little worlds. They would "work among" Baptists and Presbyterians as they would have worked in a store or a factory. It amused them a little to hear an ardent young girl try to tell what, to her, this new profession meant.

Once a group of us sat together, after a lecture on child-caring. There were perhaps thirty or so there, the women in trim suits (the sort that presently came to mean "social worker"), the younger girls in tailored dresses, the young Jewess (I) in a little schoolgirl dress. The lecturer had spoken of a new religion for children—the right of every child to healthy parents, freedom from venereal disease, education.

It had been wonderful to me, who had always known that it was not the child, but the group, the race, that counted, in my childhood. I came out feeling as if I had heard a new language. But I was shy among these older women. One of the women, later to be a leading social worker, leaned forward and said, "It was a good talk. Splendid. I think that if we could persuade the State of Illinois, where I come from, to pass the sterilization law—"

"Oh," I cried out then, for once forgetting that these women were older than myself, "don't you see that it isn't so much Illinois that matters! It's important only because it is a place to start. But the idea's bigger—it goes to all children, and all people! If we begin to give the child his rightful heritage of health, of education, we'll have to give it toleration of its opinions, of its—"

"It's what?" smiled one pretty woman from the South. "I'm not interested in idiots in Illinois, either; I'm from South Carolina."

I joined in the laugh. But I went on, trying to explain: "I come from a town where every one is Scotch-Irish, Presbyterian or Catholic—or Jewish. In our city the Catholics and Presbyterians and Jews all live apart, as if they were each in different worlds, as if this weren't one America. It's that which is the essential thing—to think of all youth as the future, the childhood of America, and not as Jews or Gentiles or Catholics."

My classmates looked at one another; there was a discreet silence. The subject was changed, but before it was some one said, smoothly, "Just so." During my year at the school not one Gentile girl invited me to her home.

It was "just so." For presently I was looking for a job. I had specialized in settlement work because of my earlier experience in it. I wanted to get a position in some settlement house, at no matter how small a salary. I wanted to find whether, perhaps, in real work this new social work would be found.

The school offered to help me find a job. It gave me a list of available openings, in the "Middle West and East." I asked why not in the West and South, and was told that it would not be advisable to try: "Jews are not usually wanted there."

The first opening was in a settlement in New York. The head worker met me herself, smiled affably, interviewed me, and then told me to come to see her in a week. I was living on the remnant of my former savings; mother was helping me out. I waited a week. The head worker, a harassed, middle-aged woman, had a board member with her, a pretty young woman with dark, sweet eyes.

The two of them interviewed me together. "And

you have had experience in club work?" she asked, in a high, sweet voice.

"For more than two years," I told her.

"With girls? Or women, too? We may want you to have women, too."

"Just for a year with women, but a whole two years with girls," I said, "and with girls not easy to lead—Jewish immigrant girls."

"Jewish?" repeated the high, sweet voice, pausing on the word.

I explained that I had lived in the neighborhood, how well I knew the girls, and what I had been able to do.

"Oh, thank you so much for coming," said the sweet-faced board member. "We shall let you know in a week."

I waited a week, but did not hear from her and, when I called her up, was told that they were so sorry, but they had engaged a former candidate, one having experience with the sort of work they did—Protestant girls.

It was almost two months before I learned that I could not expect work in a settlement house as a Jewish worker. I gave up. I went to the school to ask what I could do. There was nothing to do but wait; perhaps a Jewish settlement house would want a Jewish worker. "But often," said the pleasant director of the "personnel department," "even Jewish settlements ask for non-Jewish workers, you see."

It was necessary to earn some money. I went to teach. I taught school in a foreign night school maintained by a labor organization—and my students were Jewish.

Then, to my astonishment, I received a letter. I

was offered a job. The head of one of the departments of a settlement house needed a "recreation and housing worker." The salary was tiny, but there was "maintenance" included. The name at the end was familiar; it was the name of a fellow-student at the school for social work, a graduate student who had done brilliant work in research.

He was in the office when I came in. He was slight, with kind blue eyes and the finest mouth in the world, gentle and understanding.

I gave him my name and then, before he could ask me further questions, I said, "I suppose you didn't see me in our big classes at the school. But we took the housing and children's lectures together. I want you to know I am a Jewess."

He nodded, absently. "And you are prepared to begin work at once?"

My work was not with Jewish people. It was to make a study of the homes of Polish people, to discover their various racial backgrounds, their reasons for coming to America, their social life here and so forth. I cannot, of course, speak Polish, and a young student whose native language that is was assigned to help me.

I liked my work. To gather the facts was like seeing a tapestry of history weave itself. My chief, Dr. Morton, was planning to write a book, and this was to be part of his material.

In the settlement I learned one thing—to be silent. There are few things that the social worker can do better than maintain discreet silence, if he is a man of mediocre ability. Silence can be damning. I had been damned so often by it that I respected it. I was a very silent member of the house.

At the house lived four old women, each interested in some neighborhood activity. One was the head of a playground, another director of a library, the third the principal of a public school and the fourth our head worker. The librarian was an Englishwoman, the school principal a New Englander; they hated each other with a historic hatred. The other two sat and clawed.

To me, they were like four old ghouls sitting gleefully tearing at life. And yet, each in her work, was admirable. I saw the librarian in her office, with her own hands bind the cut of a little Hungarian ragamuffin who came in one day crying, with blood dripping from a ragged cut on his hand. I knew the school principal spent hours visiting the sick and the neglected children in her classes, hours long after school was closed each day. Our head worker was a woman of great wealth, who chose to live in a settlement house, among the foreign and poor. Yet, at table, they spoke as if they hated these people with whom and for whom they worked.

"Scum of the land," said the New England teacher.

"We wouldn't allow them in as you do here," said the Englishwoman.

Our head worker smiled in appreciation.

I did not like it. I spoke of it to Dr. Morton, and he smiled. "You don't understand them," he told me. "Each of these four women is at heart a mother. They belong, however, to an era in American life when it seemed the nobler thing—the braver—to refuse motherhood and wifehood and choose a career. Each chose a career, and it is to her a child, as the people she meets in it are her family. It's because they so much fear to be thought sentimental, discovered as mothers, that they try to appear so hard."

I was to find the same attitude often. I met young social workers who looked like young men narrowly escaping complete disguise, who spoke with disdain of their people, their shiftlessness, their "lack of coöperation," their stupidity, and who were prepared to give up their lives, if need be, in the service of these very worthless persons.

I was surprised to find something else. In all my previous experience, the Gentile in contact with the Jew either resented him, patronized him or worshipped him as a super-being. These social workers, "non-Jews" who worked with Jews, were genuinely fond of them, they found their characteristics that were so often food for caricature or censure, lovable qualities that made them endearing. The emotional Jewess, too ready with affection and gratitude, was to them admirably appreciative. The studious little Jewish boys, mature when they should have been children at play, seemed to these social workers honorably eager for learning. Even the Jewish fear of poverty, that makes the Jew careful of his pennies, they found right and self-respecting.

Could it be, I wondered, that the Jew was disliked, feared, only when he was an equal?

VI

MY chief was the only male resident on the staff of the settlement house, and, although he was so young, and the others so ardently feministic, whatever he said was always greeted with a certain special respect. The elderly women who sat about the table at dinner would pause in their mutual enjoyment of gently clawing at one another as soon as he spoke.

It was interesting, too, to see that for him the boundaries that marked their likes and their prejudices stretched, as if their femininity unconsciously responded to his grave courtesy, a quality of his very voice, of his smallest contact with the rest of the world. That courtesy was part of his inheritance, for his father had been a Frenchman, his mother an Englishwoman of good family. He was the only child, and, though his youth was spent in America and he was, indeed, born in this country, many of his memories and some of his sympathies were with the two older countries from which his parents came, and to which, I found, they had often taken him as a child. When the New England schoolteacher opened the book of American history, to speak with a peculiarly intense and even personal animus to the English librarian at our same table, Dr. Morton would listen quietly, perhaps smile a little, and then would speak, very candidly but justly, to declare his own point of view.

Once, when we were going over something that had

developed in our housing study, we found, what is now of course well known, that the Polish immigrant (even in those days before the present rigid restrictive act) usually came to this country without his family, was a bachelor here for several years and lived in a boarding or rooming house with his companions and fellow workers. Sometimes, in the case of young married men living this bachelor existence, there developed rather complicated illegal relations with their landladies. The Bohemians, on the other hand, came with their families, and, when their children had gone to school for a few years, one could not tell them from "born Americans" in New York. There were a few Germans in our "neighborhood," as the sphere of our work was called by us, and the Germans were entirely domestic and utterly good husbands and fathers.

"That's the Teutonic strain in them," said the Englishwoman, commenting on the discoveries of our surveys. "The Anglo-Saxon has made whatever is worth while in the States here. I've often thought that sometimes there will be a union of England and this country, after all, through Canada, perhaps, first of all, and then—"

The New England school teacher, who always ate her food as if she despised it, and the process of eating, too, put down her fork with a thin ring of metal on china. "England?" she said, and her voice was really high. "Why, it's taken us a whole century and a quarter to forget that we came from a nation of gorging, self-satisfied men who are more allied to the beast in man than any other people on earth! Can you think of the culture of New England—and that's the culture of America—and say it springs from England? It's the colossal vanity of the British that's their worst fault! Kipling shouting and beating drums! Canada may ask us some day to let it become part of the Union, and if women had the vote, I'd vote against it; but even the slightest union between us and the English is impossible!"

From the head of the table, the head worker's dark eyes sparkled. She came from the South, and her geographical animosities, excluding the "Mason and Dixon line," were not so pronounced; but she enjoyed any sharp combat to be watched. "My father used to tell," she said, with a little smile, "that when he visited Canada in his railroading business, his hosts never felt they had entertained him like an honored guest and a gentleman before they had drunk so much that they fell asleep at, or under, the table!"

I thought of our own home, of my father and his guests sitting to midnight, and later, in the yellow light of our lamps, reading the Torah.

"But in my grandfather's house," said Dr. Morton then, quietly, "though there was the usual conviviality, I suppose, I never saw my grandfather drink to excess nor, for that matter, any Englishman—that is, no more than one may see in a restaurant in Paris or on Broadway. I don't think," he added, "I could ever become very much excited about a war between America and England—and that, although my father was a Frenchman and never cared for England."

He laughed and said, "It brings to mind something that one of the men in the gymnasium said here last week: 'It ain't my stomach-ache, and it ain't your stomach-ache; why should I go cry because he ate what ain't good for him?' I can't feel the resentment of any group of people, in the past."

Our head worker, however, shook her handsome gray

head. "That's not the proper way to think!" she said emphatically. "That's the fault with this country. We have so many nationalities here that, in the end, we find we have not one in common—not even our own. Even our grievances are put in the melting pot and boiled into pleasant broth to serve to the enemies of our ancestors! I know I don't like the English," with a smile to the English librarian, "except those who are my dear and personal friends, just as I don't like the Jews—except my own Jews."

It seemed silly, but I had to say it: "You know I am a Jewess!" Usually I was too shy to say anything at all, but now I spoke with a curious challenge. I did not smile.

"Sorry," she said. I learned that even those who did not like Jews could be surprisingly friendly to me, although I was a Jewess. I was "their Jewess." "I like Jews I know," said our head worker, smiling to me, "*you* know that, dear child!"

In New York, where the whole city seemed to be a new Jerusalem, entirely different from our small city, in which the Jews were few in number, the people who were not Jews felt toward Jews in two distinct ways. One group I could not talk to; the other troubled and embarrassed me. I used to speak, sometimes, to Dr. Morton, after dinner before the fire, or rather he spoke to me—long talks—and I tried to tell him of it. . . . The first group felt that all Jews were shrewd, sharp and bound to be successful. They did not credit them with any ethical ideals, except a bizarre sort of honor that held with their own people, like thieves with one another. The Jews to this group were, it appeared, a Midas people, making gold out of the very air of the city. They, themselves, made themselves the hangers-on of Jews; they came to Jewish homes, ate Jewish meals and even attended religious Jewish ceremonies, such as weddings or funerals. But all the time, they never for a moment permitted their Jews to forget that they saw them as Jews, the Jews of Dickens, ridiculous, kind, and very keen at making money.

"I like Jews," one of these said to me at the home of a cousin of mine. "They're so kind, and they have such good gefüllte fish."

They are kind, I acknowledged, explaining to Dr. Morton carefully, and they do have gefüllte fish. But this young man I recalled was the close friend of the girl at whose home he was calling. He was a classmate of her brother's at college, and called often. He took her to the theater and to dances. But, as she said candidly, she had not the least intention of ever marrying him. "Marry a Goy?" she said. "Oh, I like to show him off, and he's very handsome looking, not fat like our boys, you know. But I wouldn't think of marrying him. He's not the kind you marry. Could you imagine what the family would say if I did!" She laughed. Eventually she met a stout Jewish teacher of history in one of the high schools, and fell in love with his full cheeks, snapping eyes, full mouth and little bulging body. She immediately dropped all friendship with her non-Jewish friend, but he transferred himself unperturbed to her sister. And when he married a thin, yellow-haired and extraordinarily pretty Western girl, he did not so much as send them announcements, though he had attended the wedding of both girls. They, however, sent him a wedding gift, which he—and not his wife—acknowledged with a pert, patronizing and distinctly conclusive note.

This man thought of the Jew as a vaudeville character who had a knack of making money. "You people certainly can make the mesuma!" he said, smacking his lips. Although he was a classmate at college of the girl's brother, he did not, when his mother came to New York from their home in Kansas and he entertained her, ask his Jewish classmate to meet her, although it was at the latter's home that he spent most of his time.

These young cousins were distant cousins, really cousins of my mother's. Their father was a highly successful merchant, who had a number of big stores in various cities over the country, most of them managed by relations whom he had brought to America, helped to become Americanized, and then set up in his big businesses. The young classmate of his son spoke to him with a lofty and, perhaps, a not uningratiating condescension, and the older man accepted it with a little deprecating smile. He was proud of his son, lived in the boy, and planned everything wonderful in the world for his Simeon. He was proud to have his son's friend speak to him. Did not he himself talk with a pronounced accent? He was uncouth at table. It was hard to think of this stout, diffident man, trying hard to please his children in the expensive house he maintained for them, and then to recall him at our house, where, with my father, he would sit with his skullcap tilted back, his cheeks flushed, reciting page after page of Hebrew, to the admiration and wonder of the assembled scholars about him. He had been a young rabbi in Galicia, had begun to teach Hebrew when he came to New York, saw his family starving, opened a little store, prospered, and opened another, and found himself at last with four children who were college graduates, American, residents on West End Avenue, and members of an exclusive reformed Jewish temple. They bore a kind tolerance for "Daddy,"—which he himself pronounced "Deddy"—adding to me once, whimsically, his shrewd old eyes understanding enough, "It means dead, eh—deddy?"

Simeon, his son, was like my brother Robert, tall, thin, intense, very handsome. He troubled the old man because he did not have that Jewish quality—a purpose, something definite and real for which to work. It might be a doctor's degree, or a store, or the back room of a chemical laboratory, but one ought to know to what one was aiming, the "Zweck." That was what his father felt. But Simeon would look at him with that impersonal, unseeing glance that he seemed to reserve for his father, and would sit, utterly silent, while the old merchant spoke. Once he made me come in to listen, to ask that I intercede with Simeon, persuade him to choose something to do, not to waste the whole year after graduating. But Simeon looked at me with his beautiful, dark glance, and said,

"Don't ask Leah, dad. She's making a long detour from the way you'd want me to go! You'd be sorry!"

His father flushed, looked at me doubtfully and was silenced. Simeon threatened him always with becoming a Gentile, at least dropping from the Jewish fold.

The old man wanted to know what I really was doing. He was kind to me because my mother had written to him to ask him to be good to me. But he wanted to reassure her, he told me, that I was still a Jewish girl. He did not expect religious formalities of young people in this country, he admitted, but he hoped his children—and I—would still be Jews here. He spoke with fervor and with a quaint sort of diffidence to me, a young girl, whom in my own home he would have addressed rather loftily, because he was a man. But in his handsome apartment in New York his children made him see himself on another plane; here he was different.

I did not know what to answer him. I had come to New York to break away from Jewish ties, to be whatever I wanted. But I did not feel resentful and at the same time impotent to change, as did Simeon. I was not afraid, if I felt it to be right, to say what I thought. That I had from my father. Simeon knew that he might make his father unhappy, but he did not dare to offend his "dad", who held the purse strings, and would have cut him off—cut his own heart as he did it, too—if he were "not a Jew," observing Jewish laws.

One day Simeon said to me, abruptly, "See that fellow there?" and pointed to a young man passing, for we were on Broadway. "He's the big gun in one of the fraternities in our college." He was quiet a bit, then went on in a low, colorless voice, as if he were speaking of something utterly out of his sphere of interest: "He asked me to join the rowing team in my freshman year—heard I was a—a Jew—and told me they didn't need a new man. They got another fellow two weeks later, though—a vacancy then!"

I felt hurt with that strange, sharp pain in his voice. I felt older by years than this cousin of mine. "Didn't they know all the time you were a Jew?" I asked.

His dark eyes burned like a flash around to mine. "Did I have to shout it with a brass band?" he asked, and we went on, for a while, without speaking.

He said, after a long interval: "Fred—you met

him at the house—is my best friend. Told me he was in love, showed me his girl's letters. Came to our house—and made fun of dad. Took Beta out—and treated her as he wouldn't treat any girl in his crowd. I—I told him he'd have to cut it out. He said he was sorry and—and behaved differently to her. And she asked him, one day, was he cross at her, that he behaved so distantly to her, 'cold as ice!'" His lips were pale, his eyes grew dull. "What's the use of living, of doing what one wants, if your family's a crowd of clowns to make your friends laugh?"

It seemed to me that he might have changed it, that they were clowns because they allowed themselves to be, that any people would be clowns to their friends if they allowed it. It was the way one thought of one's self.

"He's not that way with you," I said lamely.

Simeon turned to me: "No. And since he married, he's not asked me to meet his wife, just as he didn't ask me to meet his mother. But dad invested some money for him—that he spent for his home. I—I sent him the china on which they dine. He accepted it—with a grin, I guess—and closes the door on me."

But I did not tell Dr. Morton of what I thought when I thought of Simeon.

In my pretty cubicle at the settlement house I would think of Simeon and his life. He was like Professor Raphael, but he had not any brilliance, any great light to illumine him, making a splendor wherever he stood. He would, perhaps, enter business with his father, be moody and unhappy, marry a wealthy girl, go on the board of Jewish Charities, the Temple, and feel that his life was limited and blighted because he was a Jew.

Professor Raphael was the other sort of Jew, that non-Jews resented. But my sort they liked. It made me wish they did not.

Once, when I had been asked to the home of a board member with Dr. Morton and one other member of his staff, our hostess sat speaking of books and of people. She was an artist, the wife of a famous actor, and was living these last years of her life in good works for her city. She had not the technical interest in social work that the professional worker had, nor the desire to fill an empty place that animated the souls of unmarried women in the field. To her it was an expression of the love she had for all human beings, and particularly for the quaint and the hurt.

The other girl in our group, Nellie Frost, a plump and healthy girl with beautiful clear skin and eyes, laughed with her usual merry enjoyment of the people she met, as she described the boys' clubs she led. "Tonio wanted to be the leader of the game," she said, "because he felt he was most important, as the only fellow who had a parent in Sing Sing!"

Dr. Morton described the houses we had found in one street, a row of old homes turned into unspeakable tenements. In one was an old woman, a Bohemian, with a baby in her arms, a little child at her knee, a pot of coffee, some bread, a dish-pan with hot water for her feet—and a little body of a boy twenty hours dead,—on the table. The child had died of pneumonia. Her daughter was working in a flat in the Bronx and would not be home until the following day. She was waiting for the mother to come home, with the child there on the table.

Dr. Morton pointed to me and laughed a little. I had not been wise and resourceful, as I should. I had not immediately informed the city authorities of the death, taken the little children to the Children's Aid, and the old woman to the C.O.S. Of course I knew —had I not been taught?—that was what I should have done. But, instead, I lifted the old woman to the bed, put the dead little body on two chairs and covered the tiny face, so still and frozen and thin, wrapped the two other children and then ran out to buy milk and crackers and meat at the corner delicatessen.

I cleaned up the house, washed the boy and girl and then sat and waited for the mother. I forgot about the settlement house—my job.

I did not speak the old woman's tongue, for she was Hungarian. Then the mother came into the room, a big, robust woman with red cheeks and friendly warm eyes, her strong arms full of parcels.

She saw me standing. Her parcels dropped. She came over and pulled back the cover. There lay her son, dead.

The servant girl from Hungary and I bent over the little body. We washed it and dressed it. The old woman lay, moaning, crying harshly. I helped place the little figure in the coffin. I watched the mother bid it good-by. In those days servants were not ladies of importance; a good job was precious. She could not even go to see her child buried, and I went. I went with the old grandmother and heard her anguished cry.

The undertaker took me back in the one cab to the settlement. And then they heard the story there.

Our head worker was not pleased. It was a touching story, she said. But I should not have written my part in it as I did. I should have called her up, or the Charity Organization Society. They would have sent a visitor, as I knew (had I not tried to be a "visitor" myself?) and she would have arranged everything. I had simply put the settlement out, wasted my funds, and—this said with much kindness, however—I had taken a day and a half of the time which I was supposed to devote to work for which the settlement paid. A dozen years later, in my own settlement house, I was to see things as she did. But not that day, at twenty-two!

I offered to resign, I remember. But she shook her head and said, "Of course not! But we must do things according to practical rules," and left me to Dr. Morton.

He looked down at me, standing by his desk, and did not speak for a while. Then he said, "Do not be unhappy about this. One meets things in one's life according to one's own lights."

But I shook my head. "That's just it," I said. "I don't feel one meets a social problem by set rules just because the people one finds in it are below the line of self-support" (the popular phrase). "I wouldn't do the thing differently, if I did it again. That's because, you see, Dr. Morton, these—these people are like myself. I've been so awfully poor that when people don't have money they don't seem different for that reason. They're—just people without money. If I happened to hear of a woman of means who'd lost her child—and was alone—would I call up the C.O.S. to help her? The thing is, Miss E—— sees people when they're poor as in a special circle, in a different world. I don't! And as long as I don't, I can't respect the rules of social work. I cannot be a social worker!"

He smiled then. "That's where you're mistaken," he said, quietly. "This work is new. It's so new that now it is mainly rules—rigid, perhaps. That's because in a new profession boundaries have to be set, rigidly, that they may be recognized. I'll wager in twenty years social work will have swung around the circle—it will be what you want now—the rules will be there, to be relaxed, in every case. Do you see?"

I thought I did. But I saw more that he was kind and understanding, that he was my friend. He teased me gravely, using a catch phrase of the day, sometimes, to curb my enthusiasms: "This is my funeral!"

This evening, after dinner, he repeated to our hostess the story of the servant woman and her children and mother. "We want a place for those two children for a month or so," he said. "Some farm, if possible, with their grandmother."

Our hostess said, "I'll take them to my farm. There's a lot of room there, and the housekeeper is, it seems to me, Hungarian—or German, anyhow."

I had not spoken, but now I felt as if my heart filled, as it always did when something beautiful happened. I was afraid to lift my eyes. She spoke to me then of the children, of their ages, their appearance.

Then, as we left, she put her hand under my chin and lifted my face. "You have a look of wonder in your eyes," she said, kindly and sweetly. "Don't let life erase it." She held both my hands and said, "You told me you are a Jewess?" For I had spoken of that some time earlier.

I nodded, embarrassed. I did not like to be told I had a look of wonder in my eyes. I think I wanted to be thought practical, mature. I thought all my feelings were considered conclusions.

"Don't lose the spiritual sweetness of your people, then," she said. "It'll never get you anywhere—the impractical Jew is the most forlorn creature in the world. But perhaps not the less loveable." And, to my embarrassment, she kissed me.

I did not like it. I was enchanted by her beauty, her genius. But I did not wish her to see me as carrying a pale golden torch for my people. I wanted to be myself, apart from every one, from every people. What was the use of having come to New York, of having a new profession, if I were to be no different from my own father as I knew him, simply a fine Jew?

On the way home Nellie Frost, who understood me, grinned and spoke mischievously of her sorrow at being "nothing but a Methodist." "You know, Dr. Morton," she mused mournfully, "I think I'll become a converted Jew. A poor little Methodist hasn't a chance here in New York! If you aren't an interesting Jewess, not a person wants to notice you!" She spoke, with mischief, of Rose Pastor Stokes, of Mrs. Rose Walling, of all the Jewesses who were then holding the imagination of New York in a strange captivity.

"Anyhow," she sighed as if in infinite relief, "if I can't be a romantic Jewish girl, at least I can be grateful I am not a young Jewish man!"

The only person who seemed to forget that I was a Jewess was Nellie. She had grown up in a big city among Jewish girls and boys; she knew them and their customs. She had had Jewish beaus at high school, and a "crush" at college. They were simply people to her. I found her dear to know.

Our head worker was always excessively careful now not to speak in depreciation of Jews in my presence; since the day she found I was a Jewess, there had never been mention of Jews at the table. But, of course, her feeling and judgments had not changed, I knew. I felt uncomfortable in her excluding kindness.

Dr. Morton was my chief. I knew that he liked my work and that he enjoyed hearing me speak, too. To him it was not a question of the work I did being done by a Jewess or a Gentile. It was well done, if not brilliantly. Perhaps no one, therefore, made me so happy as did he.

For, here, in his office, I was not a girl representing a race. I was not a Jewish maiden responsible to a race, as at home. I wasn't a strange young woman who took jests about her people with sensitive, chilling quiet. I was a worker, with an intelligent mind, doing the work of the community.

We completed our study, analyzed our findings. Dr. Morton wrote the thin pamphlet that gave the results of our work. In its preface he had a short sentence: "The research in housing was done by Miss Leah——." It was the first time I had so much as thought of seeing my name in a book, a real book. I used to look at that page and that line, and find it as if it glowed in light out of all the surrounding text. Once I had thought to write, but I had not ever expected to be *in* a book—to have my thought and work in it.

And then one day Dr. Morton turned to me and said, "Perhaps you have heard that I have been asked to go to——to take charge of their housing and recreation work there?"

VII

IT did not seem strange to me when he asked me to go with him and to be his wife. I had known for months that I loved him. That was why I could speak to him of those things I felt most deeply, and why I felt the peace of my work. I knew that I would not be happy unless I was working at something I believed—but it would have to be some work done with him, too.

I did not think, when he asked me to be his wife, that he was not a Jew. I only felt that, if he asked me that moment to pour out my life for him, in our kiss, it would have been sweet to do it. I did not think, then, that he was a man and I a woman. He was my love and I his.

We had been to the park, walking home from the library. It was early spring, and the bushes near the little lake in Central Park were all sprigged with buds, and yet it was cold. I had gone over all the books in our big office, to "take back" those that we had been using in our work. And, just as I was about to go out, he called and asked if he might go with me. We went out together, riding to the library and completing our work quietly enough.

Then we went out, and he asked if I would like to walk. I had not walked with him—all our talks had been in his office or before the fire in the library after the rest had gone to their clubs or classes, or up to their cubicles to rest.

We walked fast, and sat down near the little lake to rest. But it was too cold to sit; only walking was one happy, and so we walked. He began to speak of the little park in London where he used to play as a child, and that one in Paris to which his father would take him when he was a bit older. "I remember," he said, "father used to boast that I knew two hundred French words when I was two years." He laughed. "And our folks marvelled,—and did not think that a child speaking a language daily would as naturally know two hundred words of that language as of English."

I told him that I had spoken Hebrew when I was not three, for my father used to play with me by teaching it to me, my elder sister and brother laughing as I lisped the words.

He looked down at me, and smiled: "Rebecca and the student do not belong." But I would not have that; I was no Biblical Rebecca sorrowfully pleading for her race. I was an American, now, just as he was.

Above me his dark blue eyes twinkled, and he brushed back his heavy hair that sometimes looked gold and sometimes brown red—"Carrotty", his English cousins called it, he told me later. His mother had auburn hair.

He spoke of his new work, its scope and a curious idea he had—new then, twenty years ago—that play is as necessary to mankind as work, as health. He was to be in charge of housing and recreation, but, he said, he meant to do something that would startle his board of directors. He meant to stress the "recreation" part of his program and make the "housing"

—the solemn part of the work—secondary. He felt that to the worker and the citizen, play—music and plays and books and rest—were as important to life as food, as money; to provide play as essential as to give medicine or work or clothing.

I felt my eyes shining. Had I not planned that, too? To be sure, I had not done so in New York. I had all my life never had the chance to prove that I felt play essential to my life, for I had worked hard. But some day, I had always been telling myself, I would play. I'd dance, go to the theaters, just sit and read,—not for a purpose, as Simeon's father felt all things ought to be done—but just for the *pleasure* of it.

"But," I could not help asking, "is it sensible—I mean, will they think it is practical—to say that play and recreation are really not just frills you ought to add on when you haven't any other thing to do with your budget?"

He laughed out then, and said, "I should like to meet the social work agency that has anything left out of any budget! It's easy to see that you haven't had the bitter end—the administrative end—to meet yet, young lady!"

Then he explained that he felt in a few years even business houses,—yes, even factories and mills—would provide their working people with periods for recreation. It seemed rather funny, for I knew mill workers. I had heard, since childhood, their stories. Play for workers—paid by employers?

But he told me of what was being done in Europe, in Germany, for working people. He described to me how physicians had found that a man, after resting a bit, could do better work than if he went on without pausing all day. "Why, some day," he smiled, "people won't work on Saturdays! It will be a holiday in which salesgirls and mill workers together will go out to play and forget."

It did seem funny, then!

But when he went on to speak of his plans, the singing groups he would organize, the classes in summer playgrounds, the clubs for mothers, country games for children and vacations for the families out of tenements,—it seemed real and beautiful, so real that I said, "Why, I should like to do that, too!"

He looked down at me then, and said, very quietly indeed, his voice low, "And will you not do it with me—with me all my life?"

That was what I had wanted him to ask me, of course, ever since I had known him; though I had not known it. I had loved him all the time, and he me. He was tempered steel to my fire; he was quiet to my swift running. He was reality to my imaginings. We were very happy.

Then there were my mother and my father to write.

It is needless to tell how bitter was the cry of my father. I felt, for a time, that I could not endure to hurt him so. I broke my engagement. But can one do without that which is part of one's very living? My lover came to me and asked me if I had not him, too, to consider. He asked me just two things: if I loved him and if I was certain of his love for me. I knew the answer to both. So we were married, and in my own city, and with my mother giving us her blessing. Her eyes were swollen with crying, but she spoke her blessing to us and called my husband "my son." That is what he has always been to her.

Curiously enough, my husband's people did not even

find our marriage incongruous. They were artists, writers, cosmopolites. They had no real religious or, perhaps, even national ties. They accepted me for his wife and a woman, and I entered our new life.

The settlement house was shocked, however. It was apparent that they felt a good man had gone astray. Our head worker gave us a set of silver butter-knives, and said she hoped we would be happy, but she spoke as if she hoped we would repent. The New England lady looked as if she knew that was what one could expect of a man whose father had come from England —and she gave us a set of Emerson. The English lady kissed me, strangely enough, and whispered she had been in love, once, and my husband was a fine man.

Not one of my cousins in New York would come to see us. I had married a Gentile. But Simeon sent me a very lovely little jade god that he must have sought for weeks, and with it came a note: "New gods."

VIII

LOVE stories, says Merrick somewhere, are full-length portraits; marriage stories are bust-length. Only in the past decade has the story of marriage been told without a tongue in the cheek, without tragedy as its excuse in this country's literature.

We went for the month of our first love to northern Maine, along the sea, to a little village where strangers had surely never come before, and we lived in a house in which the master had gone to eternal quiet for many years, a tiny house that had been closed almost a score of years before we took it. We cooked our meals together in the bright kitchen; we scoured the wood, that had been covered with dust for years, to bright yellow again; we put curtains in the low, squeaky windows, and a bright cover on the high, old bed. We brought logs into the square, prim parlor, and in the evening, with the wood burning in the little fireplace, we sat and felt how beautiful it was for us to be together.

My lover was a Doctor of Philosophy and twenty-seven, and I a staid social worker, a Bachelor of Arts and twenty-two, but the education of our time had not thought it necessary to teach two young people how to be man and wife. We went to our little house, and for a little while we were just brother and sister, only clinging close to one another, seeking one another.

It may seem curious, but this is just as it was with us.

Then we bought an old medical book and read about marriage, and in the little house we made our marriage solemn and complete, in the sunlight and the warm summer. It is strange that so much has been written about the love of men and women not married, and so little of the love of man and wife!

We were young, and we were well. We were mysterious and beautiful to one another. I had, all my life, thought of the womanhood in me as something rather to be deprecated; a man, I knew, of my faith, must absent himself from his wife, as from defilement, at certain holy times of his life. And, always, she must humbly beg God to pardon her that she is a woman. Had I not read, in the prayer book, the words my brothers, my father, all my uncles, spoke daily—thanking God they were not woman?

But my love found me God-worthy because I was a woman. He found me holy.

I wished, though I did not speak my wish, that I were big and tall, made like a great vase, for my lover; not small and slight and white, like a fragile boy. But he seemed to love me for just that which I was. "Little Boy," he called me; and that is his name for me to-day, though I am not now young, only tall and slight still, as then, nearly eighteen years ago.

My father, when he had married my mother, had spent four days in the public eye, listening to the songs and impromptu verses of the bad-chan, or bard, and the long rabbinical speeches of the twenty rabbis whom his father-in-law, as a great rabbi and a wealthy man, had invited to his only child's marriage to a brilliant young scholar.

My lover and I spent our first days in the sun, by

shining waters, with none to see us, to speak to us, but our own hearts. Only the stout, lame old captain who took us out sometimes to sea, would come, grin at us and say, "Eh, well, it's good fishing to-day." We would be shy lest he should see how much we wished to be alone; we would go with him and come back to the warmth and the perfect peace of our home, shut off from all others.

We read and we dreamed a great deal. We planned together a life that was to remake the world. I was not to be like the women I knew, tied down to children, a home, drudgery. I was to be free, free with my love to enrich my freedom. I was, of course, a suffragist, in those days when to be a suffragist was to be something erratic and even immoral. I wanted a career and love, not a career and the sacrifice of love, as had the old women in the settlement house, as did the young women going even now into social work.

To paint a full-length portrait of a marriage there must be the physical life of man and wife in it. That is very difficult to do. Writers who describe love processes or manifestations describe the effect of love memories or love desires upon themselves. They do not seem to be able to write of love, even when they are fiction writing, apart from their own personal memories or disappointments.

My own life had been spent, all through girlhood, in a home where the dominant thought was religious, the culture based on religious literature. My father was a fragile, slender man, a scholar. Women were supposed to be strong and well, to function as mothers and wives of the race. Men were best when they looked to be students, so absorbed in the spiritual life of

God and the intellectual absorption of the Talmud that they were just men enough to be able to carry on the race. The Mosaic tradition made for candor in the discussion of all marital relationships, and the European background from which my folks, European Jews, came made for the utmost lack of embarrassment in discussing marital arrangements, results and failures. A childless woman was considered not only a pitiful spectacle, but a failure in the community and a burden to an unfortunate husband, denied through her the blessing of fatherhood, the highest in Judaism, which aims to give to God many sons for His honor.

All through my girlhood I was accustomed to hearing myself spoken of disparagingly because I was so thin—thin as a boy. I had no great, firm breasts, no splendid hips, such as my cousins and aunts possessed. During college I had lived with my uncle and aunt, near the University buildings, because our town was too far away to make walking to school convenient. Besides, on Friday after class I would have had to ride home, and then perhaps be late, intruding on the Sabbath, if I had lived with my parents. My aunt was an uneducated woman, inferior to my uncle, a handsome peasant Jewess from a Lithuanian village, whom he had seen while a student and had married against the wish and, indeed, to the horror, of his family. She had wide shoulders, splendid thighs that swung as she walked, a lovely straight back and a bust like a rampart before her. Her dark, bright hair she refused to cut, and wore like a great silk cap on her head. She ruled my uncle absolutely; scholar though he was, writer and acknowledged leader, he dared not deny her authority. She treated him like a child, but an inspired child. Yet he did not question her; she was so majestically a female, a "woman who came out of the Bible."

She used to fret over me. She fed me goose fat on bread, made me eat warm dough, and one day put glass caps on my skinny young arms to bleed me, to "get the thinness out" of me. She was fond of me and concerned because I was so utterly thin. She had no girls. She was a mother of men, seven handsome sons each of whom has become a factor in American business life, none of them inheriting the intellectual or spiritual urge of their father, my uncle.

But all her care did not make me any stouter. I remained looking like a thin young student, who might have come from and been, one of the emaciated "day students" in the Yeshiva that my father and her husband knew—young boys half starving, studying and living as best they could on the piety and kindness of the community that kept alive, but barely alive, its holy men.

My father's father was an ascetic, who fasted three days each week. My mother's people, though wealthy, denied themselves the grosser needs of the body.

I knew that workingmen, ignorant men and peasants, were strong, vulgarly robust. But scholars must be thin, even perhaps rather sickly. The thinner and sicklier the better!

My husband I had noticed, even as a student, the first summer I saw him, because of his difference from the rest of the students. The others were Middle Westerners, husky and even freckled with sunshine. He was thin, tall, ascetic, the type made familiar in New England. His fine, colorless skin might have been the skin of a scholar in my own childhood. His shoulders did not have the Jewish rabbinical stoop, but they were not flung back in animal arrogance, as were those of the men I knew. He did not look at me masterfully, and with the violent impulse of possession, that some of the other men who liked me had expressed.

I found that I was right in my intuitive judgment of him. Gentle he was, kind as the kindest, dearest, father. He was a lover who made no demands, who asked little of me.

Our love, though it was new and mysterious to us, so new to love, was not something violent and overmastering that carried us away and made us realize one another in a new way. It only made us meet one another more closely. We did not find the "grand passion" that one reads of in books; for that matter, at the time I had not read of grand passions. I was interested in poetry and in economics. I seldom read novels, and never foreign novels. The love stories I knew were in the Bible, and they were stories of love in the light of God's approval or disapproval, not those of the hunger of the lovers or their happiness. I did not think of love as something that was a hunger. It was a service, a gesture one made, to express the closest companionship, trust, if it can be put so. And I think my husband felt so, too.

More dear to me, more thrilling, too, maybe, was the fact that my husband, in this new communion and daily living together of our minds, wanted me to write. He felt that now I must write real things, and that I could. Not as a way of earning a living. That never entered his mind, but as something that would fulfil my life, perhaps as a child would later. He meant me to use all that I had seen of life and would see in books, as I would have used it in music were I a musician.

That I, too, dreamed. But I did not want, just then, to write. Once, as a girl, I had thought I might act, because I could recite at school, it may have been. I went to the local stock company and saw the manager, but when I began to speak to him and saw his loathsome face, coarse, beer sodden, I left. My father had taught me to loathe low-grade men. I never thought again of the stage. Later, I planned, perhaps, to write for the newspapers. But I did not even know how to go to ask for such work. In our life, with my father knowing only Jews, and Jewish scholars at that, no one even understood me. I sent a poem in English, once, to a Jewish newspaper in New York, that published an English page, but I never again heard of it. I decided I could not write. Then, when Professor Raphael betrayed my faith in Jews, made me see the Jewish intellectual and artist as a coward hiding under the shelter of Christian marriage, I decided I could not write, not for a long time, at least.

One thing I knew I would never do. I would not teach. My father taught Hebrew and hated teaching. He hated the juvenile mind, though submitting to the torture for the glory of imparting the holy tongue to unregenerate American youth. I would not teach, I told myself.

When I left college, one of my friends, another Jewish girl, tried to obtain a position in a small college as instructor in Latin. Her record was excellent, and she was charming in many ways, admirable as a leader of young girls. She sent her credentials, was asked to come to see the board, passing their testing questions, and then when asked her religion, replied she was a Jewess. She was refused the position quite bluntly. Another girl I knew, though bearing a college degree, had waited for years in high school in our town, and finally in despair took a grade school class, "until a vacancy occurred in high school." Long after my third child was born, she was still teaching in grade school.

I would not submit myself to humiliation by people I knew. Even if I had to work to live, I would rather work in a shop. Then I heard of social work, the new beginning in human relations. I was to find there that when people of limited minds come even to new ideals, they bring their limitations with them. My experiences in social work taught me that to be a Jewess was as much a handicap in social work as in education.

Only my husband had loved me as a woman, and for my woman's mind. Now he loved me for the gift he said he found in me. He pointed out to me that it was a rare and womanly gift I had, a beautiful one. He wanted to cherish and protect me so that all I knew would keep my point of view apart, delicate, feminine, unembittered. I would write lovely things.

I wanted to write. The thought pulled at me and urged me, as it had since, as a little girl of twelve, I wrote my first novel in a yellow tablet in Yiddish, while the rest of my class sat studying geography. But I did not know whether I wanted to live apart from life. I did not know whether I wanted my writing to be a gem on our love, or an instrument, keen and decisive, with which I would cut a pattern in life for myself.

I did not know whether I wanted to be a wife, living in my husband's love, or a woman building her career.

That first year I did not really try to know. I was happy. Never had I had a friend before, and here was my friend. I had had the authority of my father, to obey, and to obey without question, with loss of his love as penalty if I did anything to displease him. My husband gave me his love, and the authority was mine to exert over him. My wish—how sweet it was—was always enough to make a law for him.

I had read books—and my people had not even understood them. They had not approved my reading them. Here, in my lover, my friend, I found one who walked side by side with me, who found delight in discovering the ways in which my mind chose to go, and who walked with me, full of wisdom, of clear light.

I had wanted to know—well, things—about art and music and great people long dead, not great just because they were Jews, which alone my father knew, or great because they were in history books, such as my teachers knew, but because of things which I honored. And these people in the past my lover knew; he had read so much, he knew so much. Books that I had never heard of were in his mind's memory, and people came from his stored-up mind to me like a procession of glamorous heroes. How beautiful it all was! And he was like a captain of ship on a sea he loved to sail; he made the journeys with me with pride, with a tender sort of radiant pride.

Of children we did not speak. At that time birth control was not a word spoken. There was a sin called preventing the conception of children, but Margaret Sanger had not yet appeared. Girls became pregnant and had abortions.

But married women had as many children as fate

chose. If they were much advanced they might live only at certain times with their husbands, and have protection against pregnancy so. That was mentioned, in an awed whisper, by prurient minded, but kindly, married women, to young brides. One spoke of it to me, and made me feel as if she had torn the door open on our love by even mentioning my husband and me in this way.

No, I did not think of children. Sometimes I wanted a child, to look exactly like my husband, and perhaps one to look like my mother. But we did not speak of that to each other. We only hoped that we would not have a child soon. We wanted to know and enjoy our dear, rare friendship, without another, even our own child, for a little while. Once, a friend told me she did not mean to have any children at all; she meant to have a job, and her husband knew it and agreed. But I did not ask how she meant to accomplish this thing. I was not even interested that her husband agreed.

One thing only remained with me. She meant to have a job. She spoke of that job of hers with decision. She described it quickly, in detail. She had been training for it before her marriage, had been working at it since her marriage. She was to take a postgraduate course now, and then get a position. She was sure she would have the chance of becoming a leader in her work. It was a new work—technician in hospitals.

She spoke of her work, this married woman, not as something to be done in spite of something else, or because she had nothing else to do, or apologetically. She spoke of it just as a man would; she spoke of it not as an amateur, but professionally, just as my husband spoke of his. There was no tender note of protection her husband used to her in speaking of this work of hers; he saw it just as his own. It was her career. Their jobs were equally important to each of them and to each other.

A strange restlessness came, as always, to me then. That was what I had planned. I had meant to do social work, to learn about life, to earn my living, to *write.*

I had always meant to write.

Love—that I had not thought of. It came, and it was dear to have it. But must I really give up the *career* of writing because of my career of marriage?

My husband was modern. He said I must not give up my writing, that I must do anything I wanted to do, just as he did what he chose. Only, he added, *he* must earn our living. Whatever *I* did I could do without thinking whether it was successful or not; only whether it made me happy.

I took his hands in mine, I recall, and put his palms against my cheek. But he did not feel how hot my cheeks were against his palms. I kissed him. But as I kissed him then, I know I wished he had said that my work was as *practically* a need to me, as his—that it was as essential to our life as his. If work was to be judged by him by its practical value to his life and mine, I would have wanted him to see that which I chose to do, too, as practical, and helpful as his own.

I know that, in the back of my mind, I put my writing away then and there. I had no faith whatever in my ability as a writer. I could not earn money by writing; that was it.

But I could earn money in another way. I could do social work.

I AM A WOMAN—AND A JEW

My husband was amused when I told him I meant to do social work after our marriage. "You needn't," he said, holding me close. But he felt I was so young that to wait for writing would be well. He thought I might do social work as a volunteer, without pay. I was, however, determined not to do that, not to be an amateur. I wanted to work just as he did. I would not be happy otherwise, I told him.

He took me on his knee then, kissed me, and told me I was a violent feminist. But he liked it in me, I know. In fact, he was, himself, in his quiet way a feminist, too. I had been a member of a committee to arrange a meeting for Anna Howard Shaw, and when she came, he did the then striking thing of standing at the door of the little hall and greeting each person as she came in—for alas, only one other man came. I did not go with the suffrage party to Washington on any of its trips, but I saved money from lunches, and sent it to them anonymously.

"So you want a career," he smiled, "and a husband tacked on?"

It was a striking thing, but I said, seriously, "Haven't you one with me tacked on?"

He kissed me then, and laughed, very tenderly indeed.

I meant to try to get some work, some social work, as soon as I could.

Was I not a college woman, a trained social worker? I had a gift—not a brilliant gift—but a fairly rare one, of making all people trust me, of winning their minds and making them show me what they thought and felt, of making them remember, back in the past, and tell me of it, because they always knew I understood. I was not academic, not statistical, as often I so much wanted to be—exact, rapid, impersonal—but I had the quality of persuading people to give me facts. It was valuable in social research; it would be easy, said my husband, to find some one to put my facts into long tables and records. Mine was the delicate job of winning from the human mind and heart the precious material of human life for those who wished to analyze, to study it. I did not quite believe him, I thought he was so kind only because he was blinded a bit with love of me. But I let myself be lifted in his arms, held to his heart, and dreamed of the work—that wonderful work—I would do, to prove to him that I could be wise and effective, too, as well as be his love and his little friend.

We left our tiny house to go to his new work, and opened a home there, a truly wonderful house to me, whose own home had always been rather poor, made for piety and not for beauty. We brought to it pictures found in New York, books, old bits of furniture of my husband's mother—and the little jade god my cousin Simeon sent me. There came, too, a gift from some one to whom I had not written of my marriage, from Professor Raphael—without his wife's name, or their address—a lovely picture of Chase's girl in the gray kimono. My lover could not understand why he sent this picture, but one evening, as we sat in the soft light, he put down his book, went over to me and said, "Why, it's you, dear!" And though of course most vague, there was a certain resemblance, but only for one who wished to see it. I did not feel anything but wonder that I had ever had that long, sharp stab in my heart, when I heard, five years before, that my ideal was to marry another woman. I have never been able to think of myself as living with my life dissevered from my love. I have always felt that the years before he came were simply like the long prologue to a story, and the beginning came with great banners flying, with music. It was not until years later that I thought, one day, of what Raphael had said to me: "Don't marry a Jew." But to me the real words were: "Do not marry any one who is not your husband." There could not have been any other.

There was work that would be open shortly in the city, a job for which my training and ability would fit me. We were told, though, that there would be some difficulty. The board would object to giving a job to a married woman. A woman who married ought to—though it was beginning to be debated by these modern women—stay home!

The only thing that mitigated my wanting the work was that my husband, of course, was a social worker. And social workers get much honor (sometimes); they have great responsibilities; and they have such small salaries. A salary earned by me would help, and it was needed.

When I had worked on my husband's staff before, my salary had been $15 a week and "maintenance." His salary had been $25 a week and also maintenance. I had always had more than enough money. I used to send some home to mother.

Here he received a great increase, a really fine salary, $2,000 a year. But our rent now was $40 a month; our maid cost $8 a week, for I was helping him as a volunteer in order to have the necessary experience in the city, in case I would need a job later (and also because his staff was too small, alas). It was very difficult, apparently, for two to live on less than one—with a house to maintain instead of "maintenance."

I hoped that the job would come. I went to see the board director who was most friendly to us. He smiled, listened again to my plans and said he was certain he could persuade the board to take me, even if I were a married woman. After all, I had unique training; the only other applicant was a former stenographer.

I went home, elated. I wanted to be at work; to begin my own work. I felt rather tired and dizzy with the suspense. I lay down to rest, our little maid with me. I felt dreadfully ill. I fell back, nearly fainting. She lifted me up, held me to her broad darky bosom, and said, "Thah! Thah! honey! Little honey! Doan't be skeered! It's nature, don't be skeered!"

I was to be a mother in six months.

IX

I HAVE had hundreds, many hundreds, of women come to me with the story of the coming of their first baby, since that day, some of them young brides, some frightened, foolish girls meeting the unexpected penalty of a sin, or a bit of pleasure, other women coming to tell me that their dreams were to be at last realized in the coming of a child to their marriage. I have had perhaps a hundred or so young women come to me, asking me for jobs and telling me that they were expecting a child. But that is all within the past five or six years. Invariably, when a young woman came to tell me that she wanted some work, and wanted it although her baby was coming, I have managed to see that some sort of work was found for her. In fact, in the past few years, many of the women I know have entered, or have certainly, continued, their work in their careers—professions, or business—until nature demanded that they give themselves to the ordeal of bringing forth their child. And then they have, oftenest, gone back to their jobs, as soon as it was possible.

But eighteen years ago, for a woman to be pregnant and to expect to hold a job would have been so horrifying, so unnatural a thing, that even to think of it was impossible to me. An "expectant mother" waited for her infant, and thereafter she devoted herself to it. Whatever nonsense she might have picked up about wanting a career (and, perhaps, she was not so much to blame for wishing these inconsequential, unimportant activities in the absence of her natural work) was, it was assumed, simply blown away, like chaff before the wind of reality, when her real and her one job came—to be a mother. To be the mother of a child, and to have a "job" besides was not to be thought of, unless one were at the same time a widow or the wife of a very ill-paid workingman.

I did not think of it for myself. I was dismayed, of course. I did not whisper to my husband any of the honored sentences made famous in novels and plays by young mothers-to-be. I sat during a long afternoon in our parlor and wondered what we would do. We had absolutely nothing saved, for my husband was a dreamer, almost excessively unfamiliar with the management of money, of which he had always had enough for his own exceedingly simple needs. His mother, who had a small income, had put him through college, but thereafter he had been responsible to himself. She was living in England and had only sent us a most kind and loving letter with a check for the purchase of a gift. We had, immediately, bought a piano with it. We had planned, as if it must be so because we wished it, not to have children for some time—oh, for a long time.

We had not spoken of it. Eighteen years ago even wives, young and shy, did not speak of everything to their husbands, I think. But we had understood. All our plans, as we discussed them, were for a few years of love and work, of development of my life, with rest and companionship a sort of crown after the years of poverty and hard work behind. They were to be the beginning of a kingdom of achievement, in which some day, when we were ready, a young prince was to be brought.

There was so much to think of. I took out a little book the head worker of our settlement house had given me when we were married, a little book on "The Young Mother." It was most delicately worded: "When a lady is in a delicate condition, she will require much rest." "Port wine twice daily, but not to excess, is excellent, and helpful later in providing a rich supply—" I blushed deeply, put my hand involuntarily to my breast and put the book aside. I had not thought of that; that this was my body I was giving, not only my future, my time—but all of me—to my child.

I was no more practical than my lover. I suppose I should have gone to a physician and "made arrangements." Instead, I did not so much as speak of it to him for over a week. I lived in a daze, and when he asked, troubled, what was ill with me and pleaded that I should not be so tense and expectant about the new job I had been promised, that it was almost certainly mine, if I just waited, I looked at him and did not see him.

The letter offering me the job came, and I wrote a letter in answer, saying that for reasons which had arisen I could not take it. I thought I was very discreet, that I jealously kept a secret by writing so. But a little while later, at a luncheon to which a number of the social workers had come, and to which my husband persuaded me at last to go, too, the wife of my friendly board member came up, put a broad motherly hand on my shoulder, and said, kindly, "Be sure to come to me, and let me help you, my dear. Be sure to come, please."

I could not speak; again that burning blush came to my face. I looked toward my husband, and, alarmed at my appearance, he drew me aside. "What is it?" he asked.

"I am going to have our baby," I whispered.

My mother's five children had all come easily, as if nature had planned her for that function; she bloomed before each child. Her childhood in her father's big home, where she had play and sunshine, servants and good food, to make her strong and well, stood her in good stead.

I had been all my life my father's child, a student. In the house, when Hannah and Etta had helped the old colored woman, and mother, with the housework, I had done the "sitting work," sewing, mending, writing for father. Later, I taught, tutored. I had been too incompetent at cooking and housekeeping for mother to waste time on me. Because we had two other girls in the family to do it so very much better, I had done no housework to speak of. I was, consequently, a very poor, a very inexperienced housekeeper. Our colored servant, coming in for "light work" to our pretty house, knew well how little I understood the work I so gravely ordered her to do. She had things her own way, and it was only because of that innate kindliness of negroes that she did her work really well.

But I saw that we could not face a baby and keep a servant, too. I must keep house alone, and why should I not, I demanded to my husband's sharp protest, when there was nothing else I had to do now, for a while, anyhow? It would be fun to learn!

I was to find that, of all jobs, housework is the least fascinating for the student to learn. I could not become excited about cooking dinner, about dusting the house, nor even about making the beds. It was not, try as I did to tell myself otherwise, just as interesting as meeting twenty people to talk over a new issue, to help devise a plan for the city's play, to hear about books, music, to discuss the success of a great undertaking in a far state.

My husband thought I was getting thin. But in the evenings we sat and talked of the future, of our child. We would not say whether it was to be a boy or a girl, just a little living thing. Then I was supremely happy. But it did not seem real to me, except when we two spoke of it together so. At other times the illness that came increasingly over me was like something dreadful, alive and not part of me, that had taken possession of me.

I worked madly to try to forget it. I dusted, scrubbed, tried to learn new recipes. It was, in a way, fun to do the recipes. They were so shocking!

This was the reason. I had eaten "unclean" food —made outside Mosaic dietary law—for years now. But I had never seen that food prepared. I now, myself, made food such as would have set my home by the ears. That was a sort of perverse wildness! My husband laughed aloud at this wickedness in the kitchen. But as I moved about the kitchen, I thought of my mother. I wanted her, I needed her so that I could have cried, all the way over the long miles between us, the long years, for her to come. I wrote her a letter, telling her I was expecting a baby. A very little letter came, guarded and loving, but she did not say she would come to me. My child was a Gentile's child, I understood.

I did not want strange women to come to speak to

me, intimately, of my coming motherhood. I had not the glibness they seemed to have in describing physical and mental disturbances. I would receive my guests and listen, but without speaking myself. They were kind, but I did not seek kindness. I wanted my mother with me. I did not want these strange, kind women.

It was interesting, however, to note one thing: that all these women in our social set seemed suddenly to have appeared from behind a wall, where non-Jewish women had hidden before from me. All non-Jewish women, at high school, college or in my work, had been of three sorts. One was cold and distant, simply greeting people and saying little beyond the necessary words. The second was almost effusive, speaking too quickly, too smoothly, too anxiously and pleasantly. The third was abrupt, curt, businesslike, making no attempt to get through her conversation quickly, but permitting no smallest bit of personal color to enter into her conversation.

This last type I liked best. I was too shy, too quiet, to be happy with cold, crisp people; I was too shy to feel comfortable with gushing women. I liked the impersonal, businesslike women best.

And, suddenly, here I found scores of friends of all ages and kinds, who were just like the women I had known in my mother's circle, in mine as a girl. They spoke amiably to one another, yet "whispered behind their backs." They were kind and gentle, and yet envious, too. They were hard and vain, and yet marvelous mothers. They spoke English, and not Yiddish with Galician, Polish, Hungarian or Austrian accents, but their speech was just the same as that of all women I had known.

It was not until much later that I realized why I saw this new aspect in American women revealed. It was because no one knew I was a Jewess. When I declared I was a Jewess, it did not appear to matter, since I had married a non-Jew I was accepted as my husband's wife. I was just "Mrs. Morton." Our friends did not feel the need to wear a friendly, a too friendly, a gushing or a defensive mask with me now; they were themselves, just women.

But for all their friendliness, I did not want any of them. I wanted something more in a friend than I was offered. I wanted something spiritual—something that my husband used to describe to me, tenderly laughing, as "sacrificial." It was so: I wanted a friend who could feel it in her to sacrifice herself for an idea.

And soon I found her. Her husband was a young newspaper man, she a trained nurse. He had been all over the world, had gone to China as a cook's assistant, to Turkey, even to Siberia. He could talk, quickly and well. She was small and very dainty, with gray eyes, bright, dark hair, and little, quiet, competent hands. They had a child of seven, a husky boy. I used to think that I wished our son—if he were to be a son—would be like that boy of theirs, with his dark gray eyes, quick smile and straight little shoulders.

It was to this new friend, Lily, that I told I was to have a baby.

She smiled and said, "You little goose, I knew that months ago. I saw it in your skin and eyes." It appeared one could tell a mother by many things. She described the changes that took place in me.

Then she said, "Who is your doctor?"

I had none, of course. Lily lifted her brows inquiringly, and I said, "My mother is a Jewess, and she has the old feeling that a midwife is really more sympathetic in—for a baby."

Lily nodded.

"You'll have to have a doctor," she said. She arranged for the doctor, hospital, nurse. The sum staggered me. It would be over five hundred dollars, by the time I had bought things for the baby. And there might be more! My husband smiled, and said wasn't it worth it?

At first, he had been troubled at my fears, my worries. But bit by bit, as the months passed, a warm radiance seemed to come from his eyes to me. He had lived much alone since his mother went abroad and his father died. I was all he had. Now there would be a child.

"Oh, we'll manage," he said, when I spoke of our limited means.

He insisted on having the servant again as the months crowded to their end. And then a servant became necessary. I became suddenly ill, so terribly ill that for a little while, it was thought I would die. I lay at the point of death. And out of that hour in which I touched the hand of death, two months before her time, came my daughter.

I spent nearly a year as an invalid. It was a strange world, a world of white hot pillows, of long backaches, of the little cooing voice of my child. I had to see her walk while I lay in bed; I held my hands out to her as I moved about in my wheel chair.

She was sweet, and she was unbelievably beautiful. She was a little Jewish rose, though, gold and amber, with skin like that of a Spanish princess; she looked like my mother's mother. She was tiny, but vivid and gay. Was there anything I could have dreamed more lovely?

To my husband she was a star from heaven. I was "Little Boy"; she was "Little Maid." I was so dreadfully ill and so happy that year!

My friend Lily would come in, play with my baby, give quiet orders to my nurse and our servant, then sit and talk. Sometimes she brought in her little son. We were so happy that it seemed wicked. I used to feel glad I was ill, because, surely, then God would not think I was too blessed!

My husband in the evening would lift me in his arms, carry me from room to room that I "might see the house," for I was, ridiculously enough, rather in awe of the capable housekeeper Lily had found. I had to see how she ran my home only when she went out in the evenings. My nurse was different; she was sweet and quick and young. I felt at ease with her. I have had big women responsible to me since, but I always remember in my subconscious mind, the respectful fear I used to have for that housekeeper, Mrs. Norris, widow of a floor-walker, a good Methodist, and clean as a Dutch street! She was so good to my baby, so dreadfully capable with me!

As long as I live, that year I lived will be my husband's year, for me to repay. I was not wife, nor sweetheart, nor even child and playmate—not so much as a friend, to him. He just gave me his life that year, and gave me mine with it.

One evening Lily did not come, and when she did she was quieter than usual. It was late in the year, I was sitting up, and even eating custard with my baby at table now. I felt that I was becoming a woman again.

"Where's Tim these days?" I asked Lily, for he had not been over for a long time.

Her gray eyes looked toward me, and she stood up. She was very small, very tiny, as she stood there, so small that she seemed not much bigger than my little girl. "Tim's gone," she said then, her voice quite even. "He went away—and got married." She did not look at me, but her eyes came to me presently.

I did not understand. "How funny!" I cried. Tim was so funny!

But my husband had risen, too. He stood tall, immovable, at the head of the table. It was to me, though, that Lily spoke. "I couldn't tell you before; you'd have broken off with me, and I wanted to come over," she said. She did not say she wanted to come over because I needed her, that my people had refused to come, and she alone had been my friend.

She said, "Tim and I—you know Tim. He was always a free-thinker, he didn't believe in marriage." There was just beginning talk then of a new freedom, so new that it went beyond marriage, but even tolerant social workers did not speak of it except with a smile. I looked at her, my eyes wide, so that they seemed to strain in order to see, to strain until they hurt.

"Tim and I—well, he met a girl and they were married about four months ago," she said. "He's sending a check for Timmy every month," she added conscientiously.

This was sin. The scarlet woman. My best friend.

I thought of the times Tim had been drunk, and she had gone out to work, so that they might have food. I thought of the time he had the grippe, and she had nursed him, and when it became pneumonia she had not taken off her clothes or gotten into bed for four days and nights. "Tim, dear," she had said, very quietly, sitting by his bed, calling him back to life, bringing him back. She worked for her living, for she was a trained nurse, and that, folks felt, excused people. Trained nurses were not very high-grade people anyhow. One of our friends had warned me that, though she was a nice woman, I ought to be less —well—close, because trained nurses were what nurses are!

And was it not true? She was not married to her child's father.

I put my head on the table, and did what I never do, what I have so seldom done in my life for myself. I cried. Because I was so weak, and life was so hard to put into rules, I cried.

Was this the scarlet woman of the Bible? Magdalen? Magdalen had glamor and beauty and a high nobility crowning her. This woman had poverty, work, neglect and only a great love, empty at last.

There is no need to say that Lily has remained my friend. She taught me that life is bigger than human rules, just as I had learned that religion was wider than human creeds. She has been my dear and my true friend to this day, and her son is my son's friend, a wise and older friend.

X

THEN came the end of the year and the reckoning. I could walk, I could send my servants away. And I looked into the future. We were over a thousand dollars in debt. My husband's salary was not increased. The baby needed me and took all my time.

If anyone tries to tell me that poverty is necessary for young people, he will not find a sympathetic listener. Nothing in all the world is more terrible, more destroying, than poverty to young life! Ah, yes, I know one hears differently. But it isn't true.

Loyalty may grow out of work and suffering together. But there must be enough time for one to realize that loyalty, to think out one's love. Riches are not necessary, no; but poverty is a blight to youth.

We had $2,000 a year; we owed $1,000. We owed so much because of my husband's honorable position. He spoke before clubs. His name was in the newspapers. He was a figure in the city. He was an honorable figure. Was he not one of the leading, one of the far-seeing social workers? And was not he, therefore, obliged not to think of how his family was to live? Credit was given him on the strength of his position in the community; let him trouble about paying.

If we had lived in the Ghetto I could have managed, I think, on $1,000 a year. For it never occurred to either of us not to pay at once, now I was well. But we had to dress "decently," live "properly." We had a professional position to maintain. We had to have friends to dinner at times. We had our baby.

How does one do it? I do not think of it often now. I learned to wash clothes; I sat until midnight and stitched my husband's shirt, made by hand, since we could not so much as afford a machine. I remember one day he had to speak at a club, and I sat all morning putting in a patch on the knee of his trousers where the cloth was so thin his skin showed! We used to laugh at it, but it became so little funny after a long while.

On the evenings when we had guests, we did not eat dinner that evening, but waited until our "spread" was served them, making that our evening meal. We never went to a play or a concert. I had no time for books. I was a machine, keeping our home going. Everything depended on me.

Our baby was rosy and strong and adorable. Our home was tidy and sweet. People said I was "such a fine young wife." Well-to-do women patronized my home-made clothes, my tired, listless hands.

My husband and I used to look at each other and wonder, tiredly, where we had lost one another. At night we were too weary even for our love. I was a machine. I was not a man's love.

He wanted a larger salary, but his board could not increase it. He would try elsewhere, we decided. But $2,000 was large, in those days, for social workers; there wouldn't be much more.

Meanwhile there was a "survey" to be made of the city. His board allowed him an investigator to make the survey; he did much of the work after his other hours. There was one board member who did not like him; thought he was "too high toned"; not respectful enough. Sometimes when he saw this man on the street, he did not even greet him! But the truth is that he did not even see him. He is so near-sighted, so a dreamer, that he often passes me, to this day, without seeing me. He passes our house in getting home. But this did not help him at the office or in getting a salary raise. That man became his antagonist, even his enemy. A business man with money who pays your salary is to be noticed when you, a doctor of philosophy, pass him!

There was so much to do in the survey that another worker was needed. The survey was to show whether a new playground was needed in a certain Polish neighborhood. Each person in the tenements there was to be interviewed; the playlife of the children found, their standing in school, their standing in the juvenile courts of the city. It was a necessary and fine thing to do, and essentially part of my husband's work in recreation. This one man refused to have another worker added to the staff, and his insistence won out.

Long lines had been drawn about my husband's fine mouth now; there were hollows under his dark blue eyes. He came in one evening, and put down his bag, took off his glasses and slumped in the chair.

"B—," he said, quietly, naming the man unfriendly to him, "said at the executive meeting to-day he thought this whole survey was a waste; he didn't see that I had done anything but waste money up to now."

I was washing diapers; my hands were sudsy, my arms hurt, as they hurt all the time. I felt so tired and so stupid with tiredness that often I did not even think. When our baby was ill at night, I would stay up all night, for I slept lightly, then work all day. I used to go to bed right after supper, at eight o'clock at latest, my husband sitting up alone until he, too, would creep in silently beside me. In the evenings he did the dishes, and sometimes he washed the baby things. He kept the yard and lawn tidy, and, when he could, he would help me with the heavier part of the laundry. But this evening I looked up, sharply.

"What makes him say that?" I asked.

"He says I've spent two months gathering a lot of data, and what's the use of it? Just expensive cards filled with scrawling!" He looked at me with a little twisted smile I had not known before in his face.

"My dear," I could only say. And we sat, side by side, still, for a long time, until it was dark and the stars shone through the windows at us.

I knew what I could do. Had I not training in arranging records, in just this work? It was dreary, clerical and long, but I knew how to do it.

And of course I did it, as he did my work, too, for me.

We used to sit up until dawn at those records, arranging facts, drawing conclusions from them. We found the heart of that survey. It was hard; my eyes would be blinded with sleep, but it would be foolish to say I was not happy. In this hard work, in this tedious work, I found joy. All day I worked with my hands. But here, at night, I worked with my mind. I worked at something I loved to do and could do, and I did it with my lover.

We finished the study, and his report on the survey was written, and a new playground was opened because of it, becoming one of the busiest in the city. It has been acknowledged since to be one of the most influential influences in checking child delinquency in its neighborhood, for bad children are children who have not right homes, or right play—if they are but healthy children, too, of course.

I watched the playground being fitted up. And then I did a striking thing. I asked for a job as playground director. I shocked the board. A married woman, with a child—working? Shocking!

But my work in making the survey was known. It was Lily who had told of it, to one of our friends. My previous experience somehow was spoken of. I was asked one day to come to see the president of the board. I went, troubled—were they so angry that they were reprimanding their director's wife for wanting to work? But I set my lips, too. Nobody would make me say I was wrong. I knew I could do a job and have my baby cared for, too, at the same time!

The chairman of the board was a merchant, old, stout, kind, with gold-rimmed glasses and a pronounced, pleasant German accent. He was a grandfather, he told me, he had heard of our "dear little child." Then, abruptly he said, "I hear you want to work."

I felt my heart pound, but I said, "Our baby is three now. She is strong and well. But—but somehow we need a larger income, for—for several reasons. I am a professional woman—just like a doctor. Only my profession is social work. So I thought I might help —with our income—by getting some work?"

The old gentleman asked, "And let your baby be killed while you are away?"

I wanted to tell him about the working mothers who went to the mills, the factories, the stores, while their babies were at home. I wanted to talk to him about the wealthy women, even on his board, who left children to servants, not only while they sought pleasure, but when they did civic work. But I did not; I was never an arguing woman. I have not the courage. I lose courage when there is shouting, argument, noise.

I only stammered (though angered by my stammering) that my baby would be in the best care if I had a job, and that I could do other work better than housework.

"Pooh, pooh," said the old gentleman, "no woman does other work better than housework!"

I grew red and said, "Well, perhaps I could do it with less exhaustion, then. I can teach a class or do a day's work in an office and be happy and well in the evening. But housework has not made me"—and I was obliged to smile—"fat." I was, in truth, as thin as a stick, pale, hollow-eyed. I wore the coat of a suit four years old, a hat three years old, and my shoes were not resoled only because we could not afford it. I had to quarrel with my husband when he had to get new clothes, any garment—for, as I pleaded, he had to "meet people," and had to look well, whereas I was home—and what did it matter?

The old merchant had a big store. He looked at me from head to foot. Then he asked me, abruptly again, "You have what kind of education?"

I told him.

He said, "We want to open night school for the factory people in the playgrounds. You want to take the first class?"

I think I could have knelt there to thank him. I did

not speak, as he went on to tell me it would be $2 an evening, for three evenings a week, that I would be sure of six months' work. "And it is," he concluded, "at night, so you won't neglect your child for it!"

What did I care what he said? Twenty-five dollars a month! Our troubles were over!

It cost us fifty cents to have some one to stay with the baby at night, and I did all the work during the day, as before.

But what a beautiful, beautiful, world it was, now I was working in it! My mind counted! I had intelligence! I used to feel that all day was a song until evening came, and the evening its crescendo. I had a dress now, too, blue with scarlet that, my lover said, made me look like a small soldier. Our baby would touch my cheeks and cry, "Pretty!"

Some of our friends were shocked that I, a married woman, worked. "What might not happen to the baby in the evening? Trust a stranger? Suppose she had convulsions?"

At first I used to live with an ear cocked for news of a convulsion, a fire or a murder. But nothing like it happened, after all. Baby thrived, a "Little Maid," rosy and dimpled and creased in loveliness.

Other women in bigger cities were already working in the evening, I found. I received a letter from a night-school teacher in another town, asking me about the sort of people in our classes, their native speech, and so forth, and she signed it "Mrs." in parenthesis after her name. Oh, I was not so wicked, after all! I was happy.

Then the classes grew. That faculty I seemed to have always had, that I had not lost, it appeared, to make people like me and trust me, made my classes grow. The Polak people came in crowds. I had to open another class for two more nights. And then, there was to be still another class. Another teacher was needed.

My old German friend telephoned to me to come to see him. "It goes well," he said, smiling. I told him how well it was going!

He said, "You think there will be enough for four classes four days a week?" I knew there would be.

"Well, then," he said, "I notice how well you get along with the second teacher we have now. You show her her work, and she likes you to do it. It is a valuable thing to have people like you to be boss. What do you say, if I asked you to be principal of this night school?"

A sort of thunder went through my head. But I did not answer; I could not. "It will be $20 a week. It will be, too," decisively, "still evenings, not taking you away from home and your child."

Did I want it? I ran the three miles, all the way home, not even thinking there was a car line just beside me.

After that, things were different. The three hard years were over. Baby was past four. I had a job, a job. My husband had made a place for himself that was settled and established.

I found myself speaking at women's clubs, too, to my amusement—but with great seriousness, to be sure—about "my work," and even about "Opportunities for married women in professions," one afternoon. Baby was in kindergarten, I had a servant for afternoons. We had paid off our debts. I was happy, happy, that year and the following year, too.

Then, later in the fall, I felt that same illness, that

same dead dullness I remembered of long ago. I went at once to our doctor. He said, "My girl, you are to have a little brother for the 'Little Maid.'"

That was cruel. And yet, I thought it over, one could not have just one child. If I died, and my husband, who was there for our baby? Not my people; and he had none near. She was alone. My folks had never seen her.

It was then that my mother came to see me. I cannot describe her coming, its heartbreak. My husband was so dear to her, so tenderly kind. They were strangers, though. My little baby was a Gentile baby in her arms. She would not, of course, touch the dishes in my house. She brought her own. She stayed three days, three long, long, days for her, and went back home.

I did not tell her I was to be a mother. Suppose I were to be the mother of a son, now? A girl, after all, was to her just a female. But a boy, a man—he ought to be a Jew, taught Hebrew from babyhood, confirmed in the covenant at thirteen—he ought to be made a Jew at his birth!

I kissed her, and she told me that my father was bitter to me. But he loved me. "You know he is so bitter because he loves you so," she whispered. I knew that well.

I kissed her good-by; we promised to write. But though I pleaded with her to come again, she did not say she would. I knew I could not go to her home with my child. We were not to see one another for a long time.

My sister Hannah had four children; her husband had an enormous practice. She was "lovely and fat," mother said with tender pride.

Etta was married, too, to a successful lawyer, the son of a poor man, and she had "only two children, both boys, though, luckily."

Simeon, I knew, had gone into business with a distant cousin of my mother's, a little shriveled, tiny man, so wealthy he had an automobile. Once, he said, he had helped finance Taft's election, but of course we did not then believe him. But he was a wealthy man, a millionaire if he wished. He was hard as nails, and meant Simeon to make a wealthy match. Only our Robert was curious. He had studied something strange, something about life, biology, and he was teaching it. He made my father very unhappy, but mother hushed him up. . . .

They were all her children, all in the fold, but me.

She liked my home, but it made her feel strange. Not a messusah in the house—and then she blushed to remember why. No candlesticks lit, of course. The little jade god, green and glowing, on the piano. "Cousin Simeon sent me that," I told her. I did not tell her what he had said when he sent it: "Strange gods."

XI

I HAD determined that I would not live through another three years such as I had had with our little daughter. I meant to enjoy her brother's babyhood and my motherhood. I would not make dark this second experience.

It was useless to think of keeping my job—afterwards. But for the present I might. I might do so if I kept entirely to myself this thing our doctor had told me. I did not tell my husband.

I have not spoken of his own feeling toward my working. It was rather quaint. He did not want me to do the drudgery of housework under extreme poverty, and yet he would have liked me to be the head of his home, the wife. He wanted me to know how to do unusual things—for so anything outside cooking and sewing and child bearing were still called—but he did not want to feel that he owed me anything in the keeping of our home. He loved me; he was modern. But about his wife that was his feeling.

It was not apparent at first. I was so proud, so happy, that I could not keep my pride to myself, nor my happiness, when I got my job first. There were pretty things to be bought for Little Maid, for myself, too, and expensive, extravagant things for my lover, my husband. At first I spent my earnings ridiculously, just in buying lovely things for us. My husband laughed!

Then I began to purchase things for our home,

things we needed for beauty, as much as for comfort. And finally, I bought "good things"—the little things that make food not just gorging to keep alive, but ceremonies of human intercourse, flowers for the table, and little yellow cakes, sometimes a bit of rare, lovely fruit to put in a bowl, a jelly that my husband would like. It did not occur to me to speak of these things. They were bought with my earnings as they would, of course, have been bought with his, and for him rather than for me, for I do not care for food; it is he, with his continental training in boyhood, who appreciates these things.

He never saw a bill; he has never seen a bill. That has always been naturally part of my job as housekeeper, except for that one first year of my illness. But one day, by chance, he found a ruled bit of paper with items on it, and chuckled, "Swell! Tonio's, h'm!" Tonio's was the "swell" fruit store in town.

He read the list, and said, smiling, "We giving a party? Say, hello, we had this stuff last week!" And he read down the list, prices and names. "It's pretty stiff living like kings, isn't it?" he commented, amused, and tossed the paper aside. But, at the month's end, he found a bundle of papers, narrow and yellow, on my desk. He looked at them. "Checks?" And he asked, "You have a checking account, plutocrat?" I had a tiny checking account. I was proud of it, my first, and showed it to him, with him named as attorney in the book, and he looked at my checks, then said, quickly, "Most of these aren't for you at all; they're —why they're all for the house, for the table!"

I laughed then, and said, why should it not be?

But I sobered, seeing his face. He didn't like it. He didn't like it at all. He put my small sheaf of checks down, and said, "My darling, you mustn't buy things for the house! You must use your—your earnings—to make your life easier and more beautiful."

He wouldn't see that buying things for the home we both shared made things beautiful for me. He was silent and troubled about it. He spoke of it again and again. In no way would he come to see my point. It was, indeed, this little sheaf of checks he found that made him decide quite with astonishing abruptness that he must leave his present work and find another position, in another city, if need be.

I did not wish to leave. We were happy. I had friends here, Lily and others. I had a plan in mind, besides, that I meant to carry out here. I meant to get a large number of pupils and form a private night school, with the students paying a small fee, and to teach them. Many of my pupils in the night school were earning fairly good salaries; they could afford to pay twenty-five cents a lesson and would appreciate having the hour set to their convenience. We would hold classes in one of the labor organization's offices, unused in the evening. We would have splendid evenings that would be socially attractive, as well as arranged for education. School closed in summer, and I could have "my" school in summer to begin.

I began at once to arrange these classes, for the summer that was approaching. My students were enthusiastic. To them it promised the continuance of pleasant acquaintances, even of all the social life many of them knew. From room to room I went, telling that I would have a school in the summer, what the fee would be, and asking who wanted to come. My board chairman thought it was a splendid plan, as it was. For those who wished to go back to school in the autumn could do so, and continue in the public classes. I would have my private classes. I expected my baby in early September. My classes would be over by the middle of August. It was ideal in arrangement.

The plan worked. My pupils came and brought others. I had mothers' clubs, children's groups. But the women were few in my classes. It was their men who came. Lily helped me, and soon there was enough for a class for her, too. I put aside the money for my new baby's clothes, and even a bit for the doctor. I was thin, and so my approaching maternity did not become apparent. I was happy in my plan and in continuing busy. Nor was there the hard illness of the previous time with Little Maid; I was well.

In May I told my husband. Surely no man but an absorbed scholar would not have guessed for four months. He was silent, looked at me quietly and said nothing when I told him of my plan to teach. He spoke nothing while I taught, all through July. But at the end of that month, he said, one day, "My dear, drop it. Please drop the school. I—it shames me to have you work—at this time."

With all his love, he could not see that to do this work was living to me, that it made for contentment, that it was my happiness. I was not the woman to sit brooding in maternity. My mind must work, create, even while I created with my body. He did not urge or plead, and did not so much as refer to it again. But I saw his flush when I went to my classes. His flush would die into a miserable, white line near his gentle mouth.

I called my pupils together and told them that the school was closing for the summer. I asked them to return to the public school in the fall. I took our rocking chair and sat on the porch, with Little Maid near me, all day, and in the evening I sat with my lover, and we read and planned together. We did not speak of my night school again. But one day, passing me, he put his hand on my hair, brushed it back, and then let it lie the littlest moment there. "Thank you—wife," he said. I am very modern indeed; I feel that no man has the right to interfere in the slightest with the path his wife wishes to take, that she must live *her* life, as well as *his wife's* life. And yet, not many things in all my life have been to me what that short moment was when I felt his lean hand on my hair, and heard him thank me for giving up what I enjoyed doing most —to please his male pride.

The long summer passed. September came. But our son was late, tardy as he still is, the young dreamer. He came in late autumn, a big boy who looked so much like his father that he seemed a solemn, fat little brother to him. And that has been his name since: "Brother."

And, just as he came, came my husband's new job in the East, a real job with a salary of $3,000, and better still, a staff adequate for him to do a real work. He said to me, huskily, as we read again the letter offering him the position, "And will you help me as a volunteer worker, darling?"

I knew what he meant—that I should not try to do paid work awhile; he was earning the family income now. I might do work I could do well, but it would be as a volunteer, as a gracious pastime that I did it. But I did not answer. I just put my hand in his and sat very still.

Three thousand a year twelve years ago was a very

big salary. To us it was tremendous. I had earned $20 a week for twenty weeks; that was $400. With my husband's income we had had altogether $2,400. We were obliged to pay $100 of that for the care of our baby. I felt well now; I would not have a maid. I took care of the babies and was happy. When we wanted to go out, we paid fifty cents for some one to stay home, though always I still sat in fear all evening of the convulsion or murder at home. We had no debts. We had one another. I took a little girl every afternoon to do our dishes and to dust; sometimes she stayed with Brother when I went out on Saturday afternoons. I, of course, didn't so much as think of cards, teas or matinées. It never occurred to me that women outside books did such things. Women either worked at their careers or stayed home.

I was happy.

In this new city, however, it happened that my husband had one of his few relatives, a young bank teller, a handsome fellow with a pretty wife and a child. They called at once and were sweet to us. They at once drew us into their social circle.

My husband had his work, and that kept him increasingly busy, even in the evenings, when he attended conferences, the social workers' meetings, group meetings for making new plans. It was on me that the young wife of his cousin called alone presently. She formed for me one of those light, but not the less real and lasting affections which pretty, not too clever women, often have for serious women of their own age. She admired my seriousness, but she had not the least wish in the world—nor should she have had—to possess it.

She began to call me up in the mornings, to drop in

on me, to ask me to go out with her. Her life was a round of simple teas, of shopping and of matinées. Their maid, a rather slack Swedish girl, had complete charge of their child after public school hours, until dinner. My new cousin—Cynthia was her pretty name—did not even know what she was to have for dinner. Sometimes she saw her child only for a few minutes a day.

Presently her friends, too, began to call on me. Some of them were wealthier than she, some even owned cars, and the wealthiest had a liveried chauffeur. Her husband owned a moving picture theater, the biggest in town. Cynthia showed me off, I think—spoke of my previous work, and of my college education, for she and her friends were high school graduates, or in one case, normal school. None had ever earned her living.

These women were not rich women, not society women. Their husbands were middle-class Americans. But they did not, any of them, do one thing more for their homes, their marriage, than lend their bodies to them. Their interests were quite outside. They were not even interested in "culture," in clubs for reading or studying. They lived for pleasure. Of the whole number—and there were perhaps ten in Cynthia's circle—two had children, she and another, and this other woman's child was, fortunately, in boarding school.

It was not that these women were pleasure-loving that amazed me, though. It was that here were women with leisure, who did not even know it, who slept life away. The only thing that actually was real to them was bridge. It was dreadful to watch their faces at bridge, pinched and hard and bitter in defeat. Twelve years ago to be a bridge-fan meant having a career.

Because cards are unknown to me—my father never had to ask us not to play, for we knew no one who did—the interest in being with this group was, for me, in watching them. I used to watch them, fascinated.

Sometimes, from our back porch, I could see another young woman hanging little clothes, too, on the drawn clothesline stretching across the smooth grass of the back lawns. At times a tiny infant, hardly able to stand on its fat legs, would waddle after her, holding to the gingham dress that hung in such straight folds about her thin, girlish hips. If the baby would cry, she would bend down, lift it up, and sagging under its weight, carry it in doors. We came to watch for one another, for she, like I, would glance to see if the other's yard were empty. Across the long space of intervening houses we never crossed.

I found later that she was a college girl, like myself, that there was an even tinier baby in her house. Her husband was a teacher of chemistry in one of the high schools. They had met at college, and had married after she had taught a year, saving enough for their sparsely furnished home. His salary was $2,200 a year, and on that they lived. She had been the daughter of a country lawyer, sent to a "girls' school," and then the small coeducational college where she got her degree. She had never known what real poverty was in the little town where her father lived. Now she was like a prisoner, her day one long drudgery, followed by the long nights of caring for her baby, which was sickly. In the evenings her husband would come home, and wheel the older child up and down.

Those few minutes were her only rest day and night. One afternoon I was running by to the store, and she came out, saying, "Oh—please!" She was hesitating, flushed, shy. She needed something at the store and could not go down. Would I leave word for her? There was no one to leave at home. I did not ask her why she did not telephone; telephones in the home are an extravagance. Thereafter we would run errands for one another and speak, like runners on a long road, hurriedly, as we rushed about our daily lives. Once she said, waving a letter to me, "A round robin letter from—the girls in our class!" the last word high and brave. "Won't you run up—and see it?" She wanted to share that pleasure with some one, even a stranger, to live over college days and talk about this classmate and that. "I'll try," I called back. But, of course, that was not possible. There wasn't time during the day.

Later, many years later, when her husband had left our city, and he had reached at last the position of superintendent of schools in their state, she wrote to me, and added, "Now I have time to write my part in our round robin letters—but there's nothing to say. It's so silly to write out happy things. And one can't write the unhappy ones to strangers."

Next door to us lived a childless woman, a woman with soft gray hair and a victrola—but no child. She and her husband would sit on their porch in the evening, she knitting or embroidering, he in slippers and vest, both quietly happy in each other's silent companionship.

Sometimes, flying by in the endless grind of my work, I would catch a glimpse of her moving placidly at her tasks, and I would feel a peace in seeing her so quiet, so content. After all, there must come a time when one might rest.

But one day she came over, knocked at my door and, holding out a little red jar, said, "I made some tomato jelly; won't you taste it?"

She stopped to talk, following me because Little Maid was calling, and even to the bathroom where the inevitable children's laundry was waiting to be done.

"I'll tell you what," she said, looking at me. "I heard there is a new kind of soap—it's flakes, and you just shake the baby things up and down, and they get as white as can be." She took my hands, raw on the palm at each thumb, from daily rubbing. "Try it," she said.

It was wonderful, and it made my baby clothes really easier. I think I was happier to discover a flaked soap than I would have been to hear a beautiful concert, those days. It gave me a little bit of time, a little bit, indeed, but rest. I had been rubbing clothes for an hour a day. I did not know how to do it, and Little Maid seemed to have a genius for rubbing in dirt so thoroughly that one could barely scrub it out with one's skin.

My neighbor came again. She took Little Maid in her arms and said, "You know, I have nothing to do. I made a pair of little blue rompers, and I think I made them the right size!"

She opened a parcel she had put beside her and put a pair of blue rompers on crowing Little Maid. "They won't show dirt," she said. "I have another pair half done." She put Little Maid down. "Don't let her wear white all the time," she advised. "Blue's good enough for play!" And then she smiled down to me, "Being childless—Hubby's my baby—I can give advice to mothers!"

Had anyone told me I could love a woman who called her husband "Hubby" I would have been horrified and chagrined. But I loved her. She was my friend and my adviser. She taught me how to pour off the teapot so that I need not have to fish frantically for the darting leaves in the pot; she made me see that beef is beef one day, hash another and perhaps meat pie the third; the bills would shrink by this method. She taught me that potatoes mashed with meat and baked then made the dinner full. "It's a big dinner to-night, isn't it?" said my husband, appreciatively.

Sometimes she had "so much dessert" that they just couldn't do away with it. We simply must *taste* it. It was always so good! We did without desserts, of course.

And, often, she wanted to borrow Little Maid; she wanted to see her sleep her rosy sleep, to watch her play in her "gated garden," and then to give her her toast and milk. "Just run along and see the stores," she would say.

My dear, dear friend, what would young mothers who are poor do if there were not neighbors like you, women coming to the city from country towns, and full of a love that has no price, that asks no return, not even thanks?

One day, in the morning, as I stood, after Little Maid had been bathed and the dinner put on, so that the vegetables could be done first (as my neighbor had taught me), I saw near me my little housekeeping book, with the pencil hanging from it. I picked it up and stood so a while. And, in my tiny kitchen, I remember something I wanted to do—wasn't it long ago? To write a book some day. I put my pencil down, but my thought did not go away. All through the morning it followed me, like a bright light, shining. Write. Write.

After all, even if I were poor, my mind was there. I might write. I might write a book.

When Little Maid was asleep, I looked at her clothes, at the ironing, and deliberately closed the door. I went to my husband's desk and took some of his paper. How easily the words came! They poured out! I felt, in the writing, as if I pushed open, with magnifience, with light pouring in, a heavy door that had closed on me. Oh, if one could write!

Through the door came my neighbor. She looked at me. "Accounts?" she said, pleasantly.

My heart sank, but I stood up: "Mrs. Rahm! I —I'm doing a story—"

Her gentle brown eyes stared at me. "Dearie," she said, "I thought you were such a sensible girl!" She questioned me.

"I'm writing!" I said. "Don't you understand—I'd thought I couldn't—"

She put broad kind hands in her apron pockets. "Don't tucker yourself out with nonsense," she said. "Leave that to folks that can do it. You and I have our own work, and it keeps us busy—"

But I did not seem to hear more. I had just heard one sentence: "Leave that to folks that can do it."

What right had I to do this silly thing, take our precious time for it? If I had been a real writer, I would never have stopped because my "ideal had failed me"—silly little schoolgirl! I would not have gone into social work. I'd have written somehow.

My husband came home, and we ate our dinner. But when he went out into the kitchen he found my paper and my pencil, and he looked at what I had put there. He kissed me, as he came in and spoke to me of that which he had dreamed, that he would do his work, and I would write about it: "I will be the hands, and you the voice," he had said to me once.

"It's no use; it's no use," I said to myself. But to him I could not endure to say anything; if I spoke I would cry, and I have never cried.

I put my sheets of paper aside. I put all my dreams aside.

The hours that Mrs. Rahm gave me I spent in town, in looking at shop windows, staring at hats, clothes, expensive furniture. Sometimes I would lie down and just think, think of how strange life is, how it makes even what is most lovely, one's own love, seem dark.

XII

HE had thought that $3,000 would be a huge salary. We found that we were still breathlessly trying to catch up with our income. I worked as hard as before. I made the children's clothes. I made my husband's clothes. I made my own. Every bit of material in the clothes that I or my husband wore was used later for the children.

I know that this is done by hundreds of other young women—thousands—all over the country. I would have enjoyed doing it, for the sake of my husband and for the sake of the children.

But all the time it was so hard for me to do this; and there were other things I could have done so well, so easily. No, not making a home, not caring for my babies—that was the sweetest thing to do. But the long, hard grind of housework, the terrible ordeal of laundry, that left me with my back aching.

But at that time for a woman who was not wealthy to say she hated that, would have seemed heresy. But certainly now I may say that I, who had been trained to be a teacher, who had learned how to practice two professions, hated my housework with a strange, helpless hatred.

I should say it drew my husband and me closer together. In the books it is so. But books do not tell the truth. Love grows in mutually shared leisure and interests; I had no leisure and no interests that were my husband's. The plan he had, to make me a volunteer worker, could not work. I was needed at home, every minute.

My husband, who had been so buoyant and so gravely kind, had become a man who sat with tired, relaxed body in his chair by the fireplace, speaking little of his work, because there was so much that was not happy in it. I would sit by his side, my hand in his, feeling his thought, even though he did not express it, by the pressure of his fingers, in an unconscious telegraphy. The one thing he hoped was to find his way out, too. For he also did not fit into this field, this scholar and gentle student who was my husband.

It is the fashion now to pity women. But nothing is more pitiful than the young man tied hand and foot by his responsibility to a family. My husband, of course, could not possibly leave his profession. Could he earn, as a teacher, as much as now? Of course he could not.

One of his board members, a man who had made his money in a small store that had grown, bit by bit, to a big one, and on the profits of which he had retired now and was doing "social work," had from the beginning opposed anything my husband suggested. It was always over his voice that anything was done. It was perhaps "healthy" to have opposition, but this man made the work lag. In the end he yielded, but not before precious time had been used to persuade him. This man, like the other man we had known before, was overbearing and vain in his wealth.

My husband hated him. I do not think I have ever ever known him to hate another man than this one. Of one thing he could not persuade him. In their recreational work they had joined forces with the tuberculosis clinics; they offered to provide milk to any person coming in their work, who had T.B. This one man had opposed the plan; he yielded in the end.

But he yielded on his own terms. The milk was to be distributed, but the people were to come for it daily and ask for it, in line, one by one.

My husband's plan had been to find who needed the food, to learn if they could afford to pay for it themselves and, if they could not, to have the milk supplied them by the company dispensing the richest milk in the city. "What! Have every coughing tramp in town came to us and make us suckers!" said this man. "I'll not agree! I'll never agree to that!" He even suggested something so madly absurd as that the people benefited might sell the milk provided "to buy fool luxuries, and then where'll we be, and how'll we know?"

Nowadays T.B. work is nationally known because of the Red Cross. It was then new. This man would have objected as violently to any other new idea. To him poor men were half fools, half paupers. He wanted them all to "come in line, wait in the hall, standing, and be respectful when they come in." He would come in, himself, at times when a man was telling the most carefully guarded portions of his life to a worker who had at last won his confidence, and would sit listening, scowling, asking questions, making the applicant for help feel like a thief or at best a human derelict. My husband's idea was the social worker's, now as then: that the person helped must be given, not only charity, but, first of all, faith in the ability to help himself. It is this which costs so much in social work; it is quick and easy work to give a sum of money. It takes a long time to teach a man long down and out that he can earn that money for himself.

There was all this happening about me, my life, and my husband's, Cynthia's—and the life of all those whom my husband knew in his work.

One day, as I sat with Brother on the porch, Little Maid for the morning at kindergarten, quite suddenly I thought, "I shall write this all down. I will tell all this."

I put on my hat, my coat and my best cared-for gloves and, taking Brother in my arms, went into town. I stopped at my husband's office and did a thing I would never have thought to do before: I gave the janitor of the office building a quarter, and said, "Please let my baby play with you a little while. I—a very serious thing has just happened, and I must attend to it."

"I'm that sorry," he said. But I did not wait to listen. I had so little time! Little Maid had to be taken home at twelve. This was past ten.

I went to a big building I had passed one day, a great building in another part of town, the office of the most important publication in the city. I had worked in a small city at my first job; my home was in a modest town. This building seemed grand beyond measure to me. My heart simply banged at my breast. I knew what I wanted to write, but how I would tell it I did not know. I had never seen the inside of an editorial office; I had never seen an editor. My husband had had his reports printed, but that was by the printer, and the arrangement was made by the social agency each time. I had seen books, magazines, newspapers, but who made them I did not know. I only knew that there was something I wanted to write about, something so compelling it had to be written down. It was to be something that I would take out of my life to give to the world.

I asked to see the editor-in-chief. Because I was so inexperienced, I did not know how much I shocked the office boy at the mahogany desk. But a door opened, a slight, quick man with dark hair and the keenest eyes came out, looked at me, and I said, "Are you the editor?" breathlessly. "I am," he said, and waited. "I want—I want to write something for you," I said. "Can I ask you about it?" He smiled then, and asked me in, and I told him of my idea. It appealed to him. He asked me to write it and send it to him. "Make it five thousand words long, and let me see it," he said, in his rapid, vivid voice. "Make it real!"

That was my meeting with "my Editor."

At home I felt as if I had been blown a long way by a big wind. I could only wait until my husband came home, and say, as if the words fell out on my breath, "I'm going to write!"

I wrote the "story," and sent it in. I wrote it not one time, but ten or twelve times, mainly because I wanted it to be 5,000 words long. When it was too short I had to increase it; when it was too long, I had to cut it. I faithfully counted word by word, line by line. I typed out the whole thing with two fingers on a machine in my husband's office, in the evenings, while he stayed home with the children.

My story went away, and I heard nothing. One day, one week, passed. I wanted to pull down my telephone, to call out, to call up. What had happened? Nothing, apparently. I heard nothing.

But meanwhile I had found something. I had found something I had lost. I found I had things to write down, oh, not for one paper, but many. I had BOOKS in my mind, full of experiences, feelings, thoughts. I would write now, although long ago—that evening Professor Raphael had told me he would marry a Gentile—I had felt I could never write again. I could write—even though my neighbor had smiled to think I would. This was my language. I had found it. Now I could speak.

Then a letter came, such a letter as one receives just one time in one's life, a letter from an editor accepting one's manuscript, and not just accepting it—but full of warm praise, of friendship and of faith that one could do more. "I liked it!" that was what he had said. "You can write!" I learned that letter off by heart. I think I could recite it if waked suddenly from a deep sleep. "I liked your story."

Here was something I could do, and do at home, said our friends with approval. They spoke to me of "my nice little stories" in leading magazines, and asked if I "got" anything for them. They were a frill on my motherhood, my wifehood.

As to my husband, he made this work of mine his. Nothing was sent out under my name that was not perfectly done, finished, refinished, like a rare bit of furniture made by a master-craftsman. He was happy for me.

There were my children, my new work and my love. Could life have been more complete?

I had time to write so little, though. My work, my home, came first. But each time was a special blessing.

Sometimes I sent a check to my mother. She would write to me, her little stilted loving notes. But my father's name continued unmentioned. One day a letter came from Robert. He had read an article of mine and told me briefly that the newer science discovered one fact I quoted disproved. It was the first time I had heard of him, of any of my family. I replied at once. And thereafter he wrote to me regularly. His letters were unhappy, but in a contemplative, impersonal way. It was apparent it was because he had not found himself. He did not yet know what I had learned, that each must find his own faith. He was not like our cousin Simeon, pretending to hold to a faith because he was dependent on his father's money. My brother Robert received nothing from my father but his idealism. But he had not the courage my father had: he did not trust himself to reason out his own belief. My father conformed in his mind to the traditional Judaism. But when Robert spoke, sometimes, questioningly, my mother could always make him cease by her gentle, pleading glance. Only I was the "little Polak" who dared to question the authority, spiritual and physical, of our father, whom even love could not bind.

And yet, it would have been sweet to hear from him, to have him say he wanted to see my children. He never mentioned me, Robert said shortly in a letter.

Robert came into our house one day, unannounced. He was tall, over six feet, gangling, with fair hair. My children, delighted with his grave pranks, climbed over his hands and knees, and he let them, the serious young professor. But when he left, he said, kissing me, "The children of your brain are more Jewish than those of your body, Leah!"

"What do you mean?" I asked, startled.

"Your boy and girl are adorable little Gentiles; but everything you write is written from a Jewish memory and with the Jewish feeling—that's what."

When he had gone, and for long afterwards, I

thought of his astute comment. It was true, and not only of myself, but of others better known. Whatever the Jew has given to the written art of America has been Jewish, a heritage and gift of the Jew who came to the new land, America. My father thought he had no part in this new land; he had cut himself off from me. But every word I wrote carried his feeling, his Jewish humor and, it might be, if one were sometimes blessed and happy,—a little even of his Jewish poetry.

XIII

I HAD known it would happen; sometimes I had hoped for it. But I felt the bleakness in my husband's voice when he came in, earlier than usual, and said, "I—I'm taking a vacation, Little Boy."

He took Brother on his knee, but he did not caress him. Little Maid climbed on his other knee and began to ask for a story.

"It's such a long story," he smiled, quietly, and sat still.

It was a story I had expected. He had grown to hate that one man on his board. Everything in his profession he believed in, that one man scorned; the man made of those who came in misfortune degraded animals.

"He called me a high-faluting professor," my husband smiled. "I'd almost forgotten I had the right to be a professor."

We hadn't a penny saved.

It is such a usual story—"My husband is out of a job." How often have I heard it, and in how many differing tongues! I heard it spoken by women who came to me in my settlement house later, by wives whose stories I heard in doing post-war work, and from women who came to me when I entered business. But it is never the same story when it is your own story.

My husband was out of a job, and we had neither folks nor funds.

Getting a job in social work is not a simple matter of going to ask for it. Now there are admirable vocational bureaus, and some of the tragedy of the "lost job" is removed. The worker can choose his own work. Twelve years ago to lose your job because you couldn't get along with your "board" was a real tragedy. The people who spoke for the work you had done were your board members. If you had not their good will your work was depreciated, at the least. My husband had left against the advice of even those who were friendly to him on his board; he had lost the quiet composure that he had always so infallibly had; he had risen and said that, unless the man opposing him gave way, he would leave.

Now the social worker has the standing, sometimes, of a high-class employee in a corporation. But then, a dozen years ago, to "insult" a board member was blasphemy—even to offend his self-esteem. My husband's resignation was accepted without one protest.

We know now how young we were, but the situation might have been "handled differently." My husband need not have antagonized a man who was vain and, therefore, easily flattered. He might have yielded pride and won him, and to the good of their mutual work for the community. But the truth is that he has never been one to think that people, too, have to be considered when issues are to be met. He simply did not see the enemy he had until the work he was doing was halted by the enemy's attack.

Looking for a new place meant months of waiting, of not "looking down and out" at the same time. A man who wished to take charge of the affairs of others must look as if he were taking good care of his own, even when he had none to take care of. Clothes counted for him.

At first it was sweet to have him at home, to have the long, long days with him that we had not had since we were first married. When Little Maid was at school, and Brother asleep, it was as if we were sweethearts again, alone in our chairs on the porch or doing the jobs of the house together. For job hunting meant for social workers not going to offices to ask for work, but writing letters, perhaps putting an advertisement in the social workers' magazine. Sometimes a friendly social worker, coming to lunch, would tell of "an opening" that was to occur, and my husband would follow it. But the weeks drew into months, into four months. He did odd jobs in social work—"made a survey," filled in once when a minor vacancy opened. But the real work did not come.

If he had been a Jew, it would have been easier. Jewish social work was booming; salaries were big to our unaccustomed eyes.

It occurred to me that I might get a job; was I not a Jewess?

I went down to apply for a job. I was refused. I had married a Gentile. But the sharp-eyed, clever girl to whom I spoke said, curiously, "So you're Jewish, too? Now who would've believed it all this time!"

I had been writing for magazines and knew some of the editors through my correspondence—slight enough, but friendly. For a while I thought I might write to one, to ask for some work. But that was impractical. I had no editorial experience; I knew nothing of the mechanical part of journalism. Even in my ignorance of the field, I realized that. But another avenue occurred to me. It came, of all people, through Mrs. Rahm.

Mrs. Rahm came to our city and stopped to see the children. She brought gifts for Little Maid, and for Brother. She had dinner with us, and then she told us why she had come to our town—to attend the wedding of a nephew of hers, who was, well, she was proud of him—an editor!

She brought him to us. It was the first time I had an editor in my home; I ruined the dinner in my nervousness. He was not quick and decisive like my own first editor, who is always to me "my editor." He was young, slightly fat, and really most astoundingly funny. He had a typical American wit that glanced at everything without reverence, that glanced off everything with a light, delicious humor, like a fine rapier dancing.

"So you write, uh?" he chuckled. "Sister of the pen!"

I laughed so much that I spilled the soup; Little Maid got up and clapped her hands and said, in her grave way, "Most 'musin' man!" to his delight.

"For all this light-heartedness," Mrs. Rahm's nephew declared, while she sat simply bursting with pride, "I feel very much like Isaac being taken out to be sacrificed by Abraham. He knew he was going to Heaven, but oh, he was afraid!"

I do not know why we all thought that rather dreadful Biblical reference was so funny, and particularly so in the light of the wedding to which he compared it. Perhaps it was because we had not laughed for so long in our house. And I had thought I would have to be respectful and rather afraid, and here was an editor who was more a boy than my husband.

It may have been because we were so appreciative that, some time after, we received an announcement of their "at home." But it would have been impossible to go. I was needed in my own home. My husband had grown thin and wan.

I could not endure to see him so. We were just living, somehow; the checks that came to me, the occasional work he did, tided us over. We waited for the "real job" and the real salary. It was six months now since he had left his previous office.

One day, in one of those sudden impulses that seem to drive me always, I went down town, and in to see Mrs. Rahm's nephew. I would put my pride away. I'd ask him for some work. I could write.

It was harder to get by the office boy in the newspaper office than in the magazine offices I knew. But I wrote, on a slip of paper, my name; and then, under it, as my answer to the printed querry "Concerning ——" I added, "Something important."

The office boy looked dubiously at the message, but I was too nervous to change it. He took it in as if it were alive and might bite him. Almost immediately he came back. "Not in."

I could have cried out. But I said, "Will he be back?"

"S'pose so," hopelessly.

"Will he be back to-day?"

"S'far's I know."

I did not know this was cordiality and chivalry: he might have answered nothing. I waited twenty minutes and then rose to go. My courage, my high enthusiasm, had gone.

And then the door opened, and out came Mrs. Rahm's nephew.

He was different here, in shirt-sleeves, and rather dirty as to face. I learned that he had been in the pressroom and was all inky, but he did not feel embarrassed or ashamed about it. I followed him into a tiny office, where an exceedingly dilapidated desk stood, with a swivel chair tottering near it.

"How're the babies?" he asked.

I had not meant to start that way. I did not want to present myself as the mother of two babies. I wanted a job.

But I answered lamely and asked about his wife. His face lighted, but he only grinned, embarrassed now to the point of silence.

Then, quite outside myself, I heard a voice speaking from inside me: "You know, I have been thinking I'd —I'd like to do some writing here."

"Writing here?" he repeated, grinning. "What made you think of coming here to write? This is a newspaper office. We sell news, not writing!"

He was a different person from the man I had met in my home. Then he continued, "What do you want to work on a newspaper for? A married woman? With two such corking children?" He was plainly disappointed, puzzled, too.

I sat folding my fingers together, first on one hand, then the other. I did not know what to say. I hadn't thought the old ghost of my being a wife and mother would interfere in this work. The "writing" I still did not quite understand. Weren't newspapers written?

Then, without being able to look up, with that absurd pride that I should now never feel, because of the need to work, the honest need to work, I said, "I simply have to have—have to have a job." And, as his face turned to mine at my tone, I added, "I've worked before, after I was married, too, and—even after my first baby was born. So that's been done. But I—want a job now."

He picked up a pencil from a scrawled yellow sheet, made lines on it. His telephone rang and he answered, slangily and cheerfully. A boy came in with a long, narrow sheet of printed stuff, palpably proof even to me, and he went over it hastily, saying, "Hold till I see the Chief. I think—" He lifted the receiver, called a name, and said, almost defiantly, "Think that ought to be caps, Chief." He put down the receiver glumly. "My Chief thinks he's the whole show." He grinned: "And so he is, damn it!" Then he apologized; stuttered. I smiled a little at his sudden boyishness.

He turned on the demoralized swivel chair and said, abruptly, "Look here, you couldn't get a job here, a regular job. Regular job's getting news. Being on the assignment book. Having any rotten hole the Chief thinks of at the moment put after your name—and you have to get to it, immediately, and get the story, or get out. That's how news is built, and that's what a newspaper is for." He leaned forward, put his ink-stained hands through his hair, and said, "I take it you couldn't leave your kids to regularly sort of live down here, could you? Be on call when you're needed? That's what the news reporters do. Girls and men alike." He said, then, quickly, "And you're not the type; you haven't the brass!"

He was mistaken in making a generalization, for only a few years later it was the girls who did not even remotely suggest "brass" who began to do some of the best news gathering and news writing in the country.

He said, then, "Can you do a sob sister?"

I was startled; I blushed. Was it because my eyes were red? Did I look as if I were crying? But he grinned, "Oh, I mean spiel the sad story of why Andrew Kline killed his baby but only for love, dear readers. You know the stuff. Or why Cora Kittlemouse ran off with the duke."

I shook my head. "I couldn't do that," I said. I told myself that he was making fun of me. I half moved to rise.

But he put out a long forefinger. "Wait a minute." He sat, thinking. "For God's sake," he said, "don't build on this. But we have a new fellow the Chief put on. He's going to do the high-brow on the paper, to sell the book advertisements to the publishers. Want to see him?"

I rose now. "Do you think he might want—"

"I do not," he said, then, decisively, "I said, do you want to see him? Never can tell, that's all."

I followed him through a narrow little lane of offices, through a huge room pounding with machines at which were sitting men and women, too, and to a corner, not even screened off, where a very serious young man with very large brown eyes, a low collar, soft tie and rolled-back sleeves sat.

"H'lo, Kahn," said Mrs. Rahm's nephew. "Here's a contributor." And speaking my name, he said, "S'long; drop in on your way out, will you?" to me, and disappeared.

The young editor at the desk nodded to a chair. "Sit down," he invited me. But I was too much on edge to sit. I stood and said, rapidly, "I want to do some work—writing. Do you think I could do some for you?"

He stared at me, smiled then. "Put on the Ritz, please," he said.

I did not understand, but later, and not much later, I did. But it was that which aroused his interest, the apparent indifference that came of my desperation. "What can you write?" he asked.

Briefly, I named the magazines for which I had written and the subjects I had treated. He nodded. "Good," he said. "Do you understand anything about children? Can you write in a rather intellectual way about children?"

I smiled. "I have two of my own," I said.

He grew more formal immediately. "It is Mrs. then?"

"Mrs.," I nodded, smiling. I felt more at ease with this formality.

"Write me three columns, one for each of three succeeding issues, on any phase of child welfare, education or social work that you choose," he said, rising too. "If it's good, I'll see what will happen."

He bowed me out. He looked rather handsome and grand, bowing so.

Outside, I stopped at the door of Mrs. Rahm's nephew. "I'm to write for the paper," I said, I think as if I were strangled.

At home, my husband was amused at this work, troubled by it. "Newspaper writing is cheapening," he thought, and rightly.

But I resolved mine would not be! I wrote as carefully, as long, over each of those three columns as if I were doing an immortal book.

Mr. Kahn looked them over when I took them to him. "Righto," he said. "Go right on."

This was not the courteous, friendly, attitude of my magazine editors, always very formal and always kind. But it was "righto" for us. I received $10 a column, a huge sum in those days. But I was to do whatever reviewing of children's books there occurred. That I did gladly, as well as reviewing those books about children which began to be popular just then.

In my new work I made friends with Mr. Kahn and also with some of the women on the staff. These women worked so hard! They had tired, faded faces or young, tired ones. They had not little children to love, I used to think. But I soon found how mistaken I was. Two of the women were widows; one was divorced (still disgraceful then), and one was separated from her husband. The rest were unmarried girls. I was the only one living at home with my husband and still in love with him.

"Still believe in love's young dream, eh?" said one of them to me.

I felt foolish, but I did not deny it.

"You'll wake up," she prophesied.

She wrote the serial stories of love, married life, high life, that appeared on the woman's page. Another woman wrote the daily sermonette; the prettiest girl on the staff had a column of love letters, many of which she made up herself, and some of which, the rest said, were those she received from her own sweethearts. She was the first girl I had ever known who took love lightly. She was "engaged to three men together," she smiled, and it was true. All the three hoped to marry her.

One of the three was Mr. Kahn.

It was rather pathetic to see him with her. His cocksureness, his dignity, would fade away and leave him timorous and almost foolish. The wit and the strength I knew he had, he did not seem to know how to show her. She would come in while I talked over my articles with him, listen in a big chair, curled up there near his desk, calling out to the others passing by, and seem not to care what his eyes or lips said to her. Then one day a note told "the Chief," whom I never saw, that she'd gone. She was married. She had married a young student at the college, a young boy she had met at a public dance, the son of a well-to-do man, the office said.

I was shocked to see Mr. Kahn, when I came in the week after her marriage. He looked as if he had been ill a year. He was thin, his face wax pale. "Let's get to work, shall we?" he said at once, and we did. I went without speaking of the thing, of course.

But, as the weeks went by, he grew hollower, thinner. He grew almost as thin and as quiet as my husband at home.

It was curious about my husband. My small check meant just enough for rent and for laundry every month. His earnings supplied money for food, clothes, "extras." We were able now to live without fear of losing our home. But he treated my writing as if it were something rather delightful, femininely sweet, that I chose to do, and that, quaintly enough, proved helpful just now in the serious things of living.

"You through with your little piece?" he would ask, waiting for me to complete my work. I did not know why that wounded me. I thought the "piece" little, too; I did not take this newspaper writing seriously. And yet it was writing; it earned part of our livelihood. Neither I nor he spoke so of even the smallest thing he did to earn money.

And then his job came, a splendid one in New York, a job of a new sort, work done by a great corporation for its thousands of employees. His office, he was told, must be in New Jersey, but we chose for our home a pretty town not far from New York city, a town that was more like a small city than a suburb, and which yet had charming old streets, a good school and attractive people, who would make us pleasant friends.

I did not think then how important the choice of our home was to be. I did not realize until later that outside the tree-lined residence section into which we moved, there was a new city growing up, created by those mills on the outskirts, where Hungarians and Germans lived. It was pleasant to have Hungarians and Germans near by, because that made "help" easy to find, our new neighbors told me. These "hunkies" were not very happy with the old residents of the town, but then the war made it necessary to employ all sorts of people. Some of the factories which we knew only by the plumes of smoke coming from their stacks, far off, were manufacturing shoes, others were manufacturing clothes. In less than a year they were to be important instruments of the government, though that we did not then even guess. I did not care who was working in the mills, what sort of town this busy little city was becoming in its "business section." I had a delightful little house, a garden, a deep-fenced porch. We were all well.

We were extraordinarily wealthy, besides.

For my husband's salary was tremendous, $3,500 a year. Our troubles were over.

I had promised my friends in New York to come

often. To come to New York meant arranging for the care of the house, cooking dinner before I left and rushing back to be there to give my children their supper. Coming to New York was, I soon found out, possible only once or twice a month. I had to give up my work, of course.

My husband did not understand why I was grieved, however, to give up my work on the newspaper. He thought I ought to be glad to be relieved of it. He could not see that it had been happiness to me. "Silly little darling," he said, lifting me up and carrying me around in his delight at his luck, at our new future, "why do you have to bother doing that?"

"Because I want to!" I said. But he did not remember why I had done it. He completely forgot that I had done it because of our mutual need and the responsibility that we had shared together. The children stood by and crowed to see mother lifted up just as they were. They tumbled over him, to me, to the floor.

"You'll never work again, except at things you enjoy!" said my husband, holding me so close I felt suffocated, happy and suffocated with his intensity and his love.

"But that's what I enjoy!" I wanted to say. He didn't let me. He kissed and kissed me until my lips clung to his, until I forgot that I wanted to write, to help—everything except that I was his dear wife and we were to be happy together in this new career of his.

XIV

I BEGAN to write, and my husband stood guard over me, to see that everything I did was beautiful, finished. He thought of such great things for me to do! My first book came, and then the second and the third. And when I read lovely words about them, I felt I ought to shout out, "That's not me, that's my husband. He made me make it beautiful; it's he!"

My writing was to be a great jewel on our lives, he felt. And he saw that it should be so.

My life itself was to be in the home, with our children.

It would be stupid to say that I was not happy so. Not in all the years to come can anything come again, surely, like those years in which our home was quiet and at peace, the children growing up and my books, my short stories and articles, coming one by one, like other lovely children conceived by us two.

Little Maid was growing tall and very lovely, slender and fair; she was like my sister Hannah, but she did not even suggest the Hebraic. Brother was tall, sturdy, with eyes like corn flowers and cheeks like wild blossoms. "I see the man in your eyes, Momsie," he would say when he was little. But now he began to laugh, "The little man in your eyes is growing up, Momsie!" Little Maid was doing well in school; she wanted to be a doctor, she said, because "doctors always have automobiles, mother, and you can just ride around and around, visiting."

I used to wish my mother would see them. But that was done. I could not turn back now, even for her. She could not come to me.

Among our friends in New York were some of the writers, and a few of them were newspaper people.

One day an acquaintance asked me to go to tea with her, a "literary tea." Brother was at kindergarten; Little Maid at school. I was free part of every day now, though I still did my housework. It never occurred to me now to think of working so that I could have a maid: some day my husband would earn a salary large enough for that. Meanwhile, I did my writing, but only between the more important and necessary work of keeping house daily.

The tea was downtown, in a big old brown stone house converted, a tall old house with a garden in its rear. We entered a little hall, were met by a young lady in a pretty yellow linen dress, ushered into another room and stood there staring at five people, grown people, sitting on the floor drinking tea. I had never before seen Bohemia.

There was one man among those five figures on the floor, and he unwound himself to an unbelievable height, towered over us and, taking my hand, said, "Who is the little lady?"

Perhaps Bohemia doesn't take itself so seriously now as then; then one had to be different or die. This man did not need to try to be different. He just was different from all other men.

He had just come back from Ireland; he knew the story of the Irish Revolution, had helped to write it. He had a friend here in New York, Lord ——. Would

I like to see him? He would cherish knowing me. The friend was to be shot later by the British Government for a mad, noble attempt to bring Ireland into alliance with Germany in the war. But I just blushed, felt awkward and stammered something inaudible.

I felt middle-aged; I remembered all the time my children were growing up. I felt so settled. I was twenty-eight. I was a serious writer, with books to my name. Yet I felt silly, young and aware of something I had never known before, that, for want of a better name, one might call a "thrill." This curious man interested me because I interested him. Men had been kind to me, and my friends, since my marriage, but they had been friends to me as the wife of my husband or as friends of a married woman. This odd man would not see that I was married, a mother. He would only see that I was a woman, and one to whom he liked to speak and with whom, it appeared, he liked to be.

It was embarrassing to have him telephone to me at ten, just as I was doing the breakfast dishes, and to have him appear at three in the afternoon with books, or with suggestions for "a jaunt." I was, candidly, afraid of what my neighbors would say. My husband, though, was amused at it all. He had known writing people since childhood, and their ways. But this man, he felt, laughingly, was one of the new fraternity, not really artists, but wanderers in the field of art. He was not a little intrigued to see how bewildered was I, who took it all seriously, and seriously wished it were all over.

"How's your admirer?" my husband would ask.

He was not even anxious to see him, and my new friend appeared to be entirely unaware of my husband's existence, in spite of all my careful efforts to have him always in the foreground.

Women are friends with men now, and co-workers. But at that time, to be married and to have a man friend was to be thought more than risque: it was sin, social sin at least. I did not know what to do.

Yet it was fine to have this friend. He was queer and vacillating; he spoke an odd language. He seemed to have no traditions and no definite rules even for conduct. But he had traditions and rules that he never broke for writing. And he would read my things, carefully, almost rigidly, at attention. His judgment was always exactly right.

He did not see my writing as a frill on my life, nor even as a great jewel that decorated its leisure. He saw it as—the absolute expression of myself; as a physician's—a man physician's—work might be the expressions of his life, too; or as a missionary's work is the expression of his whole life.

He said a new thing to me, one day, that shocked me immensely. "Being a wife and a mother is the biologic function any woman can perform; you are both because you are a woman. But your real self is a writer, and it's more important—to you; we shall not speak of the community—to write than to have children or a husband."

I was too startled, too troubled, to say anything.

But he continued, "A man decides he wants a family, a wife, and he has them. But he never forgets, while he is father and husband, that he is, all the time, himself—and must live that own life of his in his career."

The new feminism had not begun to be discussed by my friends; I did not feel this was anything but sin. My religion was love and service. If I denied that this love and service must be given first to my own nearest, what was left? Was it not highest achievement for me to be mother and wife? Writing was only something I did that made me happy; I was not a great writer who could produce masterpieces, who had the right to place her work first.

My friend grinned. "Not to be irreverent," he said, "do you think your husband is a genius of the first order in his work—"

That brought the blood to my face, of course. He apologized, spoke of other things, and we did not refer to the subject for a long time. For a while I made excuses that I might not see him.

But this thing he had said troubled me. Was it true—not for me, for I was entirely happy in our life as it was planned now—was it true that a woman had the right, the real right to do something she wanted to do, even as much as she had the right to be a mother and wife? Did being a wife not destroy everything else that was lesser in one's whole life? Could writing be really, well—important—for a woman like me to do?

Of course, I realized it, it could not be. My husband was right. Perhaps, if I had to earn my living by it, there might be the excuse for seeing it as something real, something solid and serious, like my husband's own work. But now it was, as naturally, only a gift that I had and that I exercised, as I would play the piano for pleasure if I knew how to do that. I wrote in the intervals of my other work, was almost blindingly happy when my work turned out well, and when it did not, accepted with a dull sort of submissiveness my husband's, "Well, and if it did not get accepted, darling, does it matter?"

It did not really matter. It was not even important enough to grieve over.

I worried over the bills for coal and electricity; spent hours on ménus and laundry methods. I arranged a vegetable garden back of our house and tried to feel troubled when nothing came of it but roots. And, guiltily, I would scamp my work, to hurry to my room and to write. Brother became so much my friend that he would play in the same room with me and quietly watch my fingers flying over the keys of my typewriter. I used to save money on housekeeping and pay it back to myself in typewriting paper. I indulged my secret vice.

One day my husband came in and found me at my machine. He laughed, lifted me in his arms, kissed me. "You little darling!" he said. "You're all tired out! Come, let's go out for a walk!"

He did not consider that I was doing something I had been planning for a whole week. It was an assignment a magazine had given me to write. I was to receive $250 for it, almost as much as a month's salary of my husband's.

It was just something deliciously amusing, this gift of mine. I put it aside always for the serious business of walking with my husband, of hearing Little Maid recite her "selection" for school elocution.

I must say here that I have lived many years since then. I have made my work real and important in our life. But, for all that, I do not know but that having love and living it with one's husband and one's children is not the most real thing a woman can do. To this day, I wonder, and have no actual reason to think my strange, brilliant Irish friend was right and my husband wrong, although I have set my life along the way I want it to go.

XV

ONE day, our telephone bell rang, and some one said, "Do you know, I think my brother's not coming, after all. There's a war in Germany." It was a friend, a German Jew, who spoke.

"You don't think it will last long?" I asked.

And the usual answer came: "Oh, about seven or eight months."

I felt sick at the thought of war. But I closed my eyes, my mind, to this one. After all, there were things here in our country to think of.

The war made my husband restless. His father was French, and his quiet became broken by the news that came across. "I wish I could run over," he said once. He was a pacifist, but he threw aside all his beliefs as soon as his father's country took up arms.

"Couldn't you go?" I asked, though my heart sank at the thought of his going. We had never been apart once in all our married life.

"Leave my job?" he said, restlessly. "I might have a leave of absence, but it would be foolish; we couldn't afford it."

But that evening our bell rang, and a caller entered. He loomed tall in the doorway, a handsome figure, as tall as my husband. "Hello, Leah," he said, and bowed to my husband, who recognized at once my Irish friend.

There ensued a quiet first hour after he came. The

children were put to bed, and while I did that the two men were left alone. Coming down presently, I found them sitting quite silently opposite one another, smoking, the room blue with smoke.

"Sit down, dear," said my husband, and I sat down between them.

My Irish friend looked at him, at me, and then said, "I've just been talking to your man, my dear. I told him I wished I were he."

It made me smile, because this was so characteristic of my curious friend. But he did not smile, nor my husband. He said, "I'm going to Ireland to-morrow. That's that. Maybe I won't come back. I want to know this—you care for me, too, don't you, my darling?"

That has always been my husband's tenderest phrase for me. I did not know I had risen when I stood up. But I looked at my husband, at the stranger, too. I felt deeply ashamed. I suppose I should have felt triumphant, or excited. I have read of such things in books and seen them in plays. I ought to have felt flattered. But I felt ashamed.

What we said then does not matter. He was certain, at first, that I had begun to love him. He said he could tell it in the way I listened to him, as he opened my mind. He had been watching me grow, grow over to him, he said.

In the room, my husband's breath came, deeply, regularly, like the sound of an engine a great way off.

"What did I say—or do—that made you think that?" I asked then. "How could you have thought it of—of me?"

My Irish friend rose to his tall height. "It was a mistake," he said, without apology.

And without a word more, without a sound from my husband, he went out. There should have been shouting, denouncing, protesting. But it all happened in less than five minutes and in almost complete silence.

My husband came over to me, took my cold hands in his and said, "Did you admire him, Little Boy?"

But I shook my head, my eyes full of tears. I had not admired him. I had not thought of him at all, as a man. I had thought only of what he had done for me, of the new thoughts he had given me, of the new woman he had pointed out in the distance. My husband held me, suddenly and fiercely, to him. We never talked of it again. I have never seen my Irish friend again. Though I read one of his books, perhaps ten years ago, I have seen none since written by him.

XVI

OUR life went on just as before, though we began to hear much of the war. Our immigrant families in settlements and night schools, social workers told us, were returning "home" to join their native armies. There was some suffering as a result. Wages rose.

One day, perhaps eight or nine months after the beginning of the war, before the newspapers were debating whether we ought to join it, too, the door opened, and in came my brother Robert, taller, thinner, handsomer than ever. He came in dressed in an army uniform. To my amazement, he told me he had gone to Canada, joined the army there and was on his way to the British forces.

"What made you do that?" I could only ask, fear clutching me. I did not ask what my mother thought!

Robert grinned at me. "Pretty soon we'll be in the war, too. Jews will be asked to join the army. They will, but some will want to do what other Americans will want, too—to get out of it. I'm going to be one of the Jews Jewry will point to with pride when those lagging Jews will be named to the multitude! I may have a bronze tablet to my memory!"

"But we'll never join the war!" I cried. "President Wilson has promised!"

"Wait and see," said Robert, with a curious grin.

Little Maid walked beside him very proudly, her

curls dangling down her back. Brother held his finger tight. I talked it over with my husband. "We mustn't let him go!" I wanted to cry out. But, instead, I said, of course, "Perhaps he won't see real fighting. He may remain in Canada. My—mother—"

My husband was not well. He had been working hard. He had been trying to crowd two years' work into one. And the whole city was in unrest; his budget was suffering, for people did not seem to want to give money for social work, as usual. He had headaches from worry, from work, too.

"Don't make him lose courage," he said, as we waited for Robert to come back with the children.

But I could not help frowning when he came back. He brought them back, each holding a drum and a little fife. I allowed no martial toys in our house. I felt displeased, and I think I showed it. But Robert grinned. "Every one'll soon be beating and banging these," he said.

"We won't join the war," I repeated, as if to assure myself.

But Robert took the little tin drum and the rude sticks and began to drum the rhythm of "John Brown's Body."

He stayed two days and talked of everything but the people at home. Only, before he left, he said, "Father's not so well."

A sickness came over me. I wanted to ask what was wrong. But it was so late! Robert was leaving. He kissed me and was gone. I never saw my brother Robert again. He died in Canada of the influenza. In 1917 our country declared war.

Our friends seemed to change their faces before our very eyes. Men grew furtive, or strong, as we looked at them. Mothers went about with hunted eyes. Young wives looked pitifully about them. Brides increased in number, as soon as conscription was enforced. Babies began to be born. The draft was after every one.

My husband wanted to enlist at once, but I would not let him. I did not want this war! I did not want us to be in it!

And then, one day, he came in, sick with a headache as usual. He sat down, crumpled over. He went to bed, and there he remained for over fourteen months. The influenza, stalking the country, had put its touch on him, too.

When he came out of the dreadful fever, when so many were dead, he had grown to weigh less than a hundred pounds. His eyes were like deep blue hollows in a skull's head. His hair had fallen out in the illness. He looked like death.

But he was never more dear to me, never more mine, than in those weeks; never had we been so close as we were to grow in the months that followed. Nurses were impossible to get; doctors were cruelly overworked. So many were away in the war. Our nurse left as soon as the danger was over. She left the months to follow to me.

In two months the sickness was gone, but its mark was left. My husband carried it. He had lost his eyesight in the fever. He had lost the use of his feet afterwards. He was a helpless child, with the hurt, brilliant mind of a man. He could think, but could do nothing.

There was the future to think of—all of it, years and years. I borrowed money. I refused to have our friends come to see us; no one should see my lover now. I cared for him day and night, all night and all day, week by week. The children lived in the kitchen and dining room, played in the yard. Little Maid, who was so small, such a little, grave girl, was my little sister and my friend. She took care of her brother, as if she were really old enough to understand.

And then one day I knew I must get work. Not now, work to fill the time, or to "express myself," but to earn the living of my family.

I could not teach in this state, for I had not passed the examinations here. I would not do social work; our friends were social workers and they would gossip and talk. I would not write, for that was too uncertain. What could I do?

In the columns of the newspapers I searched daily for the answer to that. One day it came. A big store wanted a "personnel director." I had heard of this work. There was not the remotest chance of my getting the position, but I was desperate, and I thought I would try.

The store manager spoke to me, asked me my training, smiled to hear I was a college woman, was interested, but not antagonistic, when he heard I was married, saying, "The war's changing that," and then said, "What do you know about store work?" I knew nothing.

"But you do know social work, teaching, and how to direct people?"

"I've never had more than four people responsible to me," I explained, "and they were teachers in night school, work I knew well." I was troubled.

But this man was a new sort of person, a driving personality, quick and yet powerful, big, gray, brusque and smiling. He could be, I was to learn later, utterly cruel to an employee, merciless. But he was able and even brilliant in his work. He liked me from the first, it appeared, to my astonishment.

"We need a lady in this job," he said. "Some one that will make a high-class appearance. The girls here won't respect any other type. Now, if you prove to be what we're looking for, and I think you will, there's a big job ahead of you! But first, you must know the work. Do you want to sell for two months?"

I did not understand immediately, then I grasped what he meant. It was necessary for me to learn the business of a store—selling—before I could be part of its staff. I must be a saleswoman before I could choose saleswomen.

"Are you game?" asked the manager.

This was my one job. I needed it. He was kind and, in his unusual way, even courteous. He rose as I stood up. "Yes," I said.

I did not know what to say to my husband. My salary in this experimental period was to be small. I had to arrange for the care of the children. I got an old German woman to come in every day at seven dollars a week. The children were at school, except at noon. I cooked breakfasts and dinners, prepared them for school, put them to bed evenings and spent the hours after work with my husband.

He was too tired to care what happened. He only said, weakly, "Don't leave me alone, here, Little Boy." But he did not protest when I said I was going out. He was too ill, at first, to ask where I went. He was pleased with the servant. "Now you're resting a little," he whispered once. He lay in bed, day by day, alone.

Those who go into a store know the saleswoman as

a machine to show and sell goods. Funny writers have described her as a sort of low comedy star. The women I met were neither machines nor comedy characters.

Our store was high grade; the women working in it were, many of them, older women who had grown up with the business. They had begun to work when they left school or high school. The young girls were often high school girls. They were a vastly different type from mill workers sent out to meet life without chance or equipment. These women came from good middle-class homes, the girls from very nice homes.

They worked hard, and they were gentle with me, a stranger.

I was sent to the linen department, where were many of the older women. There I learned the uses of various linens, the process of manufacturing them, how to help women choose wisely and what to suggest to the "brides." The brides were numerous those two war years after the draft!

Presently I was promoted to the dress department, from that to the hats and then to the books. I learned the whole store. I knew merchandise, sales people, and most important of all, the psychology of the customer.

We had in the store a sharp-faced little woman who was "educational director," a thin, intense, capable creature, tiny and tireless and full of a burning faith in "store work." She taught new employees how to fill out their schedules, how to put down their "sales" properly—the mechanics of selling records. "You got it in the first lesson!" she said to me.

I read the stories of Fanny Hurst, of Edna Ferber and even of O. Henry, and try to find my friends, those I made in the store, in their books. I cannot find the women I knew there. Most of the older women spoke a simple, clear English, not a cultivated English, but as good as that used by many of the women I had known as teachers and social workers. They had a common school education, and though they read very little, they had a real reverence for education. They all had an innate love for beauty.

There was Mrs. Crocker, past sixty, white haired, with the swelling figure of the sufferer from kidney trouble. She earned $22 a week, selling "in the voiles." She supported an old mother, was sending an orphaned grandchild through school and was saving painstakingly for her "old age." She dressed in the modern, fashionable clothes the store required of its employees. Of course, she was in pain almost all the time, but she was cheerful, bustling and kind, almost to sacrifice, to the rest of us. She had meant to be a schoolteacher, but married young, was left a widow and went to work. Her husband had been a gentle, ineffective man. Her sister taught in the high school and, once or twice when I saw them together, it seemed to me that Mrs. Crocker was the finer type, not only spiritually, but mentally.

Miss Allison was the typical sales girl of the sob story, an elderly woman, still slender, with dyed hair, painted face and rouged mouth. She sold hats. She was snappy in temper, very sharp in her speech and spoke in an affected, high tone to her customers. She always preferred to deal with the "better people," and made it unpleasant for the younger girls if they did not give her opportunity to deal with the more attractive customers. She would not even go up to a customer who looked "Jewish" or "foreign." But Miss

Allison had been a great beauty in her youth. The owner of the store knew things in that past of hers that only she and he shared as memories. There had been a little boy born to him, and the child died. Miss Allison came back to the store, no longer the queen and favorite of the boss, but as proud, as unbending, as before. She lived in a sort of grand defiance of convention, lost youth and lost love. She would have died before she admitted, however, that she did so because she was so bitterly in need of her salary. One day she fainted in the little room where hats were "fixed up" for customers. She was suffering from a serious illness, due to middle age, but she would not give up. The boss himself came up, and I watched the two of them meet, the obese, not unkindly merchant, and the faded woman sitting amid odds and ends of ribbon and millinery straws. They called each other by their first names. And the little scene was not spoken in slang, in the vulgar patois of the popular "store girl" story, but in simplest, finest words. "You're sick," he said. And she nodded her dyed, tall pompadour, and said, "I think the whole song will soon be finished——" speaking his name. "Let me send you home," he urged her. But she shook her head: "I think it would be better not to. I think you'd better just get out. It will make talk——"

The floorman strutted about in his white shirt and tie. But on his $25 a week he was sending two girls through normal school. He was a decent member of his church, and gave out of his meager salary to the church work. He read books and loved music. He read everything he could find about music. He spoke shyly of his reading and interest in it.

No, the people in the store were like the people I

knew in my girlhood—they were poor, but they were exactly like those I knew who were rich. Their daily needs ate into the hours of their lives. But they had the same dreams, the same characters, whatever their work might be.

I found, again and again, that selling behind a counter does not make a woman less intellectually fine than teaching behind a desk; it does not make a man less so.

XVII

MY period of probation was to last three months. They were not easy months. But I had a problem not different from those many of the other women were facing. A great many of the women had mothers or husbands dependent on them. Almost all the married women had children whom they supported. The difference between the married and unmarried women was that the latter were often young girls, who fought or protested against life. But the unmarried girls, too, gave their earnings to their families. Sometimes, there was one who was frivolous, there were those, too, who took the easy way—and it was open in our store, as in other industrial establishments—but the great mass of working women were carrying an economic burden, like me.

From them I learned how to adjust things a bit.

I taught Little Maid how to feed her brother and prepared breakfast the night before. I would set it out on the table, and let her feed her brother, only dressing him myself in the morning. With a woman near the school, I arranged for lunches for the children, and felt easier about them. I had the old German woman come in to help my husband at noon, and take him out on the porch. My neighbors were pleasant, but I wanted nothing from them, of course. I meant to move as soon as possible, anyhow, to a cheaper place. Sometimes I would run out to my home at noon, missing lunch, but having the peace of seeing that everything was well with my husband. He was tired and lonely, miserable as he grew well enough to understand our situation; but he said nothing. He would only sit, thin and drawn, waiting until the children came home.

Presently, he was able to hobble around. He used a cane and a crutch and managed to see the children at noon. He was able to help me with them in the morning. We did not speak of my working. But he suffered the more bitterly because of it, I knew well enough.

When we had a sale at the store, I could not come home on the usual hour, because of the need to put the things away, to add up sales slips, and to arrange the aisles neatly for the following morning.

I did rather well in the linens, was transferred to the silks and then successively to millinery, books and, finally, to the jewelry, which was very fascinating, not alone because of the loveliness of the merchandise itself, but because of the completely different group of purchasers who came to buy it. Most of the department store sales were made to women, and the whole store was keyed to the tone that would appeal to women customers. But the jewelry department store was arranged to sell things for women, but to men. It was men who paid the bills for the jewelry, whether an expensive bauble for a pretty, trifling woman was sold, or a cherished, long-awaited gift for the wife of middle age.

My own work was relatively unimportant. I sold the bangles at the "odds and ends" counter, but sometimes I was called in to help guard the cases—though ostensibly to help sell—while valuable jewels were being shown. I was particularly anxious to learn the selling of jewelry, because so many of the women spoke of that department as beyond their wildest dreams. It was fascinating, but trying work, I found. All department store work, for the salesgirl, is a fight against the inexpertness of the purchaser. The saleswoman must sell goods: that is what she's paid for. But in a high-grade store, she must not press the making of a sales. She must make the customer want to buy. In stores where the "return privilege" is permitted, her sale may end in a return of the goods, if she has overpersuaded her customer. She must make her customer feel she wants the goods, trusts its value and has so much need and faith that she wants to keep it. But her customer usually knows nothing of the value of goods, outside the small circle of objects frequently bought. Often the customer does not even know what she really wants to buy: the cleverness of the counter-trimmer catches her imagination and overrides her prudence. She wants to buy what she really does not need or want.

The result is that she receives her purchase, "sent," and promptly sends it back. The store is out this much: the time of the saleswoman; the time spent in packing the parcel; the time spent in sending and delivering it; the time spent in adjusting the business of "returned" goods.

The buyer sometimes gets the blame. But the saleswoman gets it first.

In millinery, suits, dresses, the saleswomen are careful not to urge a purchase. In this field they need not worry, though. Women know these types of merchandise. They also know household goods.

But furniture, ornaments, books, furs—jewels—

they know nothing of. Selling in these departments is like a blind walk into the night; the salesgirl never knows whether the sale is really made.

I was glad not to have the real responsibility of "heavy" selling in the jewelry department. It seemed to me that my day was full enough. I found that in the evenings I would be much more tired than I remembered being before. My back ached. Often my head ached, too. In the middle of my work I could not help thinking, suddenly, "Has my little boy his rubbers on to-day?" "Has my daughter forgotten to drink the *second* glass of milk the doctor said she must have?" "Did I close the window on the right of my husband's chair: he'll have a cold to-night if I didn't." All day long, a hundred tiny things would sting at my mind from my home responsibilities. They would obtrude themselves, never allowing me to relax. I would wait until lunch time, call up then and, if I had been right to worry, I would worry then until five, because the milk had not been taken by my little girl, because my little boy, would have had wet shoes.

Our little son had frequent colds, and the doctor advised the usual operation for tonsils and adenoids. I could not have it on any day but Sunday, and the doctor came to us on that day. We put the little fellow on the table. I held the basin while the doctor snapped the thin wire inside his throat. I sat up all day with him, watched him "come through" ether, fed him water next morning and went off to work, working the usual nine hours, and then sat up until twelve with him that night.

How did I do it?

I do not know. I read of the heroic things done

during the war. Perhaps that was heroism, too. But the women working with me did it all the time. They did the daily work of a man, went home and did the work of a woman and, in addition, were nurse, dressmaker, wife, mother, to those dependent on them. Untrained, most of these saleswomen were, not highly educated, but they were one of the finest groups of women I have ever known. They asked no quarter. They were not "modern," like the young girls coming in to replace them presently. They believed in the home, in the responsibilities of the wife and of the mother in the home. But they did as much, as wage earners, as any woman deliberately going out to get a career made for herself, does, to-day. And they did so as part of their duty as "old-fashioned" women, responsible for the happiness of children, parents and helpmeets.

I had forgotten that I came to the store with the hope of another job. My weekly salary in the long, narrow, manila envelope, with my number on it, and the dollars crisp inside, was the one thing I knew here. It meant clothes for the children, food for us all. The rent was paid by my husband's salary, a salary that had stopped some months before, but had been put aside to provide for our rent for months to come.

And then one day I was called in, and faced the head of the directing board of the store, big, gray haired, paunchy, wrinkled, brusque. "Sit down," he said. I sat down in his office, wondering why I was there. The women hated him. I had seen him flay a woman, humiliate her and insult her, too, because she had made an error in filling out the address in a sales slip for a "send purchase."

"Would you like an office on the fifth floor?" he asked me.

I stared, sat up, and I think a little sigh came from me. But I could not answer. "Boss wants to try some new ideas—lectures and things like that. Books. Classes. High toned. Keep the smart young people here. Understand, no social work. Keep down the labor turnover. Keep the smart young people here. Want to do it?"

I could only put my hands close together; I couldn't talk.

He went on to explain that the work was to depend entirely on the coöperation of the floormen and the buyers. I must get in touch with them, find out who were the intelligent salespeople, particularly the younger ones, get them into my classes, arrange things to make them attached to the store, develop them. I could do whatever I liked, have a free hand, "provided I didn't ask for any money," he said, with a grim smile.

But he went on, "We'll pay $2,000 a year, begin first of this month. Well?"

Well.

It seemed they had been watching me, saw that I didn't feel "swell headed" although a college woman, had worked just like the other women, was "human." That was "the stuff"; they'd never found it before. "You've acted as if you worked for a living, instead of coming here to slum in the store," he said. "Keep it up."

As if I worked for a living.

I did not want to smile. I thanked him, and he opened the door for me, signifying that I was one of the chosen now, as good as a customer, and he said,

"Tell you what, you've got class. Miss O'Healy said it. Class goes with the girls here. Teach them to have it. Help make the store high-toned."

I nodded. I was presently shown to my office, a pretty little office with a real desk, a typewriter, a telephone and a tray—for what? For letters. It looked like the wire tray in which I drained dishes.

High-toned. Class. Worked for a living.

He thought I was doing this because I was an idle married woman who had nothing else with which to fill her time. I was to get $2,000 a year to give "class" to the sales people, keep the labor turnover down. I knew that the buyers would have looked aghast at the pittance. But—$40 a week. My husband's assistant earned $35 a week. I had never earned so much before. My own desk. My own telephone. My own letter tray. I was a woman with a career for certain now.

XVIII

MY husband listened quietly when I told him of what had happened. Then he took my face in his thin hands, and said, "You're thin."

I was thin. I pinned my skirt all around me because it would slip down. My coat fitted me like a loose sack. I wore high collars and ties, and so the boniness of my neck did not show, but the hollows in my cheeks were plain enough. But my thinness was "stylish." I was not cringing and thin; it was a proud thinness.

Oh, say what one wanted, it was a great thing!

I was successful. I was as successful as a man.

I held my little son and daughter close, and I think I smiled into their soft curls. I put my arms around my husband's thin shoulders, and when I leaned my cheek against his he did not see that my eyes were happy. After all, these three people were my own—and I was their source not only of love, but of life. That, too, I could do for them.

I wanted to write. Sometimes it seemed to me my fingers burned with the need to write. I wanted to write the things I had seen and lived, that I had learned from the women about men, from the men with me.

But I pressed all that back. Writing did not pay. And, first of all, I must prove that I was really able to take care of this family of mine, this little group, these three that I loved best. These—and my mother.

I would send her a gift, something out of my new salary.

"I'm well," I told my husband, though. "And you're getting well."

He lifted his head, grown gray these past months of illness. "I am getting well," he said then. "It won't be long you'll have to do this."

My heart sank then. Didn't he know, didn't he see, that I wanted this to be—not something I did just because he had to drop the burden of our support, but because I was as capable as he of assuming that burden?

"Little woman," he whispered. "Forgive me."

I cried then. I cried because he asked me to forgive him because he was sick. But, yes, I cried too because he felt it necessary to ask that of me; because he did not feel that I was as hungry for the full measure of human responsibility as he was.

"I like to work," I said then, quietly. "I enjoy—being important," I said with a half laugh.

He laughed then, relieved. He was delighted that I spoke like a child about my work. He kissed me and held me close. How thin and tired, how frail his arm was about my shoulder!

My new work called me to the store at a quarter after eight, because I had classes then for some of the young men at the store. It meant that I could not now dress my little son. But my larger salary seemed to me enormous. I arranged for the old German woman to come all morning, clean, dust and even to cook supper, which I would heat when I came home.

My work was divided into classes, lectures and "store work." I went to each of the buyers and asked for students for my classes. I was warned I would not meet cordiality. I did not. The buyers kept the floormen keyed up, so that their stuff would sell. The floormen kept after the saleswomen. There were, in addition, young girls and boys in each department, who were being put through training, tried out in branch after branch.

The buyers thought that the classes were a nuisance. The store was there to sell. It was no blooming school. Mr. O'Hara, the buyer in the hosiery department, was typical. A choleric, red-faced Irishman, he stood up the day I came in. "Boys?" He turned his head aside. "Haven't any to spare."

But I could not leave it at that. "I have a list of names," I said then. "Some of these boys are in your department. Couldn't you let them come to our classes for an hour—from eight to nine? They're not due with you until eight forty-five anyway."

"Waste of time," he snorted.

"Not really," I pleaded. "I am to teach them about silks—colors—dyes—part of your business—"

"Meaning you know it better'n me?" he demanded.

I hurriedly disclaimed that. I tried to tell him that if the boys understood the making of his stock, its scheme in the store, its prices, its colors, they would know better how to sell it and would be more interested in selling it.

"Can't see it," he said.

"So you refuse to let any of your boys come?"

He grunted, turned around, turned away. Then he said, "Tony and Sam can go, if you can get them. See those kids come eight o'clock in the morning!"

But Tony and Sam did come at eight o'clock in the morning. So did Jack and Fred and Tim and a half dozen girls. My first two classes were filled almost before I was aware of it.

I found that the young people in the store were of a different sort from the old. The old people represented the citizenry of the town in its youth—American. The young people were the children of the newcomers—second generation immigrants. They were Italians, Irish, Germans.

The boys were thin, tall, gawky. They were of the type later to be made into salesmen or floormen. Some of them were stupid. But two were brilliant. I began by teaching them spelling, since that was required for their daily work. Arithmetic they knew. Then—curiously enough, it may seem—I began to teach them algebra and English literature. I found that four had graduated from grade school. To these four I offered an opportunity. If they were prepared to work, I would give them high school training in three subjects. They agreed with an enthusiasm that caught at my heart, though I tried not to show that. My job was to be quiet, efficient, friendly.

I went to the board of education and had a talk there. They agreed to my request—to give my students high school credit for classes I had, provided they passed a set examination. There was jubilation when I announced that.

The girls were slower than the boys. But they caught on more quickly to other things. I taught the classes color combinations, showed them pictures, read books and articles with them. The girls appreciated more quickly beauty in color, nuances in social culture through the books I selected. "Oh, that's a swell talking," they said when I read the first paragraph of one story.

The girls were not interested for the sake of the store. They were interested in getting on—and out. They wanted to get married. They did not mean to marry "store fellows." They were pretty, well-dressed, refined and not so well educated as either the boys or the older women. What they admired above all else was fashionableness. They had an uncanny instinct for "class." They could tell a customer's social standing with almost clairvoyant promptness. Their aim was to be as "classy" as possible. A floorlady who had not class could no more have held their respect nor won their obedience than could have a dish-washer who came in without authority.

Because I was quiet and wore my hair brushed back and high, they all began to affect quiet tones, high hair-dressing and close-fitting dark suits or dresses. They imitated me faithfully and amusingly, just as my little daughter did, at home, sometimes. It made me smile occasionally. But it was all right for the store, and perhaps for them, too.

The older women I reached in a different way. For them I arranged lectures, musicales and little clubs. They were interested in books and in plays. We had "theater parties," with cut rates for clubs, we attended concerts, sometimes as the guests of organizations who sent me tickets, and we met for knitting and sewing. They did not like "heavy" books, but they enjoyed Mrs. Norris, Mrs. Rinehart and Richard Harding Davis. They enjoyed, too, the stories of such Russians as Chekhov, it must be added, and whatever fine story, translated from any tongue, that I found, and which told of love and the sweetness of bitter sacrifice.

With the men my contact was more limited. Their interests were outside the store. But I thought I could reach the young men by a plan. I arranged to have large dances for all the store employees. These proved successful, although at them the groups divided into sharply distinct social markings. The salespeople in each department stuck together, and the higher officials all stuck together. The medical department had nothing to do with the mercantile, and so on.

My work prospered, though. Our library was patronized. The young people came more regularly to classes—and so to work. My "chief" was pleased. I was to look for something nice, he said. I felt a little warmth in my heart—did he mean a raise in salary, something for the children at home, then?

I began a study of the store employees, to discover what causes kept them away from work. "Absenteeism" we called it. I wanted to find what ailments interfered with the work of the employees. I was certain most of them were simple sicknesses, easily avoided, such as colds and indigestion. I knew that the former was caused by the drafts in the dressing rooms; the latter by the hastily gulped lunches the employees were forced to eat in the limited lunch space. I meant to show the need for a rest room and a dining room.

For the first time, a real obstacle met me, however. Employees could not be asked when they were absent. But the pay rolls could be consulted, and the reason for each day's absence was given there. I went to them. The superintendent was quiet as I worked. He hovered near and said nothing. Sometimes, though, he would come, look at my charts, look at me and move away silently. He said nothing, but he did not move far away.

I found odd statements in the book he kept. Sometimes there was the word "sickness" after a name, then "excused"; sometimes there was "headache," and a blank of days absent. Sometimes there was nothing but the blank. One day I said, "Who excuses an employee for sickness?" He looked at me and said, sharply, "The boss." But that was impossible. The boss didn't have time for thousands of requests of this sort.

"I do it when he can't," he said.

I put down my pen and considered.

I understood better, as I found out the system of absences. He could write "excused" after a name, and save a worker's salary for her that day, whereas "absence" meant loss of salary. If a worker could drag herself to report and then go home, she got paid for the day. That was not, perhaps, what the business would want, but it was kind. Why was the man so sour, so belligerent?

The reason was apparent enough—and soon.

One of my girls, Mary S—, came to me with a curious look in her pretty, saucy face. "Guess I put my foot in it and made a hole in my chances," she said.

It was an invariable rule of the store not to have the girls confide their outside affairs to us. The store refused to know what sort of "lives" they led or to be responsible for them. I was there, I had been told, to do business, not "moral welfare" work.

But this girl smiled: "I told him to tell the boss what he wanted, and to go to the dickens. I'm going to leave anyhow."

My pupils did not leave; the "boss" and the leaving of a job were "store interests."

"Don't leave until you've talked things over with

your floorwoman," I advised her. "Go down and talk things over with her, Mary."

Mary's eyes flashed; her face darkened. "Tell her? Why, she wouldn't dare say anything but what he wanted! Everybody knows what she is to him! But he won't get anything out of me by writing me down 'present'—the old soak!"

This was a different Mary from the one I usually knew.

But Mary was right, I saw clearly enough, now that I had the key. The old man watched me read his books and thought I could tell where he had written "present" at his own desire, for favorite girls. It made me ill, and I dropped the study, saying that there was nothing in it. There was not. The store executives knew what was happening. But there was nothing to be done. When the old man left—he would some day, surely, die—they would replace him by young blood, clean. Meanwhile, nothing drastic. He was a good worker. And the mis-statements were too few for the store to bother—

One day a woman came in, with a smirk, to say that one of the girls was riding up and down the elevator all lunch hour, instead of going out. "A shame." The elevator boy was a mulatto, a "good-looking nigger, yes."

The girl was called into the office, given a talking to and told she would be dismissed if she didn't buck up. The colored boy was discharged. She was sent to me "to be talked to." I didn't know what to say to her. But suddenly she burst into deep, hard sobs. She was a skinny, homely little thing, in the "downstairs store," a dreary little bit of girlhood. She was Italian, she said; her father was a shoemaker. He took all her money. She worked at home after the store hours. She had no friends. Her father didn't let her go with boys—you know how Italians feel, she reminded me. She liked singing, though. And this—this colored boy—he sang. She heard him humming.. She didn't mean anything. He treated her—like a lady. He wasn't fresh. He didn't think of her at all—hardly talked to her. She didn't think of him, too. Just a friend, that was all. He was some one that made her feel grand, that was all. And now the disgrace of it—the whole store saying—she and a colored boy—she wanted to die.

I was not permitted to follow up her story. The store could make working conditions pleasing and comfortable. It could arrange for classes to keep its workers satisfied and to educate them. But it could not be responsible for anything so personal as a girl's happiness, morals, home—in the store or out of it. The colored boy was discharged. That was enough.

One had to accept one's work under the condition in which it came. But then I was younger. I chafed. I protested. My employer—the chief—I did not see. But the others simply smiled when I spoke. "This is business," they said. "But keep it up—that kind of feeling is valuable; can't help making the employees feel how personal you feel toward them."

But I was allowed to give more frequent dances, to arrange for the social life of the young girls. The floormen were ushers; they came after their long day at the store. They came without pay and because they were ordered to come.

But the young girls were delighted. They asked if they might bring friends. That was a serious question: should the store undertake something outside its own employees?

"Good advertising," was the decree. "Some stores give public concerts."

We arranged our first big dance. "Each one may bring a friend." There was to be a lecture, then music, then a dance. It was to be "swell," educational and entertaining—and good publicity.

I was so excited, myself, that it seemed to me, for that day, I was a girl again. The girls came all day about their clothes, their beaus, their cards. There were flowers to order and to see arranged, committees to keep working, programs to have ready, lights to have fixed.

The store loft was the dance hall, and it was filled. It appeared that every girl had brought not one friend, but ten friends, and as if the men had brought a dozen girls each. It was a success.

The next day my chief called me in, beamed and said genially, "Well, pretty nice."

I wanted to laugh, to clap my hands.

"I'm planning another," I said, trying to be casual. "I want to have one a week, to keep the girls—to give them enough social life, with supervision, here, under my eyes."

He laughed out then, genially and kindly, too. "Under mamma's eyes, eh?"

I laughed then, too. "Have you any suggestions?" I asked, quickly severe again.

He nodded. "Yep. One criticism. Nice dance. Nice crowd. Nice speaker. But there were too many Jews from other stores. Cut that out."

I stared at him.

He said, briskly, "Lots of the girls said they saw

sales girls from Oppenheimer's and Fields', too. Too many Jews. Spoil our class."

"But," I said, "you remember no one came here except by invitation. Those girls were invited by our men and our girls."

He smiled then. "Sure thing, that. Well, tell them they can't repeat."

I sat quietly, and then I heard my lips speak: "I couldn't do that. If I do that, I'll have to say I won't come either, for I am a Jewess myself."

He looked startled. "Really?"

I rose then. "I never thought it made any difference. But if it does, I'll leave to-day. Anyhow, I'll leave at the end of the month."

He protested, spoke rapidly of the respect he had for the Jewish business men in the city, took back what he had said and explained that he was just expressing the feeling of their customers. Hadn't I noticed how few Jewish employees they had. It was just a matter of business, that was all. As for me, no one knew I was Jewish, and it didn't matter at all.

I nodded quietly and went up to my office.

I was determined to leave by the first.

XIX

IT was time to think out this problem of my being a Jewess among the other religious groups I met at my work and in our social life. There was as much difference among them—one from the other—as between myself and any of them, I knew. In the store, most of the young women were Catholics; the older women were Protestant. The men in the sales force, and among the floorwalkers also, were Protestant; the delivery men and those doing the rougher work were more often Catholic. This was, of course, because the harder, rougher work was done by immigrant workers. The employees who came into direct contact with customers had to be not only personable men, but capable, too, of speaking a dignified English and of appearing in that odd rôle which is halfway between a butler and a host, and which is typical not only of the American "floorman," but of his brother abroad, too.

The division among the women workers, though, was due to another cause. The older women had been with the store a long time; they had come, in many cases, when the business was first begun. They were the daughters of the city—Americans. The younger women were oftenest very pretty Irish or German girls, the Irish girls predominating. There were, besides, a number of attractive Italian girls in the millinery department and in the lower-price departments downstairs." These girls came at small salaries. Most of them started at fourteen dollars a week; they could hope to earn no more than twenty-two dollars eventually, unless, of course, they would rise to the position of buyer or assistant buyer. There was much chance of that for the individual girl. It was, therefore, natural, that most of them should feel they were employed only as a stop-gap until marriage released them from obligations. The older women, however, worked steadily, and their jobs were, in a real sense, their careers.. The store, for that reason, had two religious groups, which represented, at the same time, two as distinct economic and social groups, racially alien. This was not so in the two other stores in the city, both of them owned by Jews and employing Jewish or Slavic girls.

The Protestant women, aloof and repressed, looked with intense disapproval on the very pretty Irish girls filling the store. These girls were strangers not only racially but socially.

The older women knew every resident in the city—that is, every "old resident." They felt in no way inferior to customers who came in limousines, in costly furs. They had the pride of self-respect which is typical of the small American town. The city had grown in twenty years, since first our store was opened. But these older saleswomen had not lost their feeling of security in their own dignity, with the change of the town to a big town.

The "new" girls were pert and clever. They were quick to serve. But they approached the customers with a ready servility that the older women resented and intensely disapproved. "What does Moddam want?" one older woman repeated, quietly. "That's what she said: 'What does Moddam want?' Sounded like those funny servants in a play, honest it did." These older women knew customers by name; their customers knew their names likewise. The new people who came in were "grabbed" by the "new" girls. A new store was growing up before their eyes. One of the women put it so to me: "I know every piece in my shelves, and I know how it will cut and how it will look. I never sell a thing but what I can tell exactly whether it's useful or not, or if it's a bargain or not. I know whether my customer will like it when she has it a while. But these new girls, they never think of the store, or the merchandise, or the customer. They're just anxious to sell the goods and to get the customer out of the way. They make up to the customer, act up to them and honey them into buying. 'Dear' and 'dearie' them, and flatter, them, and act as if butter wouldn't melt in their mouths until the sale is made. Then, as soon as the customer is gone, they get together and laugh at her, make fun of her. I couldn't act nice to a woman and then laugh at her. I don't feel that the women I meet selling are any different that way than the kind I meet outside. That's the difference between us and these new girls. We Americans, we feel the people we sell to are our own kind. We don't have to stick up to them, and we don't feel like making little of them, either. But these new girls that are coming into the store business, they're like all foreigners. They haven't any self-respect. They'd as lief tell a lie as not—if it's to a customer. They'd as soon make small of a woman as not, if she's not one of themselves. They've not got any real responsibility, or whatever you want to call it, outside their religion. They are, you know," and she lowered her voice, "mostly Catholics."

The Catholic girls, on the other hand, resented the other women, their aloofness, their primness, as they saw it, and their good wages. A dozen years ago the store girl was not finding competition from college graduates, as she is to-day. Her wits, her good looks, and her experience were her assets. These girls had all three of the trinity. Yet, it was true, their wages were not so high as those of the older women. The reason was valid, however, from the point of view of the store. The departments where highest-class goods were sold—to "swell" customers—were in the hands of American women and of selected American girls. The pretty, vivid Irish girls, with their charming brogue or the lilting echo of brogue learned from immigrant parents, were placed in the other departments. They hadn't the "big chances."

The result was, of course, dislike, hatred even. I found that in all the store "affairs" I arranged, one of the really difficult things to do was to preserve peace between the groups—not to make the Protestant workers feel "Everything in this store is for and by the Catholics"; not to let the Catholics feel "The Protestant women here are blocking us again."

With the men there was not so obvious a problem. They worked together amicably enough. Later, when the Ku Klux Klan made its recent entrance into American life I recalled my girls and women at the store, and I could understand the hatred of women; but it seemed hard to think that men like the friendly, pleasant workers in the delivery rooms, the garages and the packing rooms could really be unfriendly to one another.

Outside the store, my friends had been of many creeds. Most of them were Protestants. A few were

Jews, and these were German Jews of American parentage, since in this city the first residents of Jewish faith has been German Jewish peddlers who opened stores, became merchants, bred sons and daughters who, in turn, worked in the stores or studied to prepare themselves for one of the professions. There were only a half dozen or so Catholics in our circle; the Catholics belonged to the newer immigration and were still the "working classes."

Our Protestant friends were very religious, for the most part belonging to the Methodist Church, though a few were Episcopalians. The Episcopalians were less concerned about their church, its demands and its creed, than were the Methodists, however. They were, too, it must be stated, conscious of a social superiority, even in a city of small size, such as ours was. One of them was a teacher in the high school, another was a social worker, still another was a physician. The Methodists were almost all social workers or teachers, but two were business people, one the head of a prosperous insurance company, the other the president of a chain of small-town drug stores. The Methodists always spoke with a certain tight asperity of the Episcopalians; the Episcopalians were usually brightly superior to the Methodists. When, at our invitation, they met at our home, they communicated with one another with class divisions clearly marked and observed. They were uncomfortable with one another, but not with me, the "outsider." I would tease my friends about their conscious distinction among themselves, but they would only smile and say, conclusively, "Oh, you couldn't understand."

Our friends, of course, knew I was a Jewess. I had made that clear at once, and they had met my brother.

But they, too, like all the people I had met, simply could not understand that, though I had married a non-Jew, I did not myself ceased to be a Jewess simultaneously. I made it a point to let them know that I had not joined the Christian Church. My Episcopalian friends would smile and say nothing, for my husband's mother had been an Episcopalian. My Methodist friends would smile, too, but they would say, "Oh, you will join the church in good time." A distant relative of my husband's, an unmarried lady of means, sent out a "chain letter" of prayer for my conversion. That annoyed me, but it delighted my husband hugely. He is so indifferent to religion that it cannot even vex him.

The only people who did not appear to think I would come over to the Christian Church because of my marriage were our Catholic friends. One of these was an artist, a very pretty girl who painted in water colors and sold her work through the local "art store." She had been abroad, knew people and foreign languages, but she could sit through a whole evening without speaking a word, only smiling a bit when she was not addressed or smiling more broadly when she was asked a direct question. Another was the local priest, who came in contact with my husband in his work, who was a breezy, witty man, a genius at understanding people and a genius in a field he had twenty years ago put aside as lightly as one throws aside a used match—music. He had had a brilliant career as a pianist ahead of him, he had given a concert abroad, as was indispensable then if one were to succeed in America, he had even played in New York—and then, without warning, without waiting, he gave up his future as a musician, entered a seminary, and became a priest.

He had no romantic field among the poor in a mill city, or with the downtrodden in a great slum. His parish was just the middle-class working group of a small-sized town. He only smiled (showing dazzling teeth) when he spoke of his previous work. He was happy in his chosen life work now, one saw. He was deeply, passionately, religious, with that still sort of passion my father had as a Jew. He seldom spoke of his faith, but when he did he became a different man. Usually he seemed absurdly modern in his gown, because he was so handsome, so much the Gibson hero of the time, with his big shoulders, jutting chin, wavy hair and lean, strong hands. But when he began to speak of his faith, his face changed; it was as if, before our eyes, its values altered, under the hands of a painter. His eyes became brilliant, his lips became thinner, his color receded. He became medieval. He was a fanatic in his religion, a fanatic of a faith mystical, beautiful, old.

My husband used to laugh because he depressed me when he changed so before our eyes. He did not know that I was depressed because I saw the same thing I had known as a girl—the tyranny of fanaticism, the faith that "my faith alone is the right one."

Oddly enough, the Methodists could be just as intense as this Catholic priest. When they spoke of ritual, of observances, all their amenities, their urbanities vanished. They were more inimical to the Catholics than to Jews, and more resentful of Episcopalians than of Catholics, in turn. "It's because Catholics spoil the concept of Christianity," explained the wife of our friend the insurance man. "And Episcopalians are even worse; they're Protestants, and yet they imitate the Catholics as hard as they can, and then feel superior to genuine Protestants who wouldn't do such things. Some Episcopalians," she added then, each word carrying poison, "even have confession, I've heard."

The only two people who did not seem to be troubled by religious distrusts, religious animosities were my husband and myself. We were friends of people in three religious groups, and it never occurred to us to divide them into groups—except at their own choice. To us they were individuals, each with his own dear qualities.

Just that were we to one another. I was a woman to be loved, he was my man to be loved. That I was a Jewess and he not a Jew, never mattered, never occurred to us.

One reads of the unhappiness in marriages between Jews and Gentiles. *Among all our friends there has never been one marriage between Jews and Gentiles which has been unhappy—because of the difference in religion.* In one instance, a newspaper man married a Jewess because she was rich, and when she lost her money he deserted her. But every day men and women of all faiths marry into their own faiths, for money, and find happiness flies away when the money disappears. One very intelligent Jewess I came to know later married a man not of her religion, lived with him eight years, bore him a son and then fell in love with another man, a Jew this time. She left her husband for the other man. But every day thousands of American women, married in church to church members, fall in love with other men, not because they have found "one of their faith," but for a more congenial lover.

A woman we knew in our own circle married a man of whom her family disapproved. They never came into her home, and though they passed her a number of times each week in the street, they never spoke to her nor to her child. They made her intensely unhappy. She was a Protestant, and her husband was a young Catholic, a lawyer, in the city. They would not forgive her that dreadful sin of having married a Papist. Eventually, this marriage ended in a separation, long after I had left the city.

But I had no folks to make us unhappy. My parents did not write to us, and that was a deep wound in my heart. But they did not actively take a part in our lives. We were too far away. I think that marriages between young people of different faiths depends for happiness—as do most marriages, for that matter—on the absence of interference from the families of man and wife, and on that alone.

The difference in our parents' faiths did not mean anything to us, except something vivid and interesting from which we each started the premises of the philosophy of life.

The people who were really uncomfortable about my being a Jewess were the German Jews in our town. The Jewish population had been, perhaps, forty years in existence. There were about five hundred Hungarian families employed in the mills near by. It had started with two German families—the owners of the shoe store, and of the jewelry store. At present there were thirty families or so. Most of them were interested in the three big stores of the city, either as owners or as employees, usually as "high employees." It had been their stores which had provided the "Jewish girls" to whom my store objected at our big dance. The Jewish girls were not only Hungarian girls, daughters of the immigrant families, but German Jewesses, too. Nowadays, Jewish girls of good family do not enter store work, and a score of years ago they would never have thought a respectable Jewish girl could go to work at all. But ten years ago Jewish girls in smaller towns began to reach out for something —something, at least, to do. They could not marry the Gentile boys whom they met; their own Jewish men friends left for college, and thereafter for the big cities, as soon as was possible. The small-town girl looked on the desolation of her home town and turned to the less desirable men, those without gumption enough to leave, for consolation. But the Jewish girls whose fathers were the first to settle in the American small towns faced a double misery as women. They were received, very often, into the social group of the community, went to parties and dances. They had not the seclusion of the Jewish girls living even in a small city, such as I had known. As soon as they became women, however, they found themselves left alone, isolated. Their girl friends married the young men they met in churches and church societies. The Jewish girls met few, if any, of their faith. If they were German Jews they suffered another handicap, the cleavage between themselves and other immigrant Jews.

The German Jew had followed the Spanish Jew to America; he came a century later. He came as peddler and small merchant. He was followed, in turn, by the Russian and Polish Jew, who became peddler and sweat-shop worker. The three divisions of Jews are, to this day, rigidly marked. The aristocratic Spanish Jew scorns the plebian German Jew; the prosperous German Jew looks with hauteur on the Polish and Russian Jew. The Russians and Poles, on their part, return with good measure the blighting disapproval of the German Jew, and accept with proper spirit the patronage of the Spanish Jew. That is because the German Jew is the "reformed" Jew; he is the Protestant Jew. The Spanish Jew and the Russian Jew have not left the ancient faith of their people, nor have they altered its century-old observances or prayers.

To-day, the Russian Jew is a figure in the new "reform" Judaism. The leading reform Jewish rabbis are Russian Jewish and Hungarian Jewish boys who came to America as immigrants, or whose parents immigrated to America. They lead the proudest and most important Jewish communities. The young Russian Jew is taking his place, too, by right of wealth, in the boards of trustees of fashionable reformed Jewish temples, but ten, twelve years ago, the distinctions were new, and they were rigid. Nowhere were they more unbending than in the little country towns. A German Jewish girl whose father had a store in a small country town had to resign herself to being an old maid, unless she were so fortunate as to have friends in a city near by, to whom she could go for social life.

In our prosperous, busy city the shoe store was owned by an old German Jew, Gottlieb, who had come from Posen, and who, because Posen is so near Poland, felt he must mark more rigidly the divisions between himself and Polish and Hungarian Jews. He had two daughters and three sons. The boys had gone to Boston and were in business there. The girls he had sent to college, not because he believed in education, but that they might make friends, meet young men and marry. The elder went to Barnard, the other to Radcliffe. They were pretty, kind and very intelligent. But they had the natural shyness of country girls and, in addition, that odd, defensive arrogance of successful Jews. They did not find men friends. They came back home and stayed home. Because of their father's influence, they obtained positions as teachers, one teaching English, the other history. Myra and Babette Gottlieb were two gentle, slightly embittered old maids before they had passed their middle twenties.

But I liked them from the beginning, and they were my friends. They made it a point to let me know they were liberal. They did not mind my being of Russian parentage, the daughter of a scholar. They forgave me that. They had lived in big cities, New York and Boston. But they wished me to know they were large-minded. They were not friends of our Gentile friends; they were conscious all the time, even when they simply sat at the table with them, that they were of a different race. They became stiff and hard, unpleasant, when Gentiles were present. Their opinions were expressed in hard, definite statements. They laid stress on their education, their travels (really not extensive) and their father's place in the city. They were utterly unlike themselves,—their natural, reticent, shy, kind selves. They were changed because they were determined that Gentiles "should not patronize them." With their girlhood friends they were sweet and charming, even though these were not Jews. To strangers, though, they were always on the defensive as Jews.

To these two girls my marriage was simply criminal. They could not understand how I could live through it. They saw it, first, as a crime against my people—a breaking away from the fold, which was unthinkable. Then it was a breaking away from the family, my family.

Perhaps no one can really understand what that

means to the Jew. No people on earth has been so driven, so harried as has been the Jew. No race has suffered so deeply, so long,. One sanctuary the Jew has always had, however. That has been his home, his family. It has been a sanctuary of love. The Jewish family has become not only a social institution, but a refuge in which God and love come together. It has a holiness, a closeness, which no one else can feel.

That is why the Jew cannot marry out of his fold, even when there are no religious ties to hold him back. The Jewish family will hold a man or woman with its tender love when the Jewish faith itself has died away. My two friends were not religious; they were, in fact, agnostic. But they would never have found it possible to think of taking a step that would remove them from the circle of their home, of their father's love. It was he who would not approve of their marrying Gentiles. He would rather they married Russian Jews, in fact, as one of them put it, with a smile. The only men they knew who were their intellectual equals were Christians they had met at college, "or married men at home," they added with a smile. And so—they could never marry, perhaps, for, of course, they could not marry Gentiles and offend their father—and risk the displeasure of the family.

I had risked not only the displeasure of my family, but its loss to me as a family. Except for my brother Robert, and the tiny, rare notes from my mother, I was dead to my family. They had not even written to me for six years. My sisters, so far as I knew, had not even inquired of Robert about me. My father did not write to me. I was alone. I had just my husband and my children in all the world.

They were enough.

XX

SOCIALLY, being a Jewess had never, therefore, really mattered to me. The one thing which I missed, and it hurt me, perhaps, more deeply than anything I had in exchange could make up for it, was the loss of the near spiritual companionship with my mother. I used to feel, sometimes, as if I could hail the next train and run, simply to see her, to feel her firm, small hand holding mine, to see the dear tender darkness of her eyes. I saw my children growing into understanding, and I wondered how I was to bring these two generations, between both of which I stood and both of which I loved, together.

My children were taught no religion. That was my husband's wish, and I was glad to do as he wished. They were free to think and to choose to believe whatever they should find best.

Once our small son came in and said, "Dad, now that Walter, he says that he has to go to mass every Sunday morning. Now, why don't *I* have to go to mass?"

My husband loomed over the small, sturdy figure, and said, smiling, "You can go if you want to, old man."

"Oh, he couldn't—" I interposed, rather appalled, oddly enough. The Catholic Church with its tremendous circle of ritual, its close social boundaries and the mystic hold it laid upon all who came under its ancient influence seemed to me something one did not lightly permit to enter a child's life. What would our friend, Father John, say to this? He enjoyed our candidness; he liked to explain why he held his faith. He came to play chess with my husband and to share the pleasant quiet of our home. But what would he think, as a priest of his Church, at my husband's lightness in this casual permission to our son to partake in the ceremonies of a powerful church, even a religious state?

My husband's fine, strong fingers closed on mine, held them down.

Son stood with one foot on the pedal of his bicycle, the other tiptoe on the pavement touching our lawn. "Could I go?" he returned. His brown eyes grew wider; they lost their introspective look. "Guess I don't want to, anyhow!" he said, and was off before we, his parents, could look at one another.

"Would you really want him to go to Catholic services?" I asked my husband then, meeting his glance.

"Why not?" he questioned in return. "Of course, he never could go. Why should I make a ritual mysterious and desirable to him by refusal, though?"

Was not that the way that I, too, had been given my first impulse to questioning my father's faith? Perhaps I would have spent myself, all my ardor, my passion for beauty and for service, in that which he so deeply revered and wished me to believe, too, if I had been permitted to "choose and follow" my own reasoning. My husband had as a child never been taught any faith; he had, at one time, attended the Lutheran Church every Sunday morning with a German nurse and the Baptist Sunday class in the afternoons with a boy chum near their home. The processes of religious observances now interested him as psychological manifestations, as mirrors of the human mind. While at college he used to attend Catholic and Jewish services, sometimes, simply to see into the minds of the people with whom he lived. For himself, though, his faith came from the truth of intellectual processes; it was Truth to him then, and so it is to-day.

For me, there was always the need of something into which to pour my whole soul, as it were. If it were not now the Jewish religion, then perhaps it was my love for him and for my children and my mother; perhaps, though this I was not to find till much later, it was in writing. For writing can be a preaching, too, as fervent and as holy as that from the pulpit.

Nevertheless, I was not certain what to do about our children. Their religion I did not wish to build up for them. But I wanted them to feel their kinship with my people, with my family anyhow. I tried to create it by visits to my sisters, by bringing their children and mine together. They did not allow their children to come to my home; they were afraid of the Christian influence there or, at least, of the non-Jewish influence. They wished, too, not to offend our father. But once I sent my boy and girl to spend a week's holiday at the seashore in Hannah's cottage, and at another time they were at my brother Simeon's house for a few days.

They came back antagonistic and resentful. Hannah wrote a guarded, and yet rather unhappy, letter in return to mine, thanking her for her hospitality. "They're so good-looking," she said. "They were perfect little angels. They looked like little pictures when we went out in the afternoons," was the tone of it. But she did not say what they had felt. They were strangers in her nice cottage. All the little children there had been Jewish children: "Every child there went to the same kind of Sunday school, Momsie," our daughter put it. "They thought we were awfully funny because we didn't have any."

They were all going to be "confirmed." They all had "lots of spending money." They all went to "camps in Maine." They all wore "awfully pretty frocks, Momsie."

My sister Hannah's husband was very successful. He was interested in real estate and politics. He was making money.

My brother Simeon had married a wealthy woman and had no children. She was interested in Jewish charities, and was exceedingly generous. My children came home with appallingly expensive presents from her. But she had been worried and had worried them, too, all the time, with long discussions on religion, on the need of "learning Hebrew," on the responsibility of "being nice little Jewish children."

She had vexed our young son particularly, because she felt he, as a man, ought to "know something about being a Jew." Her letter was kind and thoughtful, in spite of its muddled sentences, for she was an uneducated girl. She pleaded that I let her have our little son "just for a year, so we can make a Jew out of him, so he won't grow up knowing nothing about being a Jew."

She said nothing about my parents. But of course I understood. I understood that everything my children were, said, thought, was told our parents. I knew that the fact that my daughter was tall and straight and sweet, lovely to see and dear to know, would mean nothing to them—if she were not a Jewish girl.

I AM A WOMAN—AND A JEW

The laughter in the face of my son, the clear look in his eyes, the quick, sensitive smile with which he met life, his intelligence, meant nothing to them—if these were not given to Jewish allegiance.

For the Jewish belief is that a child belongs to the people of its mother. I had married a man outside my people, but, like Esther, I was a woman, and could not cut myself away from my people. I belonged to my menfolks; my menfolks were Jews. My children belonged to my people.

My son looked out at life with the great, dark eyes that my mother had bequeathed to him; the curve of his lashes were just the exact curve of hers. He had a way of crinkling the corner of one eye, when he was particularly absorbed, that was so precisely hers. But they, the grandson and the grandmother, looked out on different worlds with those dark eyes so much alike. I did not know what to do.

"Nothing," said my husband, to my troubled questioning. "We cannot give the children to a religion, just because by accident their parents were born into it."

And, of course, it was true. Did we send them to their father's church? My children never saw my folks thereafter, and their children did not come to us.

I did not belong to the Jewish faith; my intelligence had long ago rebelled and dropped it. I lived in a world bigger than that of my people. If my people could not accept me and my children on this basis, we must part.

Yet, when war was declared by President Wilson, I saw men leaving and women coming in to take their places, young men drifting out like snow before a great wind that swept them out. The cry was not "Jew,"

"Gentile," "Catholic," "Protestant,"—it was *pacifist, slacker.*

In my heart, I was a pacifist. I could not believe in war. But I found that I could not speak against war. This country was more than my country. It had given shelter to my father, to my people. There were certain things one must sacrifice to one's country, even one's conscience—yes, "my country, right or wrong." I understood why my brother Robert had enlisted. The Jews could not be "slackers"—they had a debt to pay. And I owed that debt, not only to be paid with silence, but with action. I did not believe in Wilson. I understood clearly enough that we were entering the war not to "fight to end war," but for economic reasons, for financial interests. But I closed my eyes and said nothing. I could not speak in praise of this war, but I must not speak against it. I made bandages, knitted, very awkwardly, for the soldiers, wrote letters for soldiers, visited camps, did the usual futile things women did. If I raged against the slaughter of the youth of my land, I did so in silence. I did not think my silence was due to the fact that I was an outsider. It was due to MY COUNTRY as payment of a debt, a debt of gratitude, of honor, which my people owed it. If this were our country, we were members of the great family it made; one may feel appalled at the mistakes of one's family. But one stands by its mistakes. One feels indebted for its love and its kindness.

But one day Myra and Babette Gottlieb came to me and told me they meant to do something tremendous. They had enlisted as volunteers to go abroad. They were called upon to leave now.

It was strange. But I felt a swell, a personal feeling of pride. It was as if my sisters had come to tell me of something fine they wished to do. Our Catholic friend, Father John, had gone to France almost as soon as war had been declared. Young men enlisted from home after home in our circle, leaving college, offices, stores. Methodists and Episcopalians forgot their differences. I had been heartsick to see the young men go. But when these two young women came to say they were leaving, I felt that tremendous lift of pride, as if two sisters of mine had done something quite beautiful. And were they not my sisters, these two women, Jewesses like myself?

At home, telling my husband about them, I thought of that deep pride. I was a Jewess, of course. I had cut myself from the Jewish faith. But the group —to that I belonged. Was there a Jewish "race"? Scientists were taking sides, saying, yes, or no, as they decided. What did it matter, to us who were Jews? There was a Jewish people, something that belonged to us, so unchanging that we could not destroy it.

I had always been amused at the Jewish pride in their great men and women, the personal pride and justification Jews seem to feel in the achievements of Jews of the past and the present. Disraeli, Zangwill, Bernhardt, were great names, but I had not felt the glow that others had when they pointed out racial kinship with these great people.

But now I felt pride because two Jewesses, neither of whom I particularly admired, were going abroad to serve in a war in which I did not believe. I thought, "They're the first women to go. The two first women in this city to go are Jewesses." From all our friends these two women were mine to be proud of: I was amused at myself, but it was true—my pride.

My husband's illness came, and I dropped our friends, one after the other. I needed every minute to adjust my life to the demands made upon it. I needed every moment in working out the problem of my life, as a member of a home and a worker, a wage-earner.

But I was a Jewess in this problem, I discovered, not simply a wage-earner and a woman.

In my marriage and in the social life which my husband and I shared, it had been for me to determine the values expressed in the fact that I was a Jewess. In business, however, I found now, abruptly, the values were set; they were old. I had thought from my experience it meant nothing that one were Jewish. "One makes one's own divisions when one is Jewish," I had once said.

"No Jews in this store; a matter of business policy," the manager told me, though. "Our customers compel us to make a rule—"

If that were so, there was no place for me in the store. If my people suffered a handicap, I could, of course, seek shelter under my husband's non-Jewishness.

I might have inquired of the girls themselves what they thought of Jews; I might have tried to see whether their dislike of Jews would, for once, bring Catholics and Protestants into a common animosity. But I did not, of course. I went to look for another post. I'd work with Jews.

I went to Fields', one of the two Jewish stores in the city. They told me they could not take a married woman.

I went to Oppenheimers, and was told they could not take a Jewish woman.

They had "mostly Jewish girls," it was true. But

Jewish girls "respected a Christian woman better," they found.

They didn't really believe in this sort of work, anyhow. They had it only "to keep up with the other stores." What their place needed was an up-and-coming Shiksa who could make the saleswomen speed up a little, the smart Hungarian Jewish manager told me. I was too "refined," you know, a Jewish woman was too ladylike to be in a store anyhow, it needed one of "these athaletic Gentiles with tennis shoes" to do this kind of work. And what was I, a war widow? My husband was living? I was "diworced"? "Not-diworced?" Say, I wasn't one of these here "restless wives" they'd just begun to show up in the movies? "Say, believe me, better stay home!" I lived in a "swell neighborhood," he pointed out, anyone could see here was a lady—let good enough alone! If I had to have something to do, why not sell Liberty Bonds, or may be take charge of "these soldiers' evenings"?

I thanked the voluble manager, took up my gloves and went out.

I had to have a job.

At Fields' I was excluded because I was married. At Oppenheimer's I was not wanted because I was a Jewess.

XXI

IT was no use thinking of teaching again, for I had not taken, nor was I prepared for, the teachers' examinations given in this state. I could not have passed them, for I had no technical educational training, such as had recently been made a requirement in many schools. I had only experience.

I'd try getting a job on a newspaper, or a magazine. There was a weekly printed in the town, and I went to the editor. He kept me waiting in the vestibule for twenty minutes, then saw me in his office. He did not remove his feet from his desk, as he turned to me: "Well, what can I do for you?" I did not know how tc begin with that question.

"My name is Mrs. Morton," I answered. "I've been working as personnel director in the Blair store. I've had some newspaper experience, and I've written for magazines, too. I—I have even done some books."

He was looking at me smugly and even patronizingly, but he listened. I went on, trying to be convincing, but losing faith in face of that silence: "I wondered if there might be—some capacity in which—I could be useful to you here."

He leaned back, locked his dirty fingers behind his head and smiled kindly. "Not a chance, Mrs. Morton. I'll tell you that right away. I suppose you're one of these here college women, a college girl, now, isn't that so?"

I dumbly nodded. My eyes smarted behind their lids.

"I thought so. It's funny, the way college girls are making the same big mistake. They take their English courses and get their diplomas, and they think they can write. Now, get me, I'm not saying they can't!" He smiled again, and I saw then that his smile was simply a sort of gesture with the muscles of his face, as one might make a movement with one's hand in speaking. "They write real nicely. But for this kind of work they're just about as much fitted as a cat is to throw a baseball!"

Here he smiled broadly. "I've been a newspaper man," he went on, while I sat fumbling with my purse, waiting to go. "I've worked on a small town paper, and on a Western news syndicate. I know the game. I'm not a college man, but I can stand alongside any college man without bowing my head in shame," and he smiled. "This is no game for the college girl. You proved it just a minute ago by the words out of your own mouth. You write books. The journalist writes copy. He don't have time for high-brow stuff like books."

"You mean, then, that you have no opening for me?" I asked, getting up now.

He rose, too, and his whole face changed. It became genuinely kind. He put out his hand and took mine. "Not here," he said. "We're a trade weekly, though we have a general circulation. We need some one who understands business. Some one who can write snappy copy. Why don't you run over to the evening paper—tell the managing editor I sent you if you want to—and ask if they have an opening in the society news?"

I wanted to smile, myself, now. He was a kind little man. I should have found for myself what the interests of this weekly were, before I came here.

But he did not yet let me go. "Don't take it hard," he said, and added, apologetically: "You don't know copy-writing, do you? Lay-outs? Type?"

I shook my head. At that he brightened. "I thought you didn't have the practical knowledge," he said, and added, with real kindness, "No lady does, of course. Try the evening paper, will you? Let me know, will you?"

I was to smile, later, to remember that "no lady knows" how to write copy, how to arrange the lay-out of magazines and newspapers, how to choose type. I have friends who are managing editors of papers and magazines and newspapers, who have important posts in printing and advertising companies—and they are not only men, but women. But this was ten years ago.

I felt I was not much good. My husband was getting well, but he had not yet gone back to his work. He was considering what he should do, for we had both decided that now was a decisive time in his life. He must choose carefully the work he would select, not take the first thing that offered. I was determined upon that. It was the one thing I had stood out for, against the wish of my husband. I had made him reject one opening and another, attractive to him simply because they offered salaries. Because of my insistence, I had had my way, and the salaries and opportunities had been so unimportant that he, too, had been persuaded to see that it was best to wait. But then I had my work. It was not much, but it was a stop-gap.

What could I say to him now?

I AM A WOMAN—AND A JEW

I came home, and my husband was at the door waiting for me. He was leaning on his cane, though he did not really require it now. He had a letter in the hand clasped upon the head of the cane. "Read this," he said, his voice husky. "Read it."

It was a request for him to undertake new work in another city, a new work in a new field, where he would be not only a well-paid executive, but the pioneer to blaze a trail. He could begin in two or three months, if he wished. He would have a staff of five, "and if essential, an assistant director."

"Well?" said my husband.

I tried to speak. But what need was there for speech?

"Will you—take a job on my staff?" he said.

We talked over this work of his, for it led him into a big field outside his previous profession, and he wished to consider it carefully and wisely, before he made his choice.

"Don't let's take it just because it is offered," I pleaded. It was, perhaps, presumptuous to question fate when a door was opened. But we had both gone into whatever "openings" were offered us before. I wanted to be certain now.

Inquiry proved how big the opportunity was, not only for my husband to do real things in it, but for constructive work. It was something "to believe in."

My husband offered me not just an opportunity to assist him in his work, but to be his assistant in it. He made the stipulation in his letter of acceptance. There is a distinct difference between the two!

"As a paid employee?" I asked, my arm tightening in his.

He smiled down then: "As assistant, on my staff."

We went over his budget, apportioned the sum to be paid each of the four workers he would require: a typist, an investigator to send into the field, a part-time assistant to her and I. If my salary could be smaller, there would be two whole-time assistants. Of course, we did not hesitate to do that in the end, for this work of my husband's must be done in the most unhampered way within our means. The stenographer was to receive $20 a week; the investigator (though she was to be a college girl) would receive the same. Social workers receive small salaries: my own would be $1,000 a year. The whole budget was $10,000. We counted on a year's work. There would, most likely, be an equal appropriation the following year, but meanwhile there was just this sum to spend. My husband saw his committee and arranged with them the details. There would be expenses for trips he would have to make to outlying towns, stationery and mailing, for telephone service and office space in another agency's headquarters. Yet my salary of $1,000 was half what I had been receiving before. I was in a work utterly alien to my interests.

How false it would be to say, though, I was not thrilled, as if birds were flying in my breast, the day I and my husband walked to the office together. This was, after all, what we had planned from the day we met. We were married, had our children and we were doing *his* work together. I think that I danced along that day as I used to do when we were just young lovers newly married. I was a "new woman"; I'd just read a paper at our club on the "right of the girl-child to her own personality"—and yet I was happy to lose mine in my husband's. My husband was well. He was well enough to get to work "at once"—to-day.

The months that had stretched so long in prospect were over. He could command not only his body now, but his mind. He believed in himself again. My feet seemed to move as if they had wings.

I was very modern. I believed in my equal rights as a woman. But I was happy that day because he was head again of our life and of our home. That was something I yielded to him as I gave my love to him. It was a gift I gave to him. I knew that he was wiser than I, that he knew more than I. I had a certain knack that he had not, of knowing people, understanding them. He was impersonal. He was not interested in people, but in ideas that would help people. My gift would be brought to work side by side with his, as I lived side by side with him. That was how I would "express my personality."

The year that followed was, except that we had children, very much like the time we had worked together before we were married. Much of the work I could do at home, or at times could do according to special laws, and our children were therefore under my direct care a great part of the day. Our joint salary was $4,500 a year. Things were pleasant for us, for although living was high, our income had risen just enough to meet our simple requirements. We paid our debts and we were able, for the first time in our lives, to go to the movies, even to a play, without feeling that we ought to ask protection from our selfishness. We bought, at last, the bookcase we had wanted and the books we had said we wished to buy. We sent money to my mother, gifts for her birthday—and on Jewish holidays.

My husband's work was recognized and it was respected. I cut the clippings about him from the papers when they appeared and showed them to our children. I wanted them to grow up knowing and honoring him. It was a way of bringing our work to them, too. "Is that dad?" asked our son, his eyes wide, as he saw his father's picture one day. It was good to be living, to feel that I had found my real place in life, to be friend, comrade and helper, as well as sweetheart, mother and wife.

Women wrote to ask me to join clubs interested in "women's points of view"; sometimes I was asked to speak about my husband's work from the "woman's standpoint." What the audience wanted to know was not his work, of course, but how a woman could be a mother and a wife and at the same time work side by side with her husband in his profession. When, in one of his pamphlets, credit was given to me for work, I sent it to my college, feeling a childish sort of pleasure, I suppose. My writing had not been serious, like this. It was only books. But I was able, although I was a woman, and a mother—and even a Jewess—to write on non-Jewish subjects now, exactly like a Gentile man! I was managing the staff, helping with the writing and doing some of the investigating. My work was *real* work.

One day in late winter, a long important envelope came to the office with the name of a well-known woman in the corner. "For you, Mrs. Morton," said the typist. The letter was not in relation to the office work. "It isn't necessary to file it," I told her, keeping my voice casual.

The letter told me they were planning to open a "health center" in the industrial neighborhood where the Hungarians lived; what they thought of was a place where clinics would be held and free medical treatment given, and where, during the summer, clubs, classes and community activities would be developed. They would eventually open a camp also for children. The president of a great mill signed the letter as chairman of the committee.

They knew, he said, I had had experience in this sort of work. They had heard of my former work in the department store—from my old chief there. They wanted me to talk the matter over with them. There were a number of candidates for the position, but they had written to three whom they particularly wished to have as "first choice." The salary was stated. It was almost as much as that which my husband was receiving.

I sat at my desk, my back to the rattling typewriter of our stenographer, and looked at the letter.

Did things like this happen?

This was not "just writing." It was not "assisting my husband."

This was a real job for me to do myself, one requiring training, certain special abilities and experience.

Had I been gathering that experience in the years I was simply meeting each problem of our life as it arose? I thought over my teaching, my store work, my work with my husband. Curious. I had been an "executive"—why, for years. I had been doing these things that people thought valuable enough to train one for "a big job" all the time, simultaneously.

Here was an opportunity that any man could be content to have, and at a salary equaling a man's. We had friends teaching in the university who were earning $2,500 a year as heads of their departments. We knew a minister whose parish paid him $1,800 a year, an old man with four degrees.

My husband, whose work this was, who was my chief, received only $700 a year more than this letter offered me.

Could a woman—I—be worth this much? The war had created new conditions, of course. Hitherto, when a woman asked for work she understood she must expect at least a thousand a year less than a man, even as "executive" in a business or profession. I had women friends teaching in colleges and doing social work, who held exactly equal positions with men, and who cheerfully accepted salaries less than half of those of the men.

But every woman I knew who had an outstanding work, a "big job," was an unmarried woman, or, in a very few instances, a widow. Married women, at the head of a work as important as a *man's*—and well-paid—were still practically unknown. I could only think of two such women. I could not feel I belonged in their class. One had been separated from her husband many years; the other lived in a settlement house with hers.

In medicine the situation was slightly more "advanced." I had a number of friends who were practicing medicine, but they were all the wives of physicians, and they were all in "women's work," obstetricians, child specialists. One friend, a very daring young woman, refused to be what she called "a high-grade midwife." She insisted on specializing in "nose and throat." She came from the West, and was, therefore, considered rather wild and unconventional. She took her special training abroad and went back home to practice. Her city was puzzled. She was the only nose and throat specialist in town; she worked serenely in the hospital wards, and none of the patients died when she removed adenoids or tonsils. It took years, but the townsfolk gradually awoke to the fact that, although she did not wear trousers, but skirts, under her surgeon's coat, she had fingers that were entirely capable and trustworthy. However, had she not been married to a successful man, she would never have won out in her determination to be a specialist in a new field, and *not* a "woman's doctor." Her husband, if one may put it so, "financed" her until the community was educated to accept her on the professional basis she wished to set. When her children came, she had a second struggle, but she continued placidly, and is now the leading surgeon in her field in her home town.

On the other hand, a woman friend of mine had studied dentistry and had married. When her first baby came, she, like myself, gave up her work and gave herself to the care of home and children. Other children followed, and by the time she was forty she found herself completely out-dated. She was a "back number." Although married to a man of moderate means, and requiring the income her profession would have brought to the home, she was too far behind the time in her work, too out of it, to have the courage to fight a way back into it. She considers herself a failure, a double failure because her husband and she had planned to be partners economically, when they first thought of their marriage. Becoming a mother twisted the direction of her whole life, and she cannot find the way to make it straight again, to lead to the professional career for which she had trained herself. "If I'd stayed in my work and let people talk about the way servants neglected my children," she said, speaking of it, "I'd have been unhappy. I haven't the courage to stand against gossip. But my children would now have opportunities that we can't give them, and I'd be a successful professional woman, instead of a tired middle-aged one."

In our city, women teachers who married, automatically lost their jobs, and I had numerous friends who had taught either in grade school or high school, but gave up their work as soon as they were married. It was considered disgraceful for a teacher so much as to say she would like to continue teaching after marriage.

I was one of the few who had married, who had a husband, children and a job. But my husband had been ill; that was an excuse.

My husband was well enough to take up his work again now. I might, if I wished, be modern, and actually work with him in his work. I might help him build up his career not only as wife, but as one of his workers.

But, in the dark of our room at night, I lay beside him thinking not of helping him in his career, but of my own. I was ashamed to think of it in the light of day. I was ashamed to realize that I was considering how interesting this new work would be. I could even earn a real salary at it. I could—that I thought of now, as a recurrent hope—I could, perhaps, save some of the money I earned, enough to "finance" myself, so to speak, for a year, and in that year, whenever it would come, I could do at last what I wanted above everything else to do. I wanted to write.

I'd worked in the store, and with my husband, and in our home. That had been because of the obligations that rose and placed themselves in my hands. But all the time there had been the one thing I meant to do for *myself* some day—to write. When the children were grown up, perhaps, I could do that. I slipped downstairs into our study and stood before our bookcase and looked at the three thin books that had my name on their backs. I had marveled each time my publishers had written, "We are glad to undertake this book." I had not cared, poor though we were, that they should pay. Did I think of my lover or of my children in the light of what they paid me? They paid me by existing for me. Here were three books of mine as much my children as my two living children, as much alive and part of me. They were not splendid things, crashing a bell through the country; they were shy and quiet as I had been, as I had been in my girlhood and early wifehood. Writing was a luxury for the rich, for those who did not have to earn a living. I touched my books, felt along their backs in the darkness of the room, as I loved to do. If I opened them, they spoke to me—these living things that I had created—in my own speech. I put them back, one by one, looked up, in the darkness, and there was my husband, troubled to find I had not been resting by his side. "Are you ill?" he asked, and he wrapped me in his dressing gown, drew me upstairs again.

"No, I just went down," I answered. I could not tell him yet. I'd speak to him of this job offered to me to-morrow. I suppose I should have felt a triumph. But a few years ago to take work outside the home took courage. I did not know how my husband would feel about it. I did know, though, how most people would think, and I could not bear that anything that came to me should bring even a shadow on him.

I had been, from the first hour that I had been able

to manage it, "economically independent." I was not a burden on my husband's shoulders just because he had married me. I was—and it was precious to me to know it was so—his comrade, his love and his friend, above all. It was for that we had come together in marriage. I earned my own living; it was not for that I needed him. We gave one another the gifts of ourselves. That was all I asked, and all I would accept. My earnings were small, and my work had never been really remarkable, but it had "supported me," to use a homely phrase. I had done nothing that the average man working did not do as well. I had not sought to make a place, to find a splendid success. I only wanted to be, in truth—yes, a helpmeet to him.

But this work was utterly apart from him.

What would our friends and neighbors say if I went away every day to the office—to another office than my husband's? When I had worked at the store my husband was ill; he had been home, and the children had been under his care part of the time. What would folks say if I left my children—to do work that was not my husband's, but my own entirely?

This past year, when I had been working with him, I could arrange my home hours to stretch over the morning meal and until the children had gone to school. I had run home to see that the colored girl had their lunch whenever I could, and I had tried to be home by four. I had worked in the evenings "to make up time" for this. They were really under my care, in spite of my working.

But if I took this new job, I would be away from nine to five daily, six days a week. My work would be more exacting than my husband's. I would have to leave my children completely in the care of strangers.

But even the newest women spoke apologetically when they said, "I wouldn't go out, of course, if I had children."

Even the most modern, too, made it a point to show that their jobs were much less important than their husbands'. They were afraid even to seem their men's equals. "The Herfords" were being discussed with sympathy, not censure.

The community felt itself very broad-minded when it said, "Oh, she's not an old maid, she's an unmarried woman with a lot of brains who hasn't found a man big enough for her to marry." But the married woman who went to work had to prove that her husband was a man big enough for her to have married; she could not be "bigger" than he. She could not really be as "big."

All these things turned over in my mind. It will seem strange to women to-day; but I was afraid to take the work offered me.

Days passed, almost a week, and I could not make a decision. One laughs at these things later. I smiled, too, to think now of my fear and hesitation. But I smile as one does at something which is done by a younger sister. That woman of ten years ago was the young sister of myself to-day, and she was not ten years younger, but a generation. For in these ten years women like myself have lived through a generation, rapidly, each year compact.

We saw the whole status of women change almost before our eyes, by our will. English law opened the closed doors of unbroken precedent and took women into parliament. The United States wrote a new meaning into the sacred words of the Constitution.

I was not a fighting feminist. I did not feel that

men were the natural enemies of women, as did some of my friends. My husband was as necessary to my happiness as the very sun that shone overhead. I could not have thought of my life as separated from his, or of his apart from mine.

I had not been able to go with the suffrage groups to Washington, because I was working, of course, on my husband's staff, and had the added responsibility of our children, and the entire management of my home. However, I kept in touch with the suffrage workers in our county and did whatever odd tasks I could crowd into my days for them. One of the women, Elsa Harmon, I came to know well, and presently we saw each other once and even twice a week, principally because she made it a point to come in to the office to chat with me when she happened to be passing through our town.

I liked her. I liked her very lovely face, her very pretty clothes, the charming drawl of her voice. She was married to an architect, well-known in his profession, and she knew people who wrote and who acted, who sang and who spent money. The leaders of the suffrage movement were earnest and almost religiously absorbed in having the suffrage amendment passed. But there were many pretty women, like my friend, Elsa Harmon, who were the ornaments of the work, who came partly because they were idle, and partly because they found an emotional appeal in it.

She made excellent speeches, was usually sent when there would be a meeting largely attended by men. Her beauty and her charm were her best assets to the work. I could carry a group away by my own faith in what I said; Elsa Harmon could win a group of antagonistic men to agree without argument.

However, if one thought her pretty face held no intelligence, one was soon taught better. She had that real common sense which very pretty women often so successfully hide behind a faultless complexion. She was almost excessively practical, and in some ways reminded me of my kind old neighbor, Mrs. Rahm.

She would sit at my desk, wait until I had finished, speak of what she was doing, and then ask, in her brisk, delightful voice, "and what are *you* doing?" She was enormously interested in the office routine. It was the dream of her life to have a "regular job." "I never had anything anyone expected me to *finish*, until I went into suffrage," she told me. Even her war work she had done languidly. She had wanted to go abroad, but her husband objected. This was the real thing. "Our chairman bites my head off if I dilly dally," she declared, and it was obvious that she was delighted to have her chairman a martinet who demanded that work be done as assigned.

It was Elsa Harmon who disclosed to me that, even on a small salary, one could wear very pretty clothes, almost as pretty as her own. "Buy at the best shops; it's the best economy," she said. When I laughed at the maxim, she brought proof: "They sell the best things. The best things are made in the best way, and after the best fashion—as well, my dear, as the latest. The only thing to do is to know when to buy!"

"When you can afford it!" I concluded, dismissing the proof so.

"Exactly," she returned. "And you can afford it—at the summer sales and the late winter sales. Always buy your clothes then. Buy twice a year and buy intelligently, and you'll find you're dressed like a princess at the cost of whatever pocketbook you have.

I bought less than twice a year, of course. My hat was two years old, always. My coat was always expected to last three years or more.

My summer clothes I made myself, by hand, as my mother had taught me.

Elsa Harmon would not have that, though. "A woman has the obligation to look well dressed," she declared. She took me to sales herself, helped me buy "the best things," and chose them unerringly. She rummaged until she found among soiled blouses handmade lace, examined the "line," the "shoulder," and the "cuff," the essential items, she pointed out. She taught me the indispensable need of every woman for "good blue serge." She chose my hat and decided the style in which I must dress my hair.

"You have to look the part of a professional woman," she instructed me. "You look like a little mouselike mother."

It was, of course, delightful to look like "a professional woman," and to be able to afford it. My husband smiled when I stood before him in my new "blue serge," my freshly laundered French blouse and the tight little hat that allowed only two smooth curves of hair to appear on each cheek. "How well you look again!" he said, his absent eyes lighting up.

I smiled to myself, then. These nice things Elsa Harmon had helped me to buy made me look younger, of course. That was what he meant, though he did not know it. To him I would always look "well"—never young or old.

Elsa taught me, too, that it was impractical to have the colored girl come for a half day to "clear up the house."

"I have a maid who comes in every day, and I pay

her by the week," she said. "Why don't you find a girl whom you'll pay by the week, too? Pay her nine dollars a week."

I had been paying our girl at the rate of day work for each half day. But it was easy to find a good colored woman who came promptly to her job, and who was glad to work for ten dollars a week. I was not uninterested to learn she was the mother of a brood of children, whom she left in the care of a neighbor. "Tell her she can bring the baby along, she'll stay longer," advised Elsa. "She won't have to worry about it then." And it was just as she said.

She knew all about the practical details of home-making, home directing.

"Why don't you use that gift of yours?" I once asked her.

She shook her head, making all the small curls about her head shine. "Can't. Don Iikes living in a hotel. He hates servants. We have an occasional meal in the house, but he hates it."

That left her without a job. For the one job she could do was to be delightful as a woman, practical as a housewife. Since Don did not choose to let her be either, she was left with none.

It was to Elsa that I spoke first of the offer which had come to me. Of course, I did not tell her how I felt about it. I simply wished to see what her reaction would be toward it. She was practical. She believed both in my job in the office and in my work in our home. She was honest.

She listened as I briefly told her what had been in the letter offering me the job.

"Nice," she said. "What does it pay?"

I told her. She did not, of course, know my husband's salary. Her pretty mouth went into a silent "O" of real admiration, though.

Her lashes went up. "It'll take you out of your house completely," she said. "What does the Professor say?" That was what she called my husband.

"I haven't told him," I admitted.

Her eyes widened again. "You'd better tell him," she said. "Talk it over—and grab it. Won't the women here be proud of you!"

She didn't ask whether I wanted to do this work. She assumed I'd "grab it" because it was a "great opportunity" offered to a woman. It was something that would be, in its little horizon, a feather in the cap of womanhood. I had not considered that. But Elsa spoke enthusiastically, carried me almost immediately into plans for the work, spoke of how she would help me. She assumed that I was only waiting to "grab it."

XXII

ONE morning I turned to my husband and told him of the new offer, of the letter that had been lying under my pillow for almost a week now.

The sun was pouring into our room and fell on his face, bringing it into clear lines. I had gone to the window, pulled up the shade and turned to him. "If you lift the pillow," I said, "you'll see a letter—I wanted to show you."

He smiled, his face thin and fine in the revealing light, and turned my pillow as I came over. Sitting beside him, I slipped my hand into his when he opened it. He read it through, his fingers pressing mine close as he read.

His face turned to me, and it was grave. "You're grown up, Little Boy," he said. "What did you tell them?"

I was grown up. I was no longer the young girl of eight years before. I had not known I was growing and my husband, too, with me.

"Do you want me to do this?" I asked.

He sat thoughtful, silent, a while. "I do not know," he said finally. "It means a great responsibility. It means a real opportunity. It's a really excellent salary." His grave eyes came to mine, worried then. "It is so big a salary that I am troubled by it. It will mean that you must give yourself completely to your work. You'll have to work so hard! I've hoped that after—that store work—you'd never do anything except what you felt you might drop at your wish. I want you to feel that you are free, to do anything you like. Do you want to give up writing?"

I think, if he had not said that, I should never have answered the letter. But I understood what he wished to tell me. He wanted me to have a sheltered life, with the responsibility of our income on him and the pleasure of economic freedom for me—the fun of writing whenever I should feel I wanted to stop working, instead of the serious job of the daily task, the concrete thing, with monthly salary and hourly duties.

"I'd like to do—this," I said.

I met my board one Thursday morning, five people who met in the office of the chairman. Two were women. Of the men one was young and enthusiastic and impractical, and the other an older man with quiet voice and movement. They had heard of me, knew my work and my husband. They spoke flatteringly of my husband.

We discussed the plans they had in mind, and the work done in the past. We decided what activities it might be practical for us to begin with.

Then there was a pause.

"Mrs. Morton," came the voice of the chairman out of that pause in the conversation, "this work we are planning will take all your time and all your energy. We know you are a married woman, and we believe, I, at least," and he smiled in a very kind, fatherly way, "that married women are going to become more and more important in all kinds of work in the future, in professions and business equally. We're employing numbers of women in our bank every day. But I want to ask you two questions now. The first is this: you have children, have you not?" I nodded. He went on, slowly, "We did not know you had a family when we first began negotiations. That I will tell you frankly, Mrs. Morton. How will that come in with your work? Will your husband agree to your giving all your time to this work?"

The other four waited, with him, for me to answer. I understood that these two questions had been discussed before I came in. They had been objections raised by some one.

I thought of Little Maid, of Brother. Their rosy faces smiled at me. Had I neglected them? I wanted to smile, openly, at the question. What work would I do which I could promise to put first, before them? The fact that I was their mother answered that question. I could only work harder, give myself doubly. Nothing would ever come that could stand before them in my thought.

"I held a professional job even when my little daughter was a baby," I answered, letting that speak for me.

The larger of the two women shook her head. "But that's it, Mr. Blank," she said. "Let us be frank, Mrs. Morton. I've heard a great deal about you from Mr. Blank. I think this is your work. But I'm an old-fashioned woman," she admitted. "I do not feel quite easy about seeing young wives and mothers leave their homes. I was a schoolteacher myself, and I gave up my work as soon as I married. However, I am willing to keep up with the times," and she smiled to Mr. Blank. "I feel we ought to be intelligent. It is not clear to me, though," she confessed, "that your children do not suffer by having their mother away on other interests. I can understand that writing would not interefere so with your home. Please," she asked, kindly enough, "do not think I am being too personal, but we have to be in this matter. Can you give your children the proper care if you come to us—and are you doing social work because you want to, or just as a stop-gap?"

It was shrewd of her; she was more acute about me than was I myself.

But at the time I did not think of her acumen. I thought only how unwarranted her questions were. I thought that, were I an unmarried woman, I would never have been asked if my dependents were cared for; I would not have been asked to assure them that I would not neglect the work I was paid to do for some other interest. It was because I was a married woman, a mother, that I was in this undignified position, questioned and scrutinized in this way.

"I do not think," I said, "I care to speak about my children and the care I give them. It seems to me that if a woman is capable of arranging for the lives of several hundred people, she is equally able to arrange the lives of those dearest to her. I do not wish to discuss how I plan to do so. That seems to be the personal business of myself."

The large lady grew red. She did not answer. The chairman sat back, too. I had been "independent" to the board. I had not been suave and respectful. In other words, I had destroyed my opportunity, I saw.

I said good-by, and said good-by to $2,800 a year as I went out.

Going home, as I walked very slowly, I told myself what an utter little fool I had been, what a traitor to my opportunities. Why had I not told them I had my children in the best of care, that they were well and happy? Why had I not outlined to them my plan, so carefully prepared, to live not far from my office, to drive to and from my work, with my children in a little house, in the care of a responsible housekeeper? I had walked for days, investigating the possibilities in the neighborhood for us, had looked up schools, added up minutes which would be taken going "to and from" my work and a suitable home.

I had thrown it all away. I was coming home discredited to my husband. Elsa Harmon would raise her pretty brows.

The house was empty and still when I came in, for my husband was away, the children at school. I had to relieve myself of some of the heaviness that had fallen on me. I set to work, scrubbed and washed and swept. I tore through that house, with broom and mop. This is what "they" thought I ought to do!

My husband listened to the account of the meeting quietly. "You were right," he said, finally. "You could never have taken work under the conditions of such a start. Your board would have felt suspicious of your complete interest in your work all the time, and if anything went wrong they would have attributed it to the fact that you were giving only a divided attention to the work, that you were thinking of your children and your home. It would have been an impossible situation."

It was true, and I knew it. But for all that, disappointment ate at me. A thousand things that the salary might have bought for us came to my mind. Because I had lost it, the work seemed, suddenly, utterly valuable to me. I had hesitated, wondering if I ought to give up writing and take a definite step into social work again. But now that I had lost my opportunity, my writing seemed, as always, unimportant, fantastic, against reality.

I had thrown it all away. A man would never have done it. He would have known how to speak, how to smooth things out. Only women were emotional and hasty.

"A man wouldn't have had to meet such a situation," my husband said. "Do you think he would be asked, even if he were a widower, how he planned to take care of his children?"

I looked at him. "Did you want me to have that job?" I asked, for the second time. "Did you really want me to have it?"

He did not answer immediately. "I don't know," he said slowly. "I don't really care what you do, just so it makes you happy. I would prefer you not to have burdens to weigh you down, like, I suppose, a man carries. That's not because I don't believe you can carry them. It is just that I prefer to do that for us, Little Boy."

"Do you think of me," I asked then, "just as a—well, a little girl? Don't you think—well, that I am as mature as you, as capable?"

At that he laughed, his rare, deep laugh. "I know that is disturbing you," he replied. "You want to be thought 'just as good as a man'—in anything. You feel unhappy because you are afraid I do not see you so. I know you don't really want folks outside us two to think so, though! I remember the day you told Mr. Markley that 'we' had written the brochure the office put out—not *you* yourself! I suppose you are just as mature as a man, as capable. But," and here he smiled at me again, "it is not because you are capable and a good executive that I love you, my darling, my Little Boy."

He did not say quite what I wanted him to say. He did not say I was as capable as a man. But I was content.

"There'll be other opportunities," he said. "Meanwhile, let's get back to my work."

I waited less than a half year, and another opportunity came, this time through Elsa Harmon, who, as a member of the board, offered me the position as head worker in a settlement house that was just losing its head worker.

"Now, make things hum, dear!" she said. "The old lady that we just said good-by to was a holy mourner who'd seen 'better times' and took the work because of 'reduced circumstances.' Show them what a real job a woman can do. I'm betting on you!"

XXIII

HAVING a "big job" was much like having a lesser one, only that it took so much time. But the essentials were the same. They were using that knack I had for managing people, for "making them like to be bossed," and practicing the rules I had learned in my social work classes years ago.

I came to smile, in time, at the young girl who had been myself, a few years before. I saw that rules were necessary in all living, which is chaotic enough. Social work cannot give itself to the people who come; it can only try to bring those lives that are twisted by the breaking of rules of health, of law, of social convention, into the straight divisions again. My work was to organize the place, to collect a staff, to open classes—and then to see that all the rules which had once so fretted me were observed.

My experience in our home, in business and in managing the income we had were advantages to me. I had a practical, exact understanding of small lives that were invaluable to me. My work, I think, showed it. In the beginning, I managed to be home three evenings a week, trying to keep in touch with my home. I saw, though, that presently I would have to give my evenings, as I gave my days, too, to my work. Having the lives of people entrusted to you is not something that can be done from "nine to five." It means having your life given, too, to those who come. Presently I was spending part of my Sundays, too, at the office, "running in," to see if some one might want to come in or to go over my plans for the coming week.

My job came into our home, just as my husband's had always been part of it. The children knew, from hearing them, the names of "hard" cases; they were familiar with the processes of "treatment" they heard discussed at table. They felt that "mother's" office was as much part of the life of the family, of its interests, as "dad's."

As I sat in my living room one evening, going over some typed sheets, I heard the bell ring. My little daughter ran to the door and let in a blue-coated messenger. My brother Robert was dead, the telegram from home said.

I did not know how it is with people in families that are not Jewish, for my husband is an only child and, therefore, has no real family memories. But with us each one of the family was like another soul part of ourselves. Hannah and Etta did not write to me, but I knew that they loved me, that nothing on earth could destroy their love for me. My mother—but how can I speak of her? Even the letters she sent me were sent surreptitiously, that she might not openly offend the Jewish custom that asked her to break with me, married to a non-believer. Yet her letters came, and were full of love. And Robert was her baby, her youngest. I could remember the day he was born, and she lay, white, smiling, however, his tiny head at her elbow; I was at home, and my sisters at school. She smiled from the midwife to me and managed to say, "Little daughter, here's—here's a playmate."

We had been playmates and close friends. I had read the "big" stories to him which he could not understand, but wanted to hear, for all that. I had shown him how to throw his knife, when he played with the bigger boys, with that exact curve which meant it would bite triumphantly into the wood. When he began to study Hebrew, it was I who had walked home with him, patiently making him say over and over, "aleph, bais, gimmel," the Hebrew letters, which the impatient old teacher could not drill into Robert's head.

He had been to me my first child, my little doll and little son.

I remembered how my mother, lifting her head one day, had said, "Run!" Robert was ill, and I ran through the drifting snow of an early April day, to synagogue, to my father praying there. They had prayed for him then, changed his name, according to an old custom, giving him the name of "Alter," old man, that God might think of the little dying boy as an old man, not as youth for sacrifice. When he recovered, Mother called him "Alter," and that was the name we used when we spoke of him in intimate love.

What he had done, what he thought, no one knew. My restless, brilliant brother Robert was not given to speech. He was like our father, lost in the mystery of science, as father had lost himself in the mystery of religion. A life thrown away—a life and an admirable mind. He had thrown it away because—had he not said it?—he would not have it said that "Jews were slackers in the war."

I did not go to my mother, of course; there was no comfort for her from me, who, too, was lost to her. But soon there came occasion for my going. Not a month had passed, after Robert's death, when our father died.

He had left a letter for me. I have it put away,

written in his script that looks like print, each Hebrew letter so perfectly drawn. He told me that he loved me, that I was the daughter of his heart, as Robert was closest to him as a son. He reminded me of the women in the Bible who had married outside their faith. Esther had been one of these. But they had gone outside Judaism only to help Judaism.

I had gone out because of my ignorance, because of this land where the Jew was robbed of his most precious possession, his racial integrity, by the soft words of those who pretended to be his friends. But they really were his worst enemies, because they took from him that which alone kept him worthy of his heritage, the remembrance of the historic tragedy of his people. "The Jews need their Gollas," he said. "It has been the painful blessing of God, until Messiah shall come."

The Gollas of the Jew is the tragedy of the Jew, his wandering, his persecution, the hatred of mankind toward him. It is true that the Gollas of the Jew has kept his close solidarity, that it has held his race together, making it like a bright strain through the centuries.

My mother stood beside me as I read, her little hands tight together, in the gesture that I now know my hands have from her. She did not speak, but she waited for me to speak. Our eyes met and suddenly overflowed. "My daughter," she said then.

I had seen the wonder of my people's story always. I had felt gratitude to have part in it. But I had not felt that each of us was indebted with his whole life to keep the story unbroken. I had not agreed that each of us was obliged to offer our happiness to the continuance of that story. I had felt that the tragedy of the Jew was part of the stupidity of life, of humankind, just as capitalism, war, were part of the same endless human sorrow. To me life had become not a separation of a single group, or of one individual belonging to a separate group, from the rest of mankind. It had been the coming together of humankind that I had believed in. The whole philosophy of the Jew represented in my mother was contrary to my philosophy of life, that which had made me happy in my marriage even to a Gentile and to my interests outside the Jewish interests, and even utterly forgetful of them.

Sometimes, those friendly to Jews speak or write with humane disapproval of that which "excludes" the Jew, socially or economically. They feel a social shame in the cutting off of social privileges to the Jew, since he is admitted to intellectual and financial equality. The truth is, it is the Jew who excludes himself. The pride of his race and in his faith builds a wall between himself and all mankind. In my girlhood that division was so marked by us that even a dish, a tumbler, touched by the hands of a non-Jew, was defiled and could not be used by us except for unclean purposes again. I have heard Jewish women of no real intellectual or social background among their own people speak of disagreeable experiences with guests in hotels or with neighbors, some of whom were, perhaps, in their own circles, superior to them. These women would have been the first to acknowledge superiority of intellectual or social standing to one of their own people, for the Jew is a conventional person, believing in laws and in social rules; they would be the first to yield place to a Jewish man or woman who had gained position by success in business or, more readily, in a profession. But when they were treated with contumely by non-Gentiles, no matter how highly placed or gifted, they simply shook their heads, shrugged their shoulders, plump hands lifted, and said, "What can you expect? Goyim!" For as they knew: is it not more honorable and desirable, infinitely more, to be the least of all Jews than the highest of all Gentiles? And this is thought not only by Jews who like my parents live closely tied to the Jewish community, but by those whose daily work, whose employers and sometimes whose friends are not, like themselves, Jews. "Goyim!"

I had not, until now, felt, like Disraeli, that my "people were princes in Israel" when those of my Gentile friends were barbarians.

But now, suddenly, in the face of this great sorrow, something deep and unbreakable suddenly drew the bond tight. I belonged here.

My father's letter asked me to stand by my faith. My sisters, their eyes dim with much weeping, came up then, too, and they told me about his illness, the last things he had said. He did not wish me to be told he was dying. He had not asked to have me sent for.

That cut like a knife across my heart, but not with regret. Or, if it was regret, it was only that we had so misunderstood one another in life, we two who had so much in common, who could have been such dear friends.

I read his letter, and then I went to him.

I came to his side and looked at his face, beautiful and still in death. The watchers did not wish me to lift the cloth, for they were pious men. But I spoke decisively: no one would rob me of this little while with my father, who had been so far from me because of his faith all my life before.

His face was now tense, rigid, unbending. It was

kind. It had a great sweetness. His mouth fell into gentle lines that I had never seen in it before. I had seen his face exalted, aflame with prayer. I knew it cold and distant with disapproval of the breaker of the Law. I had seen it lit with the fine, shadowy smile that hardly showed his teeth, when some wise man had made a translation of Hebrew which was unique and greatly to be admired. But, even with little children, I had not known it to be as it was now. Even with the children of my sisters, his face had been unbending: he would not allow them to speak English amid their prayers. He did not approve of their running so fast in and out of synagogue, big boys "going on thirteen."

But now it was as if I saw that which he had written on his face erased. It was only his fanatical faith that had made him seem so hard to me all my life. This father I could have loved. I would not have feared him.

This father of mine would understand me. I bent over to him, but I did not kiss his cold mouth. I only spoke to him without words, spoke his name. I knew he would let me be free, who was himself now free—if I wished it.

Amid the confusion of talk, of sorrow, stood out the face of my sister Hannah, beautiful, stately and tragic. Her husband was a prosperous man. He owned houses; she had servants. They were members of a fashionable "semi-reformed" synagogue, which my father had sternly disapproved of, but which her husband insisted on attending, nevertheless.

So it was not only I, breaking away completely, who had lost our father, I saw. Isidore was pompous, well dressed. He spoke of his enormous practice, told me of the huge fees he demanded, and received: "I never take a case of plain fillings, mostly clinical work. I'm going to Columbia to specialize next summer." He belonged to medical societies, was chairman of a committee. He understood "the Goyim," but "they respect you more if you stand up for being a Jew." Then, with his natural kindness, he was embarrassed at the recollection of my husband, and added, "Some of my best friends are Gentiles! Fine fellows!" I could have smiled, had not that dull pain been eating at my heart, for I had so often heard non-Jews say, just in these very words, "Some of my best friends are Jews"—their "own Jews."

Isidore was chairman of an important committee on the board of their synagogue. Their rabbi "beat the old one to peanuts and blisters," he declared with a genial smile; and brought him over, a slight young man with dark hair and eyes, an orator's mouth and very thin shoulders. He was, I thought, not unlike the "yeshiva bochur" my own father must have been forty years ago. He spoke sympathetically about "my loss," told me how much he admired my father, described the intelligence of Hannah's children (who looked like angels in Italian pictures, as they stood near their mother a bit away). He complimented me on Isidore's success: "One of our coming Jews," he said. He mentioned with real admiration the success of Simeon, who was in Europe on business, and could not come here on this day. The rabbi was very tactful and very nice. He did not mention the fact that I was here in a Jewish home with a Gentile husband. He was gentle to my husband who was an alien in this home. Very likely, he knew how deep had been the break between my father and myself, but he did not intimate it now.

He left as Etta's husband came over. Etta's husband, it developed, had gone over completely to the "reform" Temple in his city. He spoke appreciatively of the rabbi, but their own was superior. They said he received $5,000 a year; in their own the rabbi got $8,000. These rabbis, I understood, were not spiritual leaders, but communal representatives of the group. They expressed the stand and the responsibility of Jewry in war work, in social work, in politics even. They were really as much organizers and politicians as religious leaders, I thought at first. But speaking to my brother-in-law, who is keen, brusque and very intelligent, I realized that the religious leadership of the Jewish rabbi was the least of his qualities.

"Up in my brother's Temple, in Massachusetts," he told me, "they have a rabbi who came to them about four years ago. He's a fine mixer and was star in the track team once. He's especially good in the Men's Club. The principal thing for the rabbis to do to-day is to fight the indifference of the men. The men pay their dues to the synagogue, and feel it's enough. You can't get them to come to services, hardly to meetings of the club. I know we arrange smokers and snappy talks for our own members here, and about half of the membership come. The women come, and they bring the children. But the men stay home."

It was the same story I was to hear just a few years later from exclusive "reform" Temples, from Episcopalian groups, from Presbyterian, Methodist and Baptist. The only religious groups that did not seem to be losing their membership were the Catholics.

Yet when the rabbi prayed his face became exalted, like a fine lamp lit up. Isidore and Ben stood, attentive to the business of arranging the funeral. They seemed hardly moved. But I felt my own heart caught, held, by the prayers. My doubt—I could only feel how unessential it was in the face of death. Even my determination to "find out the truth for myself" seemed little, unimportant. The only thing that was significant was death. Death—and the thing that came after it.

My mother sat with her hands folded, very quietly. She did not cry. She just sat looking about her, at us, her children. We were her children, but she was as much alone among us as if she were in a far counry. I had gone away first, and completely. But these others were breaking from her, one by one, little by little. Her world was my father's, the world of old Judaism, of absolute literal faith in the Talmudic teaching.

She had lost in my father not only her friend, her lover, her husband, but her world, too. She was left alien and alone amid her children now.

Even as we sat the seven days of mourning for the dead and the stream of callers poured in and out of the house to us, that new world crept up around her. The older people spoke of my father's "learning," of the faith he held, of his friends. But the younger people, after the first few sentences, spoke of their businesses, their offices, their strange interests. They described the big stores they owned, the difficulty with labor, the disagreeable strikes which the war brought on, the high cost of automobiles. They spoke with pride of their children and of the fraternity one or the other had made, for high schools and colleges now had fraternities for Jewish students. They described their homes and the impertinences of Christian nursemaids, cooks and chauffeurs.

One young cousin blushed and looked apprehensively at my mother. "I hope she didn't hear me," she said, nervously smiling. "But—well, I don't keep Kosher. My husband is a German Jew, his people are reformed and he won't let me keep Kosher."

But my mother did not hear her. She was sitting very quietly, with her hands in her lap, thinking. She was, surely, thinking of many years before, when she sat at the side of her mother, and kissed her on the lips, and said, "I'll see you again, soon. You'll come to America to visit us." She never saw her mother again, nor her father. My father and her sisters and brothers were her world, the world of her youth and of her understanding. And it was gone. She was only fifty, and she might have been a century old, watching a new life about her, one to which she no longer belonged. In American cities mothers were beginning to speak with unhappiness of their empty lives, of the "lost years" the middle-aged woman with grown children faces. They were asking for careers and a chance. But my mother, just their age, asked for nothing. There was nothing for her here, in this land where neither her faith nor her people had root.

On the day I was to leave she came to me.

"You will say Kaddish for him?" said my mother, clinging to me. I hesitated, then—"Yes," I promised.

I went back home, to my children and to my life. I thought I was free. But I found that I was no longer free.

All the years before I had been struggling against my father. I had fought to win my way to my own mind. Now the struggle was over. But in its ending my father gained that which he had not succeeded in doing before. I had put Judaism aside, said, "This is apart from me. I choose to divide myself from this people."

But one cannot do that, I found now. I could not choose to divide myself from that which represented all which is left to me of my father—his people, his creed.

This religion which had meant so much to him, which had expressed everything for him, became something which I felt I must seek because it was the only thing left me by that father I had discovered as he lay dead. I did not mean to tell myself a lie, to practice its precepts and its faith. But I must live closer to its people.

XXIV

I HUNGERED for the comfort of some religion, some way in which my father and his philosophy of life would be near to me and my life. I had not for many years asked myself what my faith was. Agnostic, I should have said. But now I sought something definite, something which gave promise to me. I did not care whether it was logical or not. Is love logic? I wanted only something to fill the long years that would come and to tie to my life those years that had passed. My husband was near and dearest to me; but in this even his closeness, his deep wish to shield me from pain and to bring comfort to me were in vain. He was my lover, but he was not my father's son.

He understood when I went to the orthodox Jewish synagogue in our city, to join there in the customary weekly prayers for the departed. I wanted to have the prayers said that would have been said by my father for me, to say those Hebrew words which he had spoken in memory of his own father. I did not know whether it was because I sought his God, or whether I was seeking him through the God in which he had faith.

I tried to attend the small synagogue where the orthodox Jews met. But they were uncomfortable at my coming. The women, sitting in the gallery apart from the men, peered not through the curtains below, as was their wont, but at me. I was married to a Gentile. I was an outsider.

The wailing and weeping, which had terrified and impressed me in turn as a child, confused me here. I was too conscious of the pitiful social problem, of the deficiencies here. I understood the mechanics of the synagogue, its simple stark needs. This form of worship had not my father's intellectual fire and his culture behind it. These poor people hardly understood their Hebrew prayers; the men themselves could, in most cases, barely pronounce the words they shouted. This was the decay of the grandeur of my people's inheritance.

I left a sum "for charity" in my father's name, as was customary, and did not return.

Perhaps, I told myself, it was the newer Judaism I sought. Young Jews had, for a generation now, been changing the forms and the very tongue in which the prayers of the synagogue were spoken. After all, even Hannah, even Etta, my own sisters, attended a synagogue in which a modernized service was held, one which they understood and with which they felt sympathy.

I went, therefore, to the Temple, where the larger number of our friends who were Jews attended services. It was rather sweet to see their eagerness, their pleasure, when they met me there. Our physician, big and stout and kind, smiled and held my hand a moment. "This will do you good. It will give you a way to find some solution to that question you ask. . . . " That question was one I felt tearing at me —the old query of the continued life of those whom we love here on earth. The Doctor had been so kind, but he had not done anything more than give me bromides and reply, "This will relieve your headaches." But here, in our Temple, he felt that I, too, as a Jewess, would receive the answer he had not given.

The bright little woman who was secretary of our suffrage club belonged, too. She had always been friendly, chirpingly cheerful. But she stopped me now one day, and said, "Try to come to service this Saturday; the Doctor is preaching a sermon you'll want to hear. . . . I lost my mother. . . ."

I had liked the "Doctor," rabbi of the Temple, whom I shall call Dr. Fishman here. He was a middle-aged man with a nobly carried head, a fine high nose, and remote, though pleasant, eyes. He looked like a Don at a British college. He spoke a meticulous, gratefully enunciated English readily and kindly, and told me he was glad to welcome me to his congregation. He recalled that once he had met my father, years ago. He was interested to know I had broken away from the orthodox faith. "Many of the young people are doing so," he said. He asked when he might meet my husband.

It was obvious that he was nonplussed to hear my husband was not a Jew, but he was not unpleasantly shocked. Immediately his attitude, which had been benignant and rabbinical before, changed and became more intimate, more—if one may put it so—that of a peer. He had heard of my husband; had read his name in the newspapers. "So he's not a Jew. Jews are Anglicizing their names so often now—matter of convenience—that one can't tell them by cognomen alone," he smiled.

He told me the younger rabbi would call on us at once; he had charge of Sunday school. He wished to know if I had children and if they would attend the Sunday school. They had a very admirable community center. A fine swimming pool was planned. And they would be glad to have our children, delighted. Did Dr. Morton—have any feeling against having the children attend Jewish services?

That had not been discussed by us anew, but I, myself, had decided upon that. My husband and I had made our decision upon that, finally, long ago, and it stood. My children would not have their religion made for them; they would choose it themselves. I did not think I had the right to enter them in the Jewish synagogue, liberal though this one was. I was finding my way to faith, not theirs.

The rabbi was not pleased, but he was kind. He spoke to me a bit about the city, asked me when his wife might call, and obtained my promise that I would not hold aloof from the Temple activities. "At least come to our social service meetings," he urged, and I consented. I could do that.

It was strange to see the congregation assemble the first Friday evening. The line of limousines before the door was a block long; there were expensive makes in it, and many of them were driven by chauffeurs in smart uniforms. My father's congregation would not, of course, ride on Friday night or Saturday, but these were liberal Jews.

The women who came out were utterly different from the traditional pious Jewesses who wore either wigs or shawls or, when they were young and daring, at least put their hands to their foreheads (in a gesture of covering the head) as they entered the synagogue. Those sat upstairs in the balcony, apart from the men; they listened to the prayers, only chiming in at far-spaced intervals. They were humble handmaidens of their God.

These women stepping down from the automobiles here and those who came streaming through the door were dressed in fashionable clothes, made in exclusive shops. They wore expensive and knowing hats. Their shoes were beautifully put together and cut. Their hair was marcelled, their hands were jeweled. They wore much too much jewelry. In that one thing alone were they different from the women I could see on Sunday mornings entering the fashionable churches where Christianity was preached. They sat side by side with their men during services, of course.

The cantor uttered the prayer, a choir (composed of Gentiles) sang sacred Hebrew songs of Sabbath, and then the rabbi delivered his sermon. His sermon took its text from a popular novel of the hour and preached upon the problem of feminism. The younger rabbi announced the program for the week—lectures, a musicale, a play ("The Wonder Hat") by young people, three dances and a card party.

In the pews of the synagogue the congregation sat as if at a lecture, immovable, well bred. This might have been a group at a Chautauqua lecture. The passion, the intensity, the fervor of the Jew was as much absent here as in a Christian Science reading room. One almost expected well-bred applause at the conclusion, which was cleverly turned. But the silence was followed by a burst of song from the choir. The audience rose, at least part of it rose. And then I understood. My eyes were blinded with tears; I managed to stand up. They were uttering the prayer for the dead.

That was uttered in Hebrew.

The one thing which had not changed in this Jewish temple was the language it spoke for its dead.

With a murmur of voices, the congregation rose, moved out, entered cars waiting and was gone.

The rabbi paused beside me, kindly. "I am glad you came," he said. "I hope you will come again, and that you will find comfort here."

I wanted to shake my head. This was not what I had hoped to find. But I was silent. After all, the orthodox synagogue had nothing to give me, and its members, on their part, did not want me, wife of a Christian.

I had broken from my faith, and now I tried to find it again. Perhaps this was the wiser way to come back: to this modern synagogue made by our priests. What did it matter, I told myself, if it were different from the synagogue I had remembered, so long as it held the essence of that faith which was my father's, so long as I could pray here for the soul of my father, pray to I knew not what—to the memory of him, perhaps, in that speech he loved and revered?

New times brought new teachers. In this new synagogue the new leaders were interpreting our faith in a different speech. It was the same faith.

My work took so much of my time that I could see little of the Jewish religious life, except on Friday evenings. But sometimes the young rabbi came to see us of an evening, and my husband and I presently felt toward him as one does to a dear young friend. From the first, we liked him. He was different from the young Jews I had known. He was not sullen and sensitive, like Simeon, nor brilliant and bitter, as had been Professor Raphael. He was not satiric and silent, like my brother Robert. To him, being a Jew was simply being a man: it was apparent that he never thought of it, except as something that had endowed him with a mission. He had always meant to be a rabbi, he told us. His parents had wanted him to be a social worker, but the Jewish social worker has a limited field; he is not free, he explained, and added that, of course, he knew that the same was true of all social workers. As a rabbi, he would be able to reach to the spirit, as well as to the body of man.

He had a quick, boyish friendliness that was winning, irrestistible. He did not speak of dogma, however, when he called. With a subtle courtesy, he seldom discussed our faith with my husband, except when the subject was brought forth by some one else. He spoke, instead, of the leading articles in the *Nation*, of the crime wave, of poetry, Joyce, Proust, Moussolini. He was a cultivated, delightful friend that the synagogue had given us to enrich our life.

One evening he came to our home when we had asked a number of friends, among them Father John, taller and thinner, more austere and more intense than before. Father John was to speak to the Knights of Columbus in our town, and was, of course, seeing us. There came, too, Doctor Perry, a fragile little pedagogue with a great head, about which flowed hair in a thick cloud, so that it looked like the pictures of God in Old Testaments with illustrations. Dr. Perry was professor of physics in a small college near by, and my husband's colleague in a number of educational interests. A distinguished jurist, visiting us, was guest of the evening. One man came later, a cousin of Myra and Babbette Gottlieb, who lived in the city, and who had come to drop in on us sometimes through our acquaintance with his relatives in our previous town.

I AM A WOMAN—AND A JEW

The young rabbi could not come for dinner, but he arrived early, just as the evening's talk took its topic.

The talk had been upon Einstein, whom Dr. Perry hugely admired and of whom he spoke as "Professor," as if he conferred a decoration. Dr. Perry himself was an Episcopalian, and he had more than once, in spite of his scientific mind, proven that he, nevertheless, felt himself in a specially selected group. I could not forbear asking, "Wouldn't there be a presupposition of error in a theory which a mere Jew taught?"

Dr. Perry laughed, threw back his head to laugh again. "There is," he admitted, however, soberly enough, "curiously, there's more than a question of scientific doubt put up to Einstein. Scientists are collecting themselves into a school with—I believe it's so—the intention of proving, if possible—it seems unfortunate—that Einstein is wrong."

"Jew baiting?" asked my husband, his mouth curling a bit. "Wagner did it in music, Gladstone in government—one rather thought we'd passed that now. I noticed, however, that the fellows who are following up the Einstein theory aren't so anxious to prove a scientist right, as that a Jew is wrong."

Dr. Perry's gentle, odd but fine and thoughtful face became troubled. "It's true," he admitted. "All over Europe, my friends seem to find a sort of frontier set up, with Hebrews pushed on the outside of it. Anti-Semitism used to belong with ignorance. But there it is—a fact," and his words ended in an embarrassed silence, as he looked toward us.

I knew that he himself did not like Jews. He was like the old head worker in the settlement where my husband and I had lived. He liked his "own Jews." He liked me, and the assistant teacher of chemistry on his faculty, and two brilliant students whom he admired, and perhaps, too, his dentist, who disclosed himself as a Jew on the Day of Atonement by closing his office then. But other Jews were alien to Dr. Perry. He was painstakingly fair to them; he made an effort to judge all students who were Jews with greater kindness than others. But they were strangers to him. They were not young people to love, as he did all the others who came into the circle of his gentle, unworldly personality. Yet, he felt the same way toward Italians, Slavs,—every one who was not an American, and preferably an Episcopalian.

It was clear, as he spoke, that, as he revered Einstein, the "professor," he felt discomfort at the thought of Einstein, the Jew. He would have preferred Einstein, the master, to be one of the rightly placed.

Or, if Einstein had been an American Jew even married to an American woman, it would have made him happier. He could never have felt enmity to a greater master—were he a fellow citizen besides—we knew. I thought of the leaders in philosophy, economics, psychiatry, chemistry, living here in the United States. The people they knew might feel alien to those of a strange creed and race—that was human weakness. But in our country intellectual genius was free, it was given homage, without thought of creed or nationality. That Dr. Perry himself showed, in his friendships with his Jewish students, and with me, whom he liked not only because I was my husband's wife, I understood, but because I was capable and could understand and stimulate him, even though I was a Jewess. After all, Dr. Perry's faith was not so much a doctrine as a social formula.

Because he was a scientist, he would have understood the religious approach of the Jew, had it ever occurred to me to do so unlikely a thing as to discuss this subject with him. The Jew, the modern Jew, intellectual and with a trained intelligence, asks of life, not what the believing Christian does, "Confirm my faith." He says, "Prove to me why these things I doubt are to be believed."

In that lay the reason for my continued faith in the Temple. I did not have from it the religious exaltation which was my father's. But that was because I could no longer accept without question a creed not, I told myself, understanding it. I could not, like a Christian, "believe," simply by wishing it. However, I thought that there was a grand ideal—if one wishes to call it that—a new decalogue, in this new Jewish church, once I discovered it. Our young rabbi, perhaps more than the older one (who was too wise in the ways of the world, it sometimes seemed to me) would disclose it to me in time, or I would discover it myself one day, suddenly, through this young priest of the new spiritual State of Israel.

XXV

I FELT proud when our young rabbi came in. He looked handsome amid the mixed group that arose at his entrance. He looked like a Jew, and yet an American, too, as had my brother Robert. He was easy, courteous, certain of himself. A certain gravity and faith in himself were charming and likeable, and to be expected in the priest of a religion, whose certainty comes from teachings he believes incontrovertible, and to which he is mouthpiece.

At first the talk was about plays of the season, a book or so, and then, as if it had been thrown into the middle of the room, some one—Gottlieb it was—mentioned the Ku Klux Klan. It was funny, in that gathering of highly intellectual, highly intelligent people, to have that white-robed fantastic ghost of old prejudices and stupidities appear.

"It's a fact. I know there are any number of them all over the country," persisted Gottlieb, Myra's cousin. "I travel all over the United States, and I know that there is a real organization."

Father John's face clouded, as it does when he is angry. "It's not American," he said. "This sort of thing can't continue. It will be wiped out."

In the silence I looked at Dr. Perry. His kind, sweet old face was withdrawn, troubled, as if he were keeping a secret. Was he a member of the Klan? The thought was almost too absurd for words. What made him look so odd, however? Was it because he could understand, even in his gentle heart, the animosities and differences that made hate of this sort? The Judge who was our guest listened intently, but he said nothing, I observed.

Father John was speaking of boys he had seen die abroad, young Polish boys, Irish, Italian—"every race that makes this country"—and, he added, "Catholics all." How could one tolerate a band of outlaws that dared so much as cast aspersion on citizens and soldiers like these? His face grew white, drawn and full of a fierce sort of tragedy. Suddenly, I knew why he looked like my father; his was that expression I knew on my father's face when he spoke of our people, even here in the United States. I remembered, suddenly, one Fourth of July when our door was flung back, and an old man, quite faint with fear and pain, fell through, and to the floor. His head was covered with blood; one of his eyes was full of blood. The hooligans and bums of the town, celebrating Independence Day, had seen him, his beard and his peddler's pack. They had hounded him, thrown stones at him and finally flung a lighted firecracker into his very eyes—in celebration of the birth of the land of liberty.

I remembered my father's words: "But this is impossible!"

It was not impossible. Ignorance and hatred lived here, side by side with tolerance and with friendship. He had said just what Father John now spoke: "It's impossible."

But these were the wretched, the poor in spirit; they were not the fine and the enlightened, of course. Most of our friends, in cities all over the country, were Jews or Gentiles, just as they happened to be born. And their friendship to us and to one another was based on human understanding and intellectual appreciation. Even those who, like Dr. Perry, felt strange with a Jew as a group—as an idea of a separate race—had friends as dear as any friend in their personal lives, among Jews.

The Klan was the voice of ignorance, of brutality. It was truly "impossible" to think of it as speaking for all of the United States.

Father John had spoken with indignation and with deep sorrow of the brutality of this secret, newly risen hatred. The young rabbi, when he took up the subject, spoke in a voice that was quiet, that was even tolerant and amused. He said the Klansmen were simply hysterical, uneducated men. That sort of thing always followed a war, and he reminded us of the aftermath of the Civil War. It was lawlessness, not religious intolerance, that made the Klan. He was dignified, logical, temperate, as he analyzed the Klan idea.

Was this the way to look at it? I did not know. But I wondered if the rabbis during the Inquisition had spoken in reasoned, temperate, understanding of the tortures of their people, had analyzed them, too, psychologically, socially, economically. My husband, across the room, met my glance, and he stepped over to me and, in passing, managed for the shortest moment to put his hand upon my shoulder. I felt his silent movement. Could it be that only by love, by love between those of us who came of different creeds and groups, this hatred and misunderstanding would be wiped from the earth?

From a chair in the corner came a sharp question:

"You were a pacifist in the war?" It was Gottlieb speaking, we saw.

No, of course not, replied our young rabbi, his sensitive face flushing.

My husband and I have friends who were pacifists, Quaker friends in England. They had gone to prison because they belonged to a faith that believed it was its message to preach peace. My people had been led by their priests into war. Yet their rabbis preached peace as an eternal duty. For whom did he speak, this young priest who was successor to Isaiah and Aaron?

His fine features were suffused in the flood of color. The Jewish rabbinate was obliged to preach for war, he said. What would people have thought, if it had not? And it was justified, for one had a duty to the country and its decrees. He quoted passages to prove that our rabbis had called upon our people to wage war many times.

"Wars for their faith," said Gottlieb then. "This was not war for our faith."

It was not for the Jew to question a war undertaken by his country, said the young rabbi, turning directly to his questioner.

"His country?" repeated Gottlieb. His florid, large face was suddenly strange, as if he had torn a placid mask from it.

He began to speak, and it was the strangest thing to hear him, as if a voice outside him had entered, to speak through his familiar lips. This large, rather stout, affable, young Jewish business man changed before our eyes. He spoke of the Jew in Palestine. He described the land in which milk and honey had once flowed for our people, fair fields in which to-day wheat blew golden in the sun, where Jewish men and women lived amid the hills which had been familiar to David when his voice rose in song. He was a Zionist. "I went to war, too," he said. "But I went because I was a Jew, and Jews couldn't hold back. Not to fight for my country. My country is the new Jewish State. We Jews have no other. Don't tell me. I've seen the Ku Klux Klan. I don't laugh at it. I don't think it's the hooligans of the country that make it: it's as American as Yankee Doodle. But it don't bother me. What does bother me is that I'm trying to arrange everything to go over there. For none of us—none of us, I tell you—belongs anywhere but over there, just as Herzl saw. That's where I'm going to live. It's the only country a Jew really has, I tell you!"

He spoke of a visit he had made there, of the hospitals and schools, the farms and the factories, that were already working there. He described the new Jewish University. "Match the staff of its faculty anywhere in the world, from Einstein down!" he exclaimed. He described the young people he had seen there, their vision and their golden dreams.

My husband's quiet eyes, blue and intent, were fixed upon this man whom we had known for months, who, when we saw him for a few hours, always spoke of shoes, the business of "selling stock," of leather, and of occasional "slack times"—and who suddenly appeared here as a prophet for his people in our living room, bringing tales of a new kingdom that had risen.

One could think of his uncle, stout, middle aged, contented, kind but not by any means sentimental—old Gottlieb. He hated to admit kinship with any Jews who were not "German Jews," and preferably from near Berlin. He would not even have Polish Jewish girls work in his store. He felt as alien to the Jews not of his precise kind, as he did to all the Gentiles with whom he had lived, as a business man, for forty years. Dr. Perry divided the world into Episcopalians and others; old Gottlieb divided them into German Jews and others. Jews were the chosen people, but Jews meant German Jews. To him, the Palestine in which all sorts of Jews gathered would have been a horror. How strange it was to hear this nephew of his, this "American" young man, express that burning fire which not only welded him into kinship with all his people, but lit the flame that blazed in the eyes of my father, mystic and believer in the oldest Judaism. He believed in the one State where he could be a citizen, that of Judaism.

My father would have been aghast that Jews dared to aspire to create that State. He waited until some divine act would bring it into being: the Messiah would come. This young business man believed that the divine will to create that State rose from the hunger and the reverence of the Jewish people. He was not religious: he belonged to the Temple. But to him the State held no creed. It was the home of the "People of the Book." To believe so was his religion.

The young rabbi listened, while words poured out in that fiery torrent from Gottlieb's lips. Father John's face responded, as if the religious fire of this other church drew his own. Dr. Perry's kind face became tinged with color, with the enthusiasm which even Gentiles who do not like Jews have for the traditional search of the driven people for their lost land. He did not feel quite comfortable with Jews on his own street, but he was thrilled at the thought of them marching with banners into their land again. The famous Judge, who had spoken little, leaned forward, and said he, too, had been in Palestine recently, and it had been like the climax to a grand story to be there. "You Jews are a great people." I think my brows lifted at that: it is a casual tribute.

But our young rabbi said, his voice slightly constrained, "I did not know you were a Zionist, Gottlieb."

Later the reform synagogue came to believe in Zionism. Then it was still solidly opposed to it.

But Gottlieb answered: "I didn't either. I never thought I was much of a Jew either. I was confirmed, and I had tickets for Holy Days once a year, and I used to go to hear the cantor singing. The rest of the year I was nothing. My wife, she's a Baptist. Then I went to Palestine. And it was funny, it got me. I'd never belonged anywhere before—excuse me, but it's so. I never believed the rigamarole the Sunday school taught me. But on the road, even if I'd wanted to be different, there I was a Jew—look at my face and see it. 'Hear about the Irishman and the Jew, Gottlieb—' I used to hear the same old jokes, always laughed when the Jew was taken off. Why not? I wasn't thin-skinned, like some, and it was good business. Then my wife, she's religious. She began to worry me about converting. Made her blue, going to church alone. Well, I wouldn't. It made her feel pretty blue. It wasn't pleasant home. Then two, three, years ago the firm said, why not take a trip? I went to Palestine, —to see what there was in the shoe trade there. And I met some of the fellows there. It, well, it's no use saying—it got me. It was the first time I belonged. That was where I belonged; every one knew it. I belonged," he repeated lamely. He spoke in a halting, embarrassed way now, as if unable to close the subject, and also afraid that he would seem less enthusiastic about it. Presently his voice drifted into a silence. But he sat back, his heavy, dark face still brilliant, vivid in color, alive.

I, too, was thrilled by the discovery he had made for himself. It was like hearing a spiritual odyssey. It was an odyssey hundreds of Jews had lived. I knew Zionists who felt toward the Jewish State as once saints seeking heaven had felt. It was as if they sought, and found, sanctuary. Some of them were practical business men, like Gottlieb, too. They saw the possibilities for business and success, but they gave up home, friends, position, here, to wander to a strange land—to seek their own people. Others left high places in professions, in medicine, in education, to give their lives, quite humbly, as one places gifts before a hallowed shrine, to Palestine.

It was thrilling. As if one saw the flight of a bird high in the heavens, high and true, in the inevitable line that made for its nest, so did this story of the Jew reaching to his home thrill one. It was enough of a religion, this traditional patriotism to a land that had existed in dreams for centuries, that was created out of a memory, and called its sons from the ages, from far-scattered lands, under its banners newly flung out.

But that was not my religion.

I thrilled to it as I would be deeply and beautifully moved by the story of a great discovery, by the final victory of the Irish people to have their own kingdom, by the true emancipation of the negro, or the freedom of India from the bonds of Great Britian.

Yet I understood that our young rabbi could feel himself undissolubly a part of this country in which we lived. He was not the secular, but the spiritual, head of his people. His kingdom was in our faith.

The conversation turned, this time, to the drama and to social work. Our young rabbi spoke with beauty of social service, and with knowledge of the literature of the modern drama, which he understood with the sensitive appreciation of our people for this art form. He knew the new writers and their works. He was much better informed than Father John, and the able Judge who was our guest was silent almost all evening as he listened. He had read more and understood more, in varied fields, than Doctor Perry. He made the whole intellectual world a treasury from which he drew, as he spoke. This was as he did at the synagogue, in his sermons, too. He was like a violin upon which all thought played—but what?

I tried to recall what I had heard in his preaching, in his conversations. Under the spell of his voice and his charm, it was hard to analyze him. But I thought back over his sermons—sometimes he quoted a Hebrew sentence from the Rabbis and sometimes he repeated a prayer in Hebrew. He read the brief, the abbreviated, service the Temple used. But his outlook, his sources of thinking, were entirely—exactly like my own—cosmopolitan. As a Jew, it seemed to me, he thought he must be urbane, scholarly, intelligent, courteous, and so prove that Jews are what they say they are—the chosen, the leaders, the princes of the world. Princes of what? Of culture, of philanthropy, of science, yes—of business, too.

My husband belonged to no church, and preached no religion. He did his work in his profession, and indirectly proved certain theses for society to accept for its greater happiness. His whole outlook, in his life, his work, in our marriage, was that of the cosmopolite.

What was the synagogue giving me, then, that was different, more rich and beautiful, than that which I had with my husband alone?

A few great rabbis were the spiritual leaders of their congregations. They were so because they were splendid orators, brilliant communal leaders, gifted writers. They were leaders in the sense that the great Catholic priests had once been leaders, too. They were great, because they were great men who happened to be Jews, and who had taken the rabbinate as their field of leadership.

But the rabbi elsewhere was not the leader of his spiritual flock. He was not teacher, father, and the interpreter of the message of his God. He was the subordinate to the purse-holder. Even our older rabbi, urbane, charming in his kind, patronizing, dignity, although he was interested in the confirmation of the children, the births, marriages, deaths, among his congregation, never took a stand on any question, even among his own people, because "it was the Jewish law." Sometimes a stand was taken on a community question; the board discussed it and decided what would be done.

The wealthy lawyers, moving-picture men, merchants, and real estate men, who were the trustees, the people with money, wrote the words which the synagogue spoke, as they did for the Church, too, of course.

The president of the Temple Sisterhood, a large, handsome woman with much jewelry, a rich, thick, contralto voice, and real good humor, insisted that my husband and I come to dinner. She had told me that she had many Gentile friends, and she was on the committees of many civic and charitable organizations to represent Jewish women. She had met me at my own office a number of times, in fact. When she spoke of her non-Jewish friends, she inevitably added, "He (or she) is a Gentile, you know?" She was proud of her non-Jewish contacts and influence, but they were never brought into her social life. Her non-Jewish friends lunched with her at "luncheon meetings" or had tea in her very handsomely appointed drawing-room to discuss policies or methods of dealing with various problems, but never at her table as her friends. She was, as an individual (as apart from her responsibilities as a personage in the community), as uncompromisingly Jewish as the women in the Ghettos, or in the newly opening Jewish sections where the prospering immigrant Jew is moving. She bought a picture from a Gentile artist—or from a Jewish, but the Jewish artist, humble as he might be, was nevertheless her own. She prided herself, in truth, on the fact that she always "made it clear I am a Jewish woman." She did not call others "Goyim"; she said, instead, in a rich, well-bred contralto voice, "She's one of us? Oh, a Gentile?"

With appreciation for this open, candid Jewishness, I expected to find her rather humble with the rabbi. She was too intelligent, too forceful, to be humble with other people. She knew that her money and her position counted in anything which won her interest, that her name on a committee made an endorsement which was often the deciding stroke for success.

My husband and I came at the appointed moment, ten to seven, to find that every one but us had arrived in dinner dress, and that our host was likewise so attired. Our host was head of a large factory. He spoke with comprehension, though not with tolerance, of labor conditions. He turned to my husband and discussed with him the passing of the prohibition law, which was being discussed as a possibility and which he thought would be a good thing for labor. He was advising all his friends in the liquor business to get out and to go into the manufacturing of sweets, he told us. He spoke of a book that had just come out, "Haunch, Paunch, and Jowl," and said the author ought to be driven out of the country, that he made anti-Semites. Then, suddenly, not waiting for my silent husband to speak, he looked at his watch. "It's ten after seven!" he said sharply. "Can't wait longer!"

His wife made a small movement with her hands, and looked toward her daughter, a lovely thing in rose and silver evening dress. Just then the door opened. The young rabbi came in, flushed, a bit disheveled, apologetic.

"Was detained by an unexpected emergency," he stammered.

"It's late," said the host shortly. We followed him to dinner.

It was apparent immediately that the rabbi was not the social or spiritual leader to this family among his flock. The young man tried to speak his opinions, to express a plucky sort of assertion, to retain his dignity. But our host bore him down, cut him off, simply brushed him aside. All the brave certainty that we knew in him was down, like a gallant plume that had been drenched in a heavy rain.

Presently, the young fellow became still, his hands fumbled as he took one of the numerous silver appliances to the luxurious dinner we were having, and he turned to me, sitting beside him, and we sat all evening speaking of the poetry of Amy Lowell, whom he greatly admired. "I'm writing a little book myself, and perhaps some day—" he said.

After dinner, the pretty daughter left for a dance. We older folks remained until eleven. The young rabbi hardly spoke, except to reply to the few questions his hostess put to him, or when there arose a matter of synagogue interest—and that was not ritual interest, but social. "We'll have the children's party at the end of the month, don't you think?" said our hostess, coming over to him. It was obvious that she came over because of her kindness, that she wished to make him feel less miserable.

The color came to his face. She did not apologize, even by a shading of voice, for her husband. It was he who replied eagerly and with evident appreciation. I left them discussing the details of the children's party; whether "Selma" or "Shirley" ought to have the principal part. "You know, Mrs. Bronsohn takes *such* an active interest," our hostess said, "I think we'd better let Shirley be the princess; she can wear a yellow wig—"

The Zionists divided Jews from the rest of the world, in the Jewish State; these Jews who were my friends divided themselves, from the rest of the world, in the Jewish social community. In neither was the rabbi—the preacher of the philosophy of Judaism—the guide.

These Jewish friends of mine had discarded the ancient observances of our Temple as useless and baseless, as I had done many years ago, myself. Liberal Catholics, Protestants of many sects, were doing the same. But Catholics did not become Protestants in observance, and Presbyterians, Unitarians—in the churches which still held the name of their old faiths.

The Jew had ceased to pray in the "Tallith," to

fast, to hold his Sabbath holy, to send his women to be purified monthly by immersion. He had cast off the shell and was holding only the fine kernel of his faith. But he did not respect that faith or the priest who preached it.

As a matter of fact, most of the Jewish families I knew celebrated Christmas, Easter holidays—with the observances of the Christian Church. They threw off the ceremonies of their own faith and adopted those of others. The very charming women I knew would meet, at Sisterhood meetings, at teas, at dinners—carefully inviting Jews only—and would relate with pride, "Why, you'd hardly know my Gloria was Jewish; she's often taken for French or even Irish!"

The leading Jews were not pillars of the synagogue; they were the synagogue. They wrote the emblems on the banners their clergy carried. And their pride, too, one discovered when one came to know them was: "'You don't look like a Jew at all,' they say to my boy at college."

Many of the younger Jewish business men we knew were college men who had inherited businesses founded by immigrant fathers or grandfathers coming from Germany, Hungary or Russia. They cashed in their education in social prestige. Their wives, too, were frequently college girls. They had carefully married for money. They carefully preserved the group unity. Their children, too, would marry Jews, come to synagogue.

But their pride was that these children of theirs, brought to the Jewish Temple, held closely in the Jewish circle, were "not like Jews at all."

It seemed hardly logical. To spend the fruits of education, wealth, power, in order to keep a social group, (a racial group if one wills,) and then to feel justified because the children brought to it were "not like Jews at all" seemed rather inexplicable.

Of course, I found that the Temple held no religious faith warm enough, beautiful enough, to take the place of the old orthodox Judaism I had lost in my girlhood.

The social unity the Temple gave I did not seek, nor feel I needed. I did not believe in it. I did not seek shelter with others of my faith—of my people.

The break with them had been final, I now knew. I simply must accept the fact that I no longer belonged. I made dear friends, and some are my friends to this day; but they were my friends, I knew, not because they are Jews, *too*, but because they are men and women whose minds and whose spirit I came to honor.

I wasn't a Jewess. I was just a woman, an "American," if one wished to put it so, I would have said. I said good-by to the Temple and said the prayers for my father myself, at home—in my "non-Jewish" home.

In less than three years I was to meet something strangely illuminating; I was to remember the day I said to the young rabbi, "I think I shall not be able to come back." I was to sit at the table of the governor of a great state, dining with his wife and himself, and as he spoke of my city, he was to mention with admiration the gentle old rabbi there, asking me, "Do you know him, perhaps? He's interested in this work, too." "I know him well," I answered. "I go to hear him sometimes at Sabbath services because he uses the old Hebrew my father spoke." "You are not a Jewess?" His excellency asked then, his face interested, alight with surprise. "One would never know it." I laughed then and said, "Oh—but *I* know it well now!" I told him why.

But that was not until three years later. I felt now that I was not a Jewess at all. I had left my faith. I did not find sympathy with my people. I plunged into my work; that was the only thing that counted. In it I was not a woman seeking justification through herself for her people; I had not entered it as a Jewess. I did not come to it, either, as "a married woman seeking a career." I entered it as a worker with definite qualifications. That was how I had been doing it, and how I now continued doing it.

XXVI

SOME day the story of how woman emerged from her ancient place in the home will be told as part of history, dispassionately and in generalizations. Now it must be the story of this woman and that one. It must be the story of a love or a marriage: of a man and a woman together.

Often it ended in disaster. I saw such stories day by day, in my own friends. One of the women I knew was the wife of a business man fond of his home, his books, his wife. She was a bright girl with a keen tongue, an unbeautiful but vivid face and a highly emotional nature. Their child was born the second year after their marriage, and they seemed to be absorbed in it and in one another.

But my friend was too restless, her mind was too active, for passivity. She joined clubs, became a member of the woman's party in her town, made speeches, neglected her home, the neighbors said. She was Catholic, and her parents conventional people. They interfered, asked the priest to speak to her. That enraged her, and she threatened to leave home if she were disturbed or annoyed, as she put it.

Because her husband was passive, she felt he was on the side of those who disapproved of her. She and he began to quarrel, and their quarrels did not decrease when she decided to go abroad during the war.

"What about Junior?" he asked her.

"You stay home and take care of him," she retorted. He had claimed exemption as a married man during conscription.

She went abroad, did fairly good work in the hospital, came home restless and unfit for the old life. Her mother had cared for her son, but she could not take up the work of being just a mother, a wife, even a restless woman in the community.

She had brains. Abroad, she found she could do one thing extraordinarily well. She had a gift with sick people, not as a nurse, but as a friend. Her inquiring, rapid mind was invaluable in the psychiatric department.

To the horror of her husband, she decided, at this late date, to study not only medicine, but "psychology," or "sick-ology," as he put it, when he was particularly angry.

She took the medical course and has just graduated. There is no possibility of their living together again. Her parents say it is the fault of this new nonsense about women—it's due to the war.

The truth is, of course, that their daughter's restlessness had been there all along. She was simply passively unhappy. The war gave her the opportunity to free herself. She is not a woman who should have married. Fifty years ago she would have been an embittered old maid; thirty years ago she would have "gone to be a missionary"; twenty years ago she married "the quiet fellow the other girls didn't appreciate." But to-day she became a professional woman, content in her job. She had the pluck and the faith to find her proper place, in spite of marriage.

Sometimes there is another side, however; the desire for the "new freedom" brings with it the illusion that there are gifts for enjoying it. One of the women on my staff was married to a chemist, a very unusual man. She was an intelligent girl whom we took on the staff mainly because she had a charming way that I thought useful with our people in club work. They had no children, having decided on a future for which birth-control offered a solution. This girl, we found, simply had no capabilities at all, except for wifehood and motherhood. She was too unstable to take steady charge of a club or even an occasional play; she was too slow, too inexpert at detail work. She was too impractical for case work; she was too inexact for even the lesser office work. We were obliged to tell her that she did not fit into our staff, but she cheerily forestalled us: she had decided to join a little theater company that was to give plays in our city. She visited us shortly to report that she could not continue with the company; she couldn't be a drudge and be ordered around by any person, "director or no director." She smiled delightfully. "You know how I am about taking orders, Mrs. Morton!" I smiled, too, for she had made it very difficult for my assistant, to whom she was responsible.

She tried, in turn, secretarial work for "an exceedingly busy executive" of a business, tutoring students lagging in high school studies, work in the new "interior decorating and art shop" just opened in our town, and finally canvassing for a "children's book house."

This girl was a college graduate; she was past twenty-five years of age. Her husband and she had never lived in a house or an apartment. They divided their time between hotels and furnished rooms.

It would have horrified her to be told that she ought

to stay home, live there and be happy. She thought herself an excessively "modern" woman, who must find her destiny "outside."

She made the same mistake that many women entering business and professions make. She felt that the wish to leave the home made the ability to fill a place outside it.

She came to find that place in the same spirit in which many women look for it. She wanted to start at the top of the ladder. She would "not take orders."

The unmarried woman in a job knows it is her work and sticks to it. She is an excellent employee, and she is, if anything, often too meek and patient. But the married woman, particularly the educated woman who is married and who goes for a job, wants the "headship."

That may be natural, of course. She is head of her home, the wife in it. She expects the same situation to meet her at work. She will not accept any other. But as a subordinate, she is often a failure for that reason.

My own training had been, fortunately for me, with my husband and before my marriage. I was one of the lucky ones who came to their jobs with qualifications. But, after the war, great regiments of married women came for work, simply because they could not endure the monotony of home. They often had neither experience, nor the ability for one special kind of work. They simply did not want to be housemakers and housekeepers.

They had my full sympathy, every ounce of it. I know that no man would choose, even for a day, between digging ditches in the company of a dozen other men, and scrubbing floors and scraping pots in a lonely kitchen.

I understood completely why these women wanted to get out, to be with people and work with people. But when I tried to tell them they ought to have training, they would be hurt, offended.

Once we opened a nursery for mothers who came to an afternoon mothers' club, where a woman physician spoke to them about preventive care of their children. We were particularly anxious for the women of the neighborhood to come, because we knew, as every social worker does now, that preventive medicine is more important than curative. We wanted to teach these working mothers how to wash their babies, how to cook their food, what diet to choose for them. Most of them had at least one baby at the breast and two or three at the toddling or creeping age. The nursery was an inspiration, for it not only would give the tired mother a chance to hear the "doctor lady talk," see movies and meet at a sort of party, but there would be, in addition, relief from the care of the children for an hour or two. They would be kept in the garden back of our office building, where the mothers could look down and see them and be assured of their care.

We advertised for a woman with experience in the care and play of children. A half dozen women came, and they were illustrative of the type of women who go out to work.

The first was a large, kindly Hungarian woman, who had been told of the advertisement by her employer. She was dismayed when she saw the crowd of children, temporarily in the care of one of our permanent staff. "Me no want caring for all so manny babies," she declared, edging away. "Me wanta haf easy wark scrobbin flars." The same distaste for caring of children is, of course, found by almost any woman who advertises for a servant and has to add "children in the family." After the war, servants did not allow children.

The second woman who came was the wife of a mechanic, a thin, clean, but obviously nervous, middle-aged, woman who told us that she had lots of time on her hands and that she wanted to earn a little extra money with that time. When she was asked if she had any children, she said, rather sharply, in relief, "No, thank heaven, I never had. I love 'em, but they make me nervous around all the time." Here was a woman with no experience, understanding, or sympathy, and she came to ask for a job with children. Of course, she was an untutored housewife, who did not understand why she failed to qualify with us.

The third candidate was a very sweet girl who was a student in the normal school. She needed the job badly, and she loved and understood children, but she could not promise to come "exactly on time," owing to the defections of the bus line at times. She did not see why we were so harsh, but we could not consider her.

The other two were married women of superior qualifications, the elder a grandmother, the other a young mother. The grandmother was one of those breezy women who seemed to come immediately after the war; a quick, extraordinarily capable woman, extremely well dressed, her figure as young as a girl's, her hair as smooth as satin against her cheek (that was the fashion, it will be remembered). She had worked with the Red Cross, had danced with the "doughboys," and had received a French daughter-in-law when her son came home. She wanted a job, and she thought this would be fine. It was with nice people—that made it so pleasant. It was nice hours, conveniently arranged between lunch and dinner. And there was even pay!

My assistant, who interviewed her, sat speechless while she spoke. She was obliged to sit speechless. For this vivid grandmother did not allow a silent moment. She told about her children, her husband, her experiences, her work, her plans, her dislikes, her favorite dessert. She spoke briskly and with real wit. It would have been delightful to have tea with her in her home, and she must have been the pusher and driver in her Red Cross circle, the "get up and get to it," member of the classes. But she simply would not fit in the professional field.

The professional field, the newcomer, entering, was to find each time, is as formal—no, more formal—for women than for men. The caller's spirit cannot be brought into it: the office is *not* the drawing-room. One of the hardest things the married woman entering professional or business life found to learn was that the little graces and amenities of her home life, her social life—which had been all the human actvity she knew—did not count, except to count against her.

How could one work with a nice old lady, youthful and active though she might be, who would cut into a plan for a year's work with: "That is precisely my idea. I told my son only last—"

It was funny, and, of course, this was not an average case. But it was enough like many cases to be illustrative.

The young mother who came—she happened to be the second to arrive—fitted in more readily than the others. She had a child, and she understood little people. She did not tell us whether she worked because she had to, or whether she simply wanted to do recreational work with children. We did not ask her. She knew what salary she wanted, and we knew what we could afford to pay. She wanted more than we had to offer her. But, when we telephoned to her later, she was glad to come at our terms, and she did very well. She is one of my friends to-day and is head of the children's work in one of the big settlements in the Middle West. I learned later she was a young widow, her husband killed abroad. She was waiting for her child to grow old enough to be cared for by some one else before taking a job.

Her problem was harder than mine had been when I went into my first job. My babies were old enough to walk when I began to work. Her baby was still being nursed. On the one day a week which she gave to us, she fed it a formula prescribed by the doctor.

The mechanics of "what did you do with children while you were away?" have always interested those who met me, and who learned (they did not learn it from me) that I had children.

My board found, immediately, that I would not discuss how I took care of my children with them. My contact with them was—my work. That was well done.

The women who came to our office and to our clubs never thought to ask if I were married or not. More and more, as the work grew, it became administrative and impersonal. It was my staff that met the individuals. I made plans, arranged the work, O.K.'d procedure.

The women on my staff were often married. I made it a point to give opportunities to married women, in each of the positions I held. But I did not make close friends of them. I found that I could live my other life, my life at home, more completely, if I cut it off from my office. At first I tried to join the two. It did not work out. I complicated things, and that was all.

That was because of my husband's reaction. My staff, at the office, knew me as the head of the place, as—I liked to think it was so, at least—a rather impersonal, quiet, decisive woman, who thought out decisions carefully, held to them and usually was right in making them.

My husband saw me as a gentle girl playing at being an executive and succeeding in deluding the world into accepting her pretence as reality. I think it amused him more to see me write a report than to read a funny story. It was not good discipline to have me projected as a charming, grown-up child. I stopped asking staff members to the house.

It was not that my husband wished to obtrude himself into my work. On the contrary, he made it a point to keep out of it, to interfere in no way, except when I asked him to help me.

During the first two years, I came to him all the time. There was hardly a decision I made or plan I considered, which I did not bring to him. He thought out each detail with me, as if it were his own work. One night he sat with me until four in the morning, writing with me my "report" to be read before the board.

He did his work and my own, too, I used sometimes to think. I was just another mouth to state his thoughts, another voice to utter his opinions. Then I began to feel sure of myself, unafraid of the responsibilities upon me. I could walk alone. He stepped aside at once, never asking me why I did not any longer consult him, nor intruding upon my new freedom in my work.

Once, when a young woman came to me with recommendations from another agency, and I was doubtful about her, afraid to make a decision—for she seemed so immature for the work we wished to assign to her—I came to my husband, asked his opinion and suggested that I introduce her to him, to see what he thought.

"It wouldn't do," he said, with decision. "Your staff must represent you. They must each be part of the machine built around their head. A girl who would fit in perfectly with my work and approach would, perhaps, be the one piece that would be out of place in yours. Trust your intuitive judgement, if you must. Take a chance."

I suppose that doesn't sound like tender love. It is different from the sentences Victorian heroines heard from their lovers. Modern wives are not supposed to hear loving phrases at all from their husbands.

But my husband, in the twentieth century, was speaking as a lover to me. He was telling me that my personality was precious to him, that the work I built up to express my personality and my ideal must be mirror of myself, and not of him, for that reason.

I know that when I was a young girl, my father, arousing himself from his studious abstraction, would sometimes say to my mother, "It is a very admirable cake, my wife." And she would laugh, pretending to be amused at his rare appreciation of food, but pleased inordinately, nevertheless.

My husband did not praise my cake or my embroidery. He did not praise my water colors, or my china painting, as the young men did with my pretty young aunts in my little-girlhood. No, he spoke in appreciation of the way I had handled a committee; he approved of the way I had organized a health drive in my neighborhood; he spoke with his quiet praise of the success of night dances we had organized in our playground during the summer months.

He admired and he gave praise to those things that were important to me. Had not the young gentlemen in "Evelina," and later in "Vanity Fair," and then in the novels of the late nineteenth century, too, always admired and praised those interests of their young ladies which the ladies chose to have?

I would smile a little when I thought of this. I smiled, too, because my husband insisted on seeing me as a young girl, while he praised my work as an unusually successful executive and a mature woman of the world.

I did not mind being charming and young to him, in our home. With our children I wanted to be young. I wanted to be as charming as I could make myself. I saw them so seldom that our time together was precious to us.

During my childhood, I had literally lived by the side of my mother, earlier tugging at her plump soft forefinger, later holding to her apron, and then playing at her side or in sight of her dark, laughing eyes.

Yet my own children, whom I saw perhaps three hours a day, were entirely happy. They were well. And—this no woman who gives her life completely to her children can completely believe, but it is so—they adored me.

I managed to spend one day a week, or an afternoon, at least, in the country with my children and my husband. The picnic lunches were always made "in the grass," as the children put it. We would cut bread, butter the slices, make cocoa, out in the open with the youngsters scampering and tumbling around us. They waited all week long for the "picnics." In winter we'd go for walks into the country, in stout shoes and woolen stockings.

At noon the housekeeper always telephoned to me how things were. It was then she was to call me up about such changes of plans as were necessary in ménu, for sudden emergencies. If the children had a slight illness, as of course they did sometimes, particularly my daughter, who is subject to slight sore throats, I left a list of places and times I was to be telephoned to about her. I would arrange to be at home for a little while to "cuddle her," if only for an hour.

I managed time to live, to be a wife, a mother and in charge of my home. I needed only to give my thought to each of these three things—and it was not impossible. I made out all checks, as before, for bills. I went over our laundry on Saturday evenings with the maid. I wrote out all ménus. I ordered all the children's clothes. I did my daily job, besides.

Was it hard? Of course it was. Did it destroy my strength? Of course it did not. For it is nonsense, as any woman knows, to say that a woman's work—with her mind—outside her house, is harder than manual work in it.

Her work in the house in easy, is nothing—if she has other hands do the drudgery for her. Her work outside, if it is mental activity, is no harder than that done by men. After I came into my job, I came to see the great jest of the "tired business man." I used to wonder what made it so hard for men who worked at business. "Being an executive," I was told.

Being an executive, I found for myself means having burdens and responsibilities to bear. But they are no heavier than these borne by the mother of a family who has the burden and the responsibility—including the very life of each member—on her shoulders.

I was not tired with my work, except as it took time.

There were women who envied me, and I understood their envy. They were as able as I, many times. But they were afraid. They embroidered, read a "paper" before clubs, or did "volunteer" work. They would not have dared work for a salary.

"Are you happy?" my husband asked me one day, coming into my study. I nodded, wrote my signature to a letter and came over to him. "Busy," I laughed. He was so much like a big boy now, and when we met for lunch he always seemed to me like a boy who had persuaded a girl to come with him for a holiday.

Was this the man who used to seem to me so—well, so much older? I had before thought of my husband not as four years older than myself but at least a generation. He was so much wiser than I, I had felt. He could do things I could not.

He could still do things I could not do. He had a mind of a keen brilliance which mine did not possess. I could not even try to think as he did—incisively, in a sort of long flash that saw principles in details.

I had only a knack to manage people and the ability to use that knack. I did not feel that it was particularly wonderful. I felt that to be a thinker was greater than to be an "executive." That was not what had made him seem to grow younger to me. The reason was another.

It was that I no longer felt I must depend on his judgement. I was once afraid to think, to decide, unless he said I should think or decide. I had simply passed from the mental protection of my father, to his.

Now I had to make decisions each day which affected not only one life, but hundreds. I thought about life according to my own vision. I had been a wife, a mother, a writer—but I had been a child all along.

I was a woman, grown up, now.

I ought to say, I suppose, that I was more interesting to my husband—or less—for that reason.

It would not be true.

Men and women do not love one another because of the work they do, because they have executive abilities or are brilliant thinkers. As my husband had said, smiling once before—he did not love me because I was capable; he loved me because I was a woman.

Marriages failed when women became independent economically or intellectually, not because the independence had been attained, but because, in the success of that attainment, husband and wife lost the dear closeness with one another—they permitted themselves to be carried away. Sometimes that was inevitable. A woman discovered herself to be a different woman; she was no longer then her husband's real wife.

But my husband and I had loved each other, first of all, as comrades. We had fallen "in love" afterwards. Our growth was side by side. It was natural that I should now grow up—to his maturity; not away from him, but closer to him. I only grew up to understand and to honor and to love him more deeply.

Our third child was born in summer, and I took a three months' leave of absence, one before the baby came, and two afterwards. I nursed him until he was four months old. A pleasant English woman took care of the little lad for the first year, and then our housekeeper, capable and faithful, took charge. For, like all women who "worked out," much depended on the sort of women whom I left in charge of my home. When our baby was two and a half years old we put him into one of the kindergartens in the city.

This was expensive, but it was necessary for the boy to have playmates and friends.

It was so expensive, however, that I realized I must look for another post. I required a larger salary to be able to afford to hold my job, if I was to give my children the proper care while I was away from them, doing it.

I happened to be in New York for a conference, and looking through the telephone book, saw there by chance a name I had not thought of for years, which I had forgotten. It was the name of the magazine of which "my editor," my first editor, was the editor.

Had I once thought of writing? In the Pennsylvania Station the telephone operator waited, as I stood with the open book before me. "Want the book, ma'am?" some one asked, and I flushed, yielding it. "Call Pennsylvania—" I said to the girl, and across the wire came the voice of my editor. "Come over," he said, "tell me what you've been doing."

But when I came I did not know what to tell him. I was directing the work of other people, adjusting the lives of people, helping others to express themselves either in work or in living.

But when he asked me what my husband had asked, "Are you happy?" I could not answer; I told him, instead, what my salary was and how tremendously vital it was for the particular sort of work we were doing, to be done.

It was work that must be done, like cooking, cleaning, "raising children." I had the knack of doing it. The only difference between myself and those other women who did the domestic work of the world was that I was receiving an excellent salary. Mine paid a regular monthly salary, just as the work of men had been paying. Many a man would have envied the salary I named, evading an answer to his query, when I replied to my editor.

However, one did not take a job to be "happy." One did one's work as an individual in the community. Which men—how many men in offices and in factories—were doing work because it made them "happy" to do it?

XXVII

EARLY in 1920 my husband entered the new work he is now doing. The analytical mind he had used in planning and creating his previous work found fuller scope and material in it. His previous education, his training and experience, have stood him in good stead. He took up a special field, and he is now at the head of it. In six brief years he has accomplished more than he had done thirteen years before.

My work had been the decisive thing in giving him the opportunity for study and for finding the real task of his life. If, at the beginning, it was to be only something added on to our life, it proved itself soon to be equally important and necessary to us as his own work. The cost of educating our children, of managing a pleasant house, of having servants to do all the various things I had done before, required everything we both earned.

I had not known how much one woman represented, as a mother, in budgeting for the home. But the cooking I had done, the sewing I did every evening, the odds and ends of fine laundering, the patching and darning, when given to be done by others were startlingly expensive. I used to put a patch in a pair of trousers between reading proofs and eating supper, after the potatoes were put on to boil. The tailor now charged thirty-five cents. I used to press my husband's ties, clean them if necessary, before he went out in the morning; they cost twenty-five cents apiece at the cleaner's now. The hand-made dresses I used to make for our little daughter cost five and ten dollars and more. I used to press my husband's suits, in the first years. I used to go over his shirts, turning cuffs, sewing up little rips. I had no time now; I was working every minute now. It cost so much to do all those many, those countless tasks that I had done without thinking of them! The servants did their set jobs for which they were paid. They could not be expected to do "extras."

My husband is not quick with his hands, and I am. But the bit of painting that I used to do—as every housewife does—in a minute or so, now and then, meant paying dollars to workmen. The lawn and the back yard were cared for by workmen whose income came from my husband's and mine.

One reads of the women in professions and in business, and hears of the difficulties they are meeting in the community. The difficulties I encountered were all told in one word: Time. It was a difficulty that grew with the growth of my success, such as it was.

My days ran away so fast. I simply ran after my days. I worked at my office, but every hour I knew exactly how my children felt, I went over their reports, I made it a point to speak to their principals and teachers if possible. The only one that troubled me was our baby boy; he was so shy and so frail. But he was well, and he attended a pleasant little day school not far from our home.

My husband did his work alone, for I was so busy that, at times, we hardly saw each other, except for the short periods in the morning when we met, with the children, for breakfast. I rose at seven, dressed rapidly, came into the dining room, met my family, had breakfast with them and then hurried off to my office. Sometimes my husband could not manage to get to breakfast, for his work kept him up at late conferences, or reading to early dawn. But our first clinic opened at nine, and I was always there promptly.

If I had a report to write, I would lock myself in my room and forego the breakfast with the family. We could see each other, then, only at dinner. It would happen, though, that my husband had a dinner engagement, and then a day or so might pass without our seeing each other.

Very often I would be asleep when he came home. Or, if I were detained in the evening at the office and then was called to a meeting somewhere, he might have gone to bed before I returned home, and I would read, relax, alone in our house, while the children and he slept.

I was speaking frequently now before women's clubs. I had a class at the little college near by. I held seminars for my new workers and arranged to lead little groups of volunteers in study courses that would explain how they could be useful to us. I was writing, too, but not as I had once planned to write. I wrote technical papers, reviews of social work books, brief pamphlets to be used for what is now called "publicity" in our work, but which we called "educational" propaganda.

Then Little Maid entered junior high school. She had her friends, her interests. She succumbed to tremendous crushes over women teachers. She became remarkably pretty. I oversaw everything, but rapidly, as if I were going over data presented me for approval by the members of my staff. Our son was still in grammar school. He was doing well, but he was not sturdy and tall, like his sister. I arranged for his care, took him to a capable doctor to have his diet written out, sent him to gymnasium. Our youngest child, the baby, we continued at kindergarten.

My housekeeper was capable, clean, conscientious. I used to smile, sometimes, to think of Mrs. Norton, the big woman who had been housekeeper for me when I was so ill, before Little Maid was born. I had been timid with Mrs. Norton because she was so big beside my smallness. I was not timid now. I was brief, quick, low-voiced, impersonal. My staff knew I would stand for no sentimentality, no nonsense. I would agree to a raise of salary, would fight for it with my board, but I expected good work in return.

No man, I think, could have run his life on a more completely satisfactory plan than I. The men I met in my work knew, and showed they knew, that I was as capable as any of themselves. In committees, my word counted. In making decisions, my opinion was often conclusive. I may say this, surely, since I am speaking anonymously here, without asking praise or acknowledgement in the future.

If my fellow workers sometimes wondered that I, a married woman, spent herself as completely as would an unmarried woman on her job, they, at any rate, never expressed themselves to me. I did not even permit those who worked with me to know, to be friendly, with my children. My children were kept apart from my work. My husband was kept apart from it also. I was not "Dr. Morton's wife," but Leah Morton. Many of the people I knew in my work would very likely have been startled to know I had a husband.

My husband and our love were part of our own life

together, of our family that we had built between us. The job was just a way of earning a living. My salary was no longer as large as his own; mine remained stationary, and his had risen, for I was in social work, where salaries, as he knew, were small. But, even if his income were to become, some day, big enough for us both, I could never now be content with nothing bigger than the home. I would be no more content there than would he, himself. It would the same as to ask the head of a business to lock himself up in a small apartment and feel happy in spending his time adding up the cost of vegetables, soups, laundry bills and the children's spending allowance.

Running my house, I still found, was easy; it was a simple thing to do, compared to running my office and my work. The two together were hard only because I did not seem to find the days long enough. I wanted more *time* for my home.

Sometimes my husband would come up, put his hand on my shoulder and say, "Tired?"

I would nod. I would often be tired. But I do not think I was unhappy. I was too busy to know, in fact, then, whether I was happy or not. My work became so a part of me that, at times, I think I must have felt the city would cease to exist if I did not arrive at nine to open my office.

The one thing I allowed to compete with it for my time was my children. It was easy to arrange for the care of babies, little children, but not of adolescents. It was easy to keep a home "going," but it is not easy—let no one think so—to manage a job and to bring up a boy and a girl stepping into adolescence at the same time. That was a problem I had not foreseen. It announced its arrival one morning, quite unexpectedly. My children needed *my time,* more of it. It was a constant fight, therefore, for time between my work and my youngsters, but I had managed it. My work was something I did as thousands of thousands of men do theirs, a sort of squirrel's cage of activity. But my children were something high and separate, something lovely. They were to me what once I had thought it would be to be a writer—the expression of dreams that I put aside. I had determined that everything I had not had they should have—a beautiful youth, health, play, a splendid education and, above all, freedom given them lovingly to find themselves.

I was not the old type of mother who could, or who would, give her children her life in immediate service, hour by hour. But I could give mine to creating service for them. That I had done hitherto for them.

In April, Little Maid needed a slight but essential operation, and I did not stay up with her, all night, as I had done years ago when our boy had his tonsils out. I sent her to a hospital, hired a trained nurse, came up in a taxi in time for the operation, stayed until she began to struggle through the ether and then went back to work. I could not stay away from the office. We were just arranging for the care of two score tubercular patients. I had to see that they were sent off, and that they would, themselves, be content to acquiesce in our plans, that they would not, with the pathetic stupidity of the immigrant, pack up their belongings and go back home as soon as they had arrived at the tuberculosis camp.

I came to see Little Maid in the evening. I missed dinner to do so, for I had remained at the office all through dinner time going over the proofs of a leaflet we wanted to distribute to mothers in the summer time, when so many children's lives could be saved if only their parents would understand that milk must be kept cold and clean. I hurried away from my daughter to attend a meeting at which I was to speak. I came home at twelve, found my husband waiting, and heard from him that he, too, had seen our daughter, shortly after I left her.

"She says she's lonely there," he told me. "Don't you think she ought to come home?"

I considered. "She'll be lonelier here," I said then. "Brother is at school, and you at the office; only Mary is in the house. Let's tell her to stay at the hospital. We can keep that nurse a bit longer; it's expensive, but she's pleasant, and daughter will like being with her."

He came over to me, put his arm around my shoulders, and said, "Don't you want to rest a bit?"

"Fearfully," I admitted. And then, as I had not done for so long, I sat down on his knee, let my head lie on his shoulder, let him kiss me quietly. In our room near by I heard our littler son's steady breathing; from the nursery came Brother's steady little snore; the clock ticked in the living room. I thought of our daughter lying with bright hair braided in curly softness about her pretty face, of her lovely eyes closed in sleep, of the white-capped nurse beside her. My arms felt a hunger, a need to have my daughter in them. I snuggled closer to my husband.

"She's doing beautifully," he reassured me, interpreting my thought.

"I know," I said, and we sat in the half-light again.

But, suddenly, something seemed to strike into my

mind. It sent me up like an arrow shot into the air. I ran to the telephone. My husband looked at me, helplessly laughing, amazed. "What happened?"

I was looking feverishly for the telephone book, though. "I have to telephone," was all I could say. I had forgotten to do it! My secretary should have reminded me!

I telephoned to a number I found, a hospital in the lower end of the city. "Maternity? This is Mrs. Morton, M-o-r-t-o- yes, Mrs. Morton. We have an emergency case—Mrs. Polacz—she's had convulsions —she will have to come sometime to-night, the doctor thinks—Is this the night superintendent?" I felt exasperated with myself because I spoke excitedly, because I was not calm, impersonal. But this should have been done as soon after eight o'clock as possible. I had heard of the need to send Mrs. Polacz just as I left my office, when her little nervous husband came in crying to tell me what had happened. Their doctor told me, over the telephone, that she would need hospital care at once. I was to arrange for it, as soon as possible, please. My assistants were gone; only my secretary was left. She had promised to telephone to me by nine, when I was due to speak, to remind me about this. She had not done so.

"Mrs. Polacz, one of the women in our neighborhood, has had a hemorrhage and convulsions," I began again, controlling myself. "Her doctor advised us that she must have hospital care at once, perhaps to-night. Could you take her in, as an emergency case, if necessary?"

"Polacz," said the pleasant, heavy, female voice at the other end. "She came. Some one telephoned from your office to expect her—"

So my secretary had done this herself. Good girl. Mrs. Polacz had, apparently, come to a serious crisis rapidly. "How is she?" I asked.

"Dead, I am sorry to say," replied the quiet voice at the other end.

I do not know why this made me turn to my husband, hold him tight to me. "Dead." That was the end of everything we did, all of us.

He held me close, smoothed my hair, sat in silence. "Let's bring daughter home," I said presently, nervously. "I'll take a few days from the office and spend them here."

But I did not have the time, after all.

Next day, when I came to work, I found I could not arrange to leave. There were things hanging in abeyance, waiting to come to a crisis. There were new things coming in to demand my "personal" supervision.

And when our daughter came home she was so well, so pink, that I felt silly to have been unnerved. She was overjoyed to be able to walk after her confinement to a chair. Then came her first breakfast at home again, a sort of feast celebrating her being herself again.

"I tell you, momsie," she said, looking at me with wide hazel eyes in their circles of gold-brown lashes, "I'll be glad to see Miss Martin again!"

"You miss her so much?" I asked.

"Life simply isn't worth living without her," declared my daughter.

I laughed, but she continued, turning to her father, "You know, dad, she's not kind, particularly. She hasn't what you'd call, well, an appearance." She groped for a word or phrase. "But she's so interested in everything you do. She makes you feel you're so important to her."

A startled glance passed from her father to me, and from me to him. "How does she do that?" I asked my daughter. "Does she pet you, dear?" That was what I meant when I told myself I must find *time* to give my children. But my query had made her laugh, for she is intensely modern and despises sentimentality, as do all children to-day. "I should say not!" she protested. "It's only—well, now, there's the Latin. That's important. She makes you do it, too, or you know where *you* get off. But, all the time, she makes you feel you're as important as the Latin is, too."

Little Sonny listened with eyes wide open, not understanding. But we turned to Brother, eating his second egg only because he wanted to see if he could knock off the end of his egg with a knife, the way an English visitor had done not long before at our breakfast table. He performed the operation, and contributed his point of view:

"I don't know. I don't like people to feel that way. I like to be let alone. I like to be all by myself. I like people to mind their own business." Was he "growing away from" us, because left to grow up alone?

We wanted him to explain, but he could not. However, he made it clear that he preferred to live as an individual, one who belonged to a home, but had no obligations to anyone in it.

"You mean, you would really like even mother to leave you alone? Me, too? Who'd teach and train you in the way you ought to go, young man?" asked my husband, pulling our boy over to his knee, to wipe the egg from his mouth.

"That's it," said our son. "Now, the fellows in my school, their mothers are always ragging them. Do this, and do that. Don't do this. Be a good boy. Now, I think it's a waste of time. Momsie leaves me alone, and I'm just as good as them, any time. Anyhow, I think I am."

"What an awful little prig this is!" laughed my husband. "So that's how you think, is it?"

Our daughter interrupted, though, "It's all right for you. But when I grow up, mother, I'm not going to have a profession at all. I'm going to marry a very rich man who can take me abroad."

A flush passed over the face of her father. "You think if you marry a wealthy man you won't want a career?" he asked quietly.

Our daughter nodded: "Well, now, dad, look at the friends momsie has. All the rich women give money to have social work done. And all the poor ones do it. Or else the poor ones are doctors or nurses or go to business, like Mrs. Ellison. The rich women just stay home and do what they want *exactly* when they want it. Momsie works all the time, though."

This was exactly what I did not want her to think. I took time to point out to her that one woman was the wife of a wealthy business man, and yet was teaching, the other was the wife of a doctor and was herself practicing. But she shook her head. "I don't believe they really want to do it," she insisted.

"Wouldn't you?" I asked her, then. "Aren't you going to be a writer, as you planned?"

She shook her pretty head. "No. I'm not," she said. "I'm going to go to college and have a good time. And then I'll get married as soon as I can, mother. You see, mother, well, every one knows it, I have a boy friend."

Every one knew it but her father and me.

Fourteen is young for a girl to have a "boy friend." But it was not too young for the girls in my daughter's school. And had not my mother's mother married at fourteen? My husband's grandmother was a widow, in France, at fifteen.

I had been arranging the lives of hundreds of girls, of women and children, but this enormously important thing had taken place in my daughter's life, and I had not known even of its beginning. She wasn't a baby any longer, needing only to be fed, dressed and kept warm and content. She wasn't now a little girl, requiring only opportunity to spend her energies safely and happily.

She was opening the door into adult life. She was having her first emotional experience. The woman who gave her time, who was her guide, unconsciously, to be sure, but none the less, decisively, was the gentle old maiden lady who taught her Latin, who had time to show her she was important in the scheme of her life. Did she know of this boy Colin, who was my daughter's "boy friend," I wondered. Very likely not.

I suppose I should have been horrified. I should have castigated myself. I ought to have talked to my daughter about giving me her confidence. In books I had read, I recalled, the mothers who "went out for a career" were suddenly confronted with their children's ruin and downfall, and they at once threw up the work of years, their most cherished plans, to "live at home and look after the children."

I knew how utterly senseless that would be. I knew hundreds of homes in which mothers stayed home doing nothing in the world but worrying about the state of the morals and minds of their children—and saw their children go just the way they wished. I knew of one woman whose daughter, just the age of my own, was the mother of a baby, the father of which was a boy in her "crowd." We had helped "place" that very baby, to hide the story. I knew of young girls, whose mothers were fine, good women, interested in church work, in community responsibilities, but in their "homes first," who were simply sliding along in the long toboggan which young people seem to have discovered to-day.

I was not in the least conscience stricken when I thought of my girl, for myself. She was healthy. She had many varied interests. If she had a "boy friend," it meant only that she was recognizing earlier than we, a generation before, had recognized, the interest of mankind and womankind for one another. This was natural, and it was healthy. She was not a bookish child, as I had been; it was her right to be herself.

I did not want her to be the "flapper," and I meant to see that she would not be. But I knew too many girls not to know that the most ridiculous, even the most dangerous thing, would have been for me to suddenly drop all my work and drown my child in myself.

What she should have was something to fill the need she had expressed to us herself, and which I had known existed before—some one to find her "important"—not some one away from her home, but in our home.

I would have liked to be that person myself, not because I would have found complete contentment in giving my life to training my child. I should have been, I think, an unhappy failure at that task alone. My children were the reason, the purpose, to which I dedicated my work. But I felt—and this I must say—that I had as much right to my work as they had to the opportunities their father and I worked to give them.

It was impossible for me to give more time to her now, however. We could not afford to have my income cut by my taking work which would give me more leisure. I simply put the problem aside, for my husband and myself to work out, so that we might find a solution which would enable us to show our Little Maid she was "important" in her own home, and to bring her brother, too, closer to his home. I was modern, yes; but, though my husband teased me about it, I did not want my son to be so modern that he would outgrow our home.

"It's seed for a complex," he pointed out to me. "You don't want to lose him. You'd rather tie him, wouldn't you, and handicap him, but make him need his home?"

I admitted it; I'd rather he were tied, even with bonds that would mean pain for him if they were broken, but which held him close to us. I wanted our home to be free—but I would not let it be weakened in its power, the power that comes from love.

XXVIII

ON my staff was a woman I shall call "Mrs. Norris" here, a highly trained expert in nursing and social service. She was, I knew, a mother, but I had never seen her children, nor did she speak of them. My contact with her was, necessarily, because she was in charge of a most fundamental part of our work, constant. But it was at the same time entirely professional. She was active in the suffrage work with Elsa Harmon, and I knew she was intelligent, but we never came close to each other.

It was through her that the "Polacz case" was treated by our organization, and she came in one afternoon with a little sheaf of paper to discuss plans she had for further work with the Polacz family. "The two older children are pre-tubercular," she told me. "The man himself is, we think, syphilitic. He should have treatment, but he has refused to submit to examination. The poor little man is broken up by his wife's going."

"Who's taking care of the children?" I asked. "Are we arranging for that, or is he able to pay some one himself?"

"He's home, taking care of them himself," Mrs. Norris said. "The place looks quite frightful, the children particularly. Formerly, they had been accustomed to exceptional care, for the mother was an intelligent woman. She was, before her marriage, a maid in a well-to-do Hungarian family, and got a lot of experience in fine sewing for her mistress. Here she worked in one of the stores, in the embroidery department; she made fine handmade things and earned as much as her husband."

It appeared that the dead mother had been employed as a "part-time" worker, and that she had taken charge, completely, of her home, besides. Some of the work, she used to do at home in the evenings when her man had had his supper and the children were, at last, in bed. Her whole life had been spent in having children and in struggling with the economic problem; it had been painted over with a glory of love and of duty.

I thought of this woman, like so many women who came to us, who performed the function of motherhood and of wifehood, busy housewives—and wage earners besides. Many of them earned as much as their men. Yet they were the lesser people. Their men, coming to America, were sought by the country as citizens. These women were not thought worthy of citizenship in America. They were, in fact, consciously inferior to their own husbands, in their own homes. I was, of course, interested in franchise for women, but my part in it was not active. I knew that, shortly, women would have the vote. It only seemed absurd that any objections could be spoken, in the light of what women were capable of doing and being, even their women who had so little chance.

"His wife held a job and took care of the children, had them, too, and things went like clockwork," said Mrs. Norris, expressing the same thought. "He's making a botch of things now he's in charge. I used to have to put my foot down, too, before, because he would abuse her sometimes; he thought she was rather lazy, because sometimes she liked to sit and just 'think about things.' She was a fine little woman, that little Hungarian."

I could imagine the nervous, high-strung little man ranting at his wife as she sat, pregnant, her work in her lap, their children asleep, and her dreams and memories of the past calling to her for a moment or so.

"Well, we mustn't let him go to pieces," I said. "Tell him to come to see me, and I'll insist that he have an examination. I shall see that he agrees to your plan for treatment. We'll send the children away for a time, and have them built up."

"He wouldn't go," said Mrs. Norris, smiling a curious, bitter sort of smile. "He has another woman there already." I must have looked startled, for she said, "Oh, it's not that he forgot his wife! But he's a weakling. He must have a woman to bolster him up—even to get over the misery of losing his own woman."

Flaccidness and shoddiness of character are not, however, possessions of men alone. I smiled and reminded her of that, rising to end the conference. But she did not get up from her chair near my desk.

"I haven't any real respect for men," she said, her large handsome face darkening. "I know them too well."

She got up, then, drew her sheets of papers together and said, "I'll have to be out of town for a week or so, Mrs. Morton. I'll arrange the Polacz case so that Miss Follimore can work at it, if you feel it will be quite all right for me to be away?"

This was so unlike her, her whole tone was so different from the usual calmness and capable certainty

I knew in her that I felt it well to ask, "You are not ill? Of course you can arrange whatever plans you think best." I knew she would be away only in emergencies.

She looked toward me then and said, "I'm not ill. It's my husband. Oh, yes, he's living." She talked rapidly then, as if to get it said, "He's been married to another woman. He deserted me almost eighteen years ago, went away, and then asked me for a divorce. He used to write, asking me for loans all the time, and I sent them. That's the kind of fools women are. Then he got married. The girl died in childbirth and left him with a baby. Do you know who took care of the arrangements for that baby? I did. I've supported our boys and myself. I never have had a thing from him but misery—that's all. Now he's sick. He wants me to be soft and sentimental and 'take him back.' Really—it sounds crazy, but that's what he suggests. He's not much good—a broken-down travelling man. I know it. But you can't drop these things. They pull at you. I can't let a man I—well, for whose children I was a mother—ask me to help him and say, no. I didn't mind his leaving me, I really did not. It left me free to go out and hustle and make a real home for the boys. I didn't care—not much—when he asked for the divorce. Yes, it hurt me when he married again, but I think that was my vanity that hurt. But I can't let him write me that he's at the end of the rope and ask me to help him, and say, no. I just can't. That's all."

We humans are strange creatures. We go about in our dark clothes, with our lips smiling, our eyes blank. We are like books that are closed. We have such strange, unthought-of stories written in our hearts and in our memories. I should not, by the furthest stretch of imagination, have thought of our capable, middle-aged Mrs. Norris, suffragist and nurse, as a wife who was so conscious of the sacred burden of love, even a love that was dead, that she would dedicate her life to the end to it.

She and I were to have gone with a group of women to the capital of our state, to lobby for a bill that Elsa Harmon wished to have put through for the industrial welfare of women. I was not much good at lobbying, for, though I could manage my office and speak readily enough from a platform, I became shy, ineffective, at once, when the loud-voiced legislators asked us questions, or when they did the more drastic thing of refusing to see us. Elsa could be winning and effective with the educated, intelligent men, but Mrs. Norris was always the one to demand an interview. She could meet a group of politicians, "jolly" them, return joke for joke. She knew how to speak brusquely. "She's a regular card," one man said of her, admiringly. And she could, in turn, be direct, compelling, driving through to her point. She understood the psychology of the politician, could suggest what clubs we ought to interest in our measures, which "names" to have behind us. She was bound to make a mark for herself as soon as women had the vote themselves. She has made a real place for herself since. And yet here was her story as a mother and a wife.

"Why didn't you marry again?" I asked her. I wondered if she really loved that man, who had been her husband, once. One could not tell her how Quixotic was her agreement to take care of him. But perhaps she loved him still.

"I couldn't marry again," she said. "I'm a Catholic, you remember?"

So this man had sinned, in the light of her religion. The child he had by a second woman was a child of sin to his wife, and yet she had arranged for its care, for its life, as a duty, a duty which was hers as his wife.

I was not ashamed of the women I was meeting in the "new freedom."

Yet all were not anxious to find their places in the community, to assume the responsibilities which were theirs as human beings as well as women. Sometimes they saw the door out of the home as simply a way out to greed and hungers repressed.

The end of the war brought the new girl in and introduced the first edition of the flapper, to follow. Galsworthy had written his novel about freedom in love, for youth in war. But married women, too, were seeking freedom there. The suffrage bill passed, and women were given the vote, to the horror of old-timers. Women took their votes lightly, though. Only those women who had wanted to be active citizens, before, took advantage of their citizenship, now that they had it. Idealists among women saw their dreams of a grand civic ideal, to be brought in by women, fade in the darkness of political corruption, which women began to share as well as the men.

Mrs. Norris railed because the mayor in our city went out openly for the women's vote, flattered them, offered them little, unimportant jobs and blinded them to that which he stood for—small-city gang politics. They became greedy for spoils, too. A Mrs. Preston suddenly appeared, who had never once been interested in a suffrage meeting and now stepped forth as the leader of a division, with two hundred votes behind her, and the mayor as her overlord. "They're no good," cried Mrs. Norris. "We should have waited twenty years and educated the women to vote, first, before we allowed the suffrage privilege to become effective," Elsa Harmon said, disheartened with the suffrage victory, when it came.

But would that have been the solution? Twenty years from now, the same human nature would have been found as now. It was not the vote, it seemed to me, that mattered for women. It was the sense that they were individuals and responsible members of the whole community. Suffrage would not purify American politics; it would make free American women, though. Its results would not be political, but industrial and social. Babies would not be left to starve while mothers filled out and cast a ballot, as had been darkly prophesied. Women would not become lost ladies because they met ward politicians in committee rooms. Nor, on the other hand, would the capital of each state become a little Paradise with senators wearing shining haloes, polished assiduously with watchful women's votes.

The change came through another way, and to other purpose. Women saw that laws affecting their work, themselves and their children, were passed. They became, in the government of the country, co-heads of the great home which is the state. They ceased to be slightly older children for whom the men, their husbands and fathers, made such rules as pleased them. And even there, the great mass of women failed to show they were "grown up." When the child labor law was discussed, later, it was not the women's vote that swung it through. It was the vote of men in the South, where women were silent, that blocked its passage.

What women voters needed, it seemed to me, was not education in how to vote. They simply needed education. They needed education in schools, but even more in life, in living. They needed to be taught faith in themselves.

Meanwhile, women like Mrs. Norris, capable as citizens, workers and mothers, were yet at such great disadvantage in the scale which weighed them and the "home woman."

There came into my office, a few weeks later, a stranger, whom I did not at once recognize, a tall man in army uniform. It took me a moment to realize who he was. This man was a college classmate of mine, whom I had not seen for many years, whom I had forgotten. He had married a girl we both knew, and I had not heard from them since I left the platform on graduation day.

"Heard of you down the hospital," he said. "I thought it must be you, though you've changed!"

We spoke of our college friends, he told me that he had heard of my husband and seen his work mentioned in the newspapers. He, himself, had been ill. He had come back from the war with a "bum lung," and though he seemed "O.K.," he'd be pretty "rocky" for some time. His profession was engineering, but he was giving that up. He was going out West.

"How's Cora?" I asked, thinking with pity of her, for she had been a tall, delicate, lovely girl, too pretty to think of anything but marriage. He had been the successful candidate among many admirers.

"That's something—truth is," he said then, "I thought I'd drop in and—"

He was so suddenly at a loss for words that I looked up. "Is she here?" I asked.

"She's in Chicago," he said. "She's—well, she's not alone."

I didn't know what he meant, still. "You have children?" I asked, carefully. Yes, they had a child, a girl.

"That's what I want to know," he said then, rapidly. "She has the kid with her—out there—and I won't have it. Now, I don't want anything public, of course. I don't want to go to a court, or anything like that. But what I want to know is this—you seem to be doing this kind of thing—can't I tell her that she has to let me have the child? She says, since I'm sick, she has the right—that's why she got sick of me—"

He looked so upright and healthy standing there in his spick and span uniform that it seemed impossible he was really "sick," marked with death. He looked so calm in his Nordic repression that one could not believe the thing he had just said.

Cora had been with him for a year. Things were rotten for her, of course, during the time. She'd taken a course and been a technician during the war. She finally got a job in a hospital. "She's a peach in looks, of course. . . ." A man had become interested in her, and it ended in their going together to Chicago, where she had now been for over a year.

"Folks think they're married," he ended, and added, "That's what they will do, in the end. But I want the kid. That's why I'm holding back. She's getting the divorce." He asked, abruptly, "Now, what I want to know is, where I can get a good lawyer to settle about the kid for me . . . when I get well. . . ."

I wanted to say how "rotten" it was to leave a sick

man, just pulling back to health, and to let him take the social burden of infidelity. But he forestalled me. "I know it looks rotten," he said. "But you know Cora . . . she always was a great 'home girl'—this isn't the life for her . . . with me. . . ."

I heard of Cora again, when the dean of our college, coming to our city for some work he was doing, telephoned to me to lunch with him. It was, of course, thrilling to meet him. It was like seeing a mirror of long ago, reflecting an image of one's self that one had thought faded away.

He was grayer, more round-shouldered. He was harassed with the burden of the modern college; there were new courses introduced and new kinds of students coming to take them. "Even the Jewish girls," he smiled, "aren't quiet and shy any longer. They aren't the type we had when you came. They're bright, smart. They are, I suppose, as Nordic as possible," and he smiled again, his gentle, self-depreciatory smile, for he carried an ancient "Nordic" name.

All girls he knew now were cocksure and overdressed and very difficult to teach anything. They dressed too extravagantly and lived too extravagantly. They were too friendly with the boys. The dean of women could not stop their drinking, not even their smoking, except in college affairs directly under her supervision. They were not respectful. "They have, in short, no reverence, I suppose," he summarized.

He had been "old-fashioned" when I was a student. He was opposed to the suffrage, and once overwhelmed a group of us, heatedly discussing it among ourselves in a deserted classroom, by coming in, standing listening and then smiling broadly and kindly, but crush-ingly, "Am I interrupting—gentlemen?" He had been opposed to divorce, to women entering the economic field. He was proud of me, but he did not quite approve of me yet, "sitting in an office, with my dear little babies at home." But, even in his wildest fancy, he had not thought of a young girlhood such as this which was arising and growing into the womanhood of the country now. "What sort of mothers will they make?" he asked, genuinely aghast.

And then he told me gossip of old classmates, and said, "Do you recall Cora Delman? Sweet young thing she was! She called at the college—she's married again—sad—a tragedy. . . . Poor Cora. Now, there was a home girl for you!"

Cora was the ideal of the young girlhood I knew. I listened as he told me of her courage, how she had had to go to work, her husband was unfaithful—and then he said, "this happiness at last." She had found a home at last.

I could not be troubled with him about the "new girl." I remembered the horror with which my people had heard that I wanted to go away, alone, to New York. I could not forget the words that were said to me when I had married not according to the wishes of my elders and guardians, but for love. I did not think that my own life was a shame to the country. And other women were doing really splendid things, great things of national importance, and many of them had been the stormy petrels of their communities, the "comic subjects" of the American press.

Even the flapper, when she arrived, though she was startling, was, at least, capable. She asked no one to offer a shoulder for her to lean upon. And I knew, among the young women of my own acquaintance, that underneath the fizz was good strong wine.

Some of our own staff wore their hair cut, rouged a little, even at the office, wore short dresses, smoked (that, too, at the office), lived "bachelor" fashion far from home, entertained their men friends in their apartments. But they were all right. They were as clean, as valuable, as the girls I had known in my youth. None had been more sheltered than those girls I had known in orthodox Jewish homes, where not even a strange Gentile had been allowed to enter. Yet there had been dark tragedies; girls had broken away and had been lost. One girl I had known had gone out with a man to a dance, had stayed out until one o'clock, was reprimanded by her father, who publicly slapped her face before her friends. That girl's "good name" was smirched forever thereafter. These girls now would not permit themselves to be reprimanded; they were capable enough, however, to take care of their own "good names." They were strong. If they presented a certain absurdity in their strength, it was only that of little boys who assert that they are soldiers. They "*will* be soldiers," they mean. But their will makes the reality, eventually. I could not be afraid or ashamed, of the women to-day.

XXIX

ON my calender there were written down, one morning, three engagements, and following them a short query. "Pageant Tuesday?" The engagements were, in order, with Mrs. Hindman, with Sam, the superintendent and janitor of our building, and with an unknown person I did not remember by the name put down—Humphrey. The query was something I asked myself, but which I was almost certain would be answered, "No."

Mrs. Hindman came in with her two youngest children, the baby still with eyes running, and the poor little body covered with the sores of a children's disease due to deficient diet and poor care. She would not send her child, as we were urging, to a hospital, and she had not the mental capacity to understand how to care for it herself or the will capacity to continue that care, had she begun to undertake it. The older child, just past two, clung to her skirts with dirty, bony little hands, its nose running with the perpetual cold from which it seemed to suffer. She wiped its nose on her apron, put the infant on the floor, and began, "I can't send my baby to the hospital, Missis. My man he fights wid me enough, and should of I go and send my baby away, it would be the end for sure. It ain't I ain't intrusted, Missis. If I work myself to the bone he says it's nothing. He says—" Mrs. Hindman did not get along with her husband. He was, I knew, a big, slow, really kind, but utterly stupid, workman who had married too young, had too large a family and could not understand even how to buck his wife up. The flabby, big-bosomed woman whose busts heaved as she began to cry now, looked at least forty. She was in fact twenty-nine years old. Yet her entire work in life was to take care of five children and to keep a little house neat and tidy. I knew women working who went to the mills, whose children were well-kept, and their houses attractive and orderly. This woman could not do the simple job her husband asked of her—simply care for home and offspring. She had not the mental equipment.

"You'll have to buck up," was all I could tell her. "Mr. Hindman is a good husband. He brings you his wages. He treats you kindly, Miss Fairland says. Now, the baby, there, ought to have a bath every day, and he must have barley-water three times a day, in clean, absolutely clean—"

She spread out her hands in a gesture of utter despair. "I can't do it," she cried out then. She seemed like a great lump of clay, trying to look as if it had the shape of a human, and her voice, thick, with its stupid, halting, speech, seemed like the speech of a woman not really completely fashioned. Through the window of my office door I could see the handsome figure of Mrs. Norton, her fine head; beside her stood Miss Fairland, slight, flat-busted, straight as a young boy, but with all the delicate beauty of the newest womanhood, athletic, ascetic, unafraid. This woman sobbing at my desk was almost revolting. No wonder Miss Fairland had been completely discouraged by her case, I thought. For two months, she had tried to fire some of her own vital life, her desire to *do* into Mrs. Hindman. She might as well have tried to bring life into a mass of dough. The baby must have care, however. The older child looked quite dreadful, too.

I was obliged to wait until Mrs. Hindman's heavy sobs quieted down, and then until the two children, whose wails rose too, were taken out by our nurse to be cared for a little while.

"Now, Mrs. Hindman," I said, speaking to her carefully, trying to think how to reach into her mind, "I know that you can take care of the children, and the house, too. We have, at least, a hundred mothers in the mills around here who have as many children as you. Lots of them are working out, besides. And they keep their babies clean, and their houses are neat. Their husbands don't have anything to complain about. Why," I said then, trying to make her see that she must brace up for the sake of her responsibility to the two sick children we wanted her to care for properly, "I have children myself. I go out to work. I used to take care of my home and my babies myself, almost all alone, when I first went to my office."

Her big, almost absolutely empty face became filled with a dull flare of expression: "You're a married missis, Missis?"

Of course, every one of our staff was called "Missis" by the people with whom we worked. Was I a married "missis"? I nodded, and said, "I have children, too, just like you."

"Your man lets you go out to work?" she asked. I had fallen in her estimation, but I had done something no one else had been able to do in the office. I had come near, at last, to her slow, almost motionless mind.

I smiled and waited for her to speak further. "If you're a married missis," she said, and she came closer, "if you're a married missis, then—"

Very slowly, with the brutality of the peasant, she told me the story then. Her husband did not have in her a wife; he was destroying her with a terrible lust, spending himself as another man would spend rage on a helpless animal without protection. "I can't do my work," she said, dully. "Maybe if he hits me sometimes, like the other mans do, it would be all right. But I can't do my work. I wisht I was dead, Missis."

Mrs. Norton, coming in later, after Mrs. Hindman had gone, looked at the memorandum I held out to her: "Psychiatric examination for Mr. Hindman. Summer camp for Mrs. Hindman and the children?" She shook her gray head. "He won't let her, I guess. I thought there must be something there! What is it? Psychopathic case?"

"We'd better ask the hospital to report," I evaded. What right had we to say what was the story in this marriage? Here was a good man, a good father, a conscientious provider. Here was a mother who stayed at home, did not waste her husband's wages in pleasure, was faithful to him, bore him children—who, at his wish, did not even go out to work.

There was nothing we could do for her, if he refused to let her go away, for the three older children would, of course, need care at home. There was nothing we could say to him; she was not a sick woman. He simply was making it impossible for her to be a human being, because he had the right to do what he wished, with his wife.

I was glad to look at the second memorandum on the calendar and to see that Sam was coming in. Sam was a Hungarian Jew; usually he was tipsy. But he was wholesome, quarrelsome, disobedient and utterly devoted to the work.

He came in with his glasses at the tip of his reddened nose, as usual, his overalls dusty with ashes, and a discontented expression in his face. "Furnace isn't working again," he announced.

I waited. Sam always began with a grievance, whether he wished to speak of the weather, the state of politics (he was a Socialist), or the need for a new fender.

"You think it's too warm for the weather?" he inquired.

"It is warm for late April," I admitted.

"I been thinking," he said, "it's so warm, maybe we might let the furnace go out a day or so early, not wait till May 15?"

Then, suddenly, as if the thought had just occurred to him, he added, "I wanted to know, they's a meeting of Local 19 to-morrow, and then we thought we'd have a outing on Sunday. They ast me on the committee, but bein's as the furnace needs attenshun, of course I said no, it ain't possible. It ain't possible, for certain." He peered over his glasses at me.

"You think we ought to have the furnace going?" I asked him.

"It could go out, and we'd save four days' coal," he said.

"You're boss of the furnace," I answered. "The office is closed Sunday. Mrs. Norton and I can light the grate if we come in for a while."

"Oh, Mrs. Morton, I love you like a mother!" exclaimed Sam, "honest so Help me God, I do. I can take that—"

But there was some one at the door, waiting to come in, a very tall, very trig and extraordinarily smartly dressed girl with the prettiest hair, the brightest hazel eyes and the most scarlet mouth in the world. This was a strange sight in our office. Even board members and "volunteers" dressed soberly when they came to us.

"Miss Humphreys," she said. "Of the *Record.*" That explained the "Humphreys" written on my calendar.

It had happened to me. I was being interviewed. Did I feel elated? To be sure, I did. The thought flashed through my mind: "I'll have to call up and tell him!" By "him" I meant, of course, my husband. I would tell him that "Sam" had said he "loved me like a mother"—me, fifteen or twenty years younger than himself. Then I'd break in on his laugh and tell him I had been interviewed. Wouldn't the children be interested?

There flashed across my mind a memory of something I had heard long ago—years ago. It was what Mrs. Rahm's nephew had told me newspaper women must be: "brassy." This pretty reporter looked like a débutante just ready for a matinée, perhaps a little too much dressed for the part.

She wanted to know "how it felt to run an organization like this, and if she could have a 'story' or two, and if having children was a handicap to a woman." She smiled, and she was like a small boy when she smiled. "It's for the women's page," she told me. "I think I'd better tell you we *don't* believe, in our paper—that is, for publication—that a woman can have a job and a husband and be married without making a mess of things. But," she assured me, "I'll quote what *you* say exactly, and then I'll have what, well, what Mrs. Carstairs says, in rebuttal, as we used to say at college debates." Her college had been Smith, she told me when I asked. Mrs. Carstairs was the president of a local women's club, and opposed to women "with careers."

What did one say, when one was asked to evaluate one's life, to defend it, so to speak?

Mrs. Carstairs would feel that a woman like Mrs. Hindman, in her sphere, was living out a natural law, that she must endure whatever hardship came with it. She would feel, on the other hand, that whatever limitations or hardships a woman like myself encountered were due to the fact that we had *broken* the natural law.

She said, I knew, that the place of women was in the home, that only the selfish, self-indulgent woman, went out of it, to seek her pleasure. Was my job, I asked myself, what I would have done for pleasure? In my desk, at home, stood my typewriter. Under it lay a sheaf of papers. That was a book I had begun four years ago. I had not looked at it since I first "went out to work." I did not cook, sew, scrub, now, it is true. I earned money away from my home. But I had put away my dreams, my pleasure, to do this work that earned money. Mrs. Carstairs did not cook, sew or care for her children. Her children were grown up, but her servants had done her work from the very moment she was born. Her servants were paid with money she had inherited, mine with money my husband and I earned. She spent her time doing work in which only her wealth and her emotional needs gave her a right to enter (if there is such a right when one enters into the lives of others). I did the same work that she did, and I did it after long training and experience. She did her work when she chose and dropped it when it wearied her—when she wished to go to Europe or to

Florida, to have a "rest cure" or to give a dinner. I did my work as I lived, day by day, faithfully, unceasingly, and, even when I was away on a holiday, I never forgot the human problems into which my position had given me entrance and which it was my job to solve.

Mrs. Carstairs did social work, giving up social pleasures for the time devoted to it—and that was fine. But I did it, giving up the one thing I wished to do, to write.

The only difference between us was that I was trained, experienced and paid, for my work; she was untrained, inexperienced and unpaid, in the same work.

Did that make my work ignoble? I thought not. I could not feel less worthy, even when placed side by side, to be measured, with Mrs. Carstairs. I felt my children received something from me which she did not give hers: the example of a citizen fulfilling an obligation steadily, intelligently. After all, sporadic charity is kind, but it is not the material by which this world we live in is built. Work is.

I gave Miss Humphreys her "story," but, long after she had gone, I sat in my office thinking it over for myself, thinking over much that I had not so much as thought of telling the pretty reporter.

I had chosen to be a mother doing social work, rather than a mother doing "home-building," as the new phrase put it. I did so because I did social work better, and it paid. I did not feel one was finer, greater work than the other. Mine was more interesting to me, it is true. But my interests happened to be communal, not domestic, that was all.

As I saw my life, it would go on in a long lane of days and of years, through which I would live much as

I was living now. I would make my place more secure in my profession. Perhaps there might be another organization which I would direct, but the work would not be much different. After all, I had specialized, when I was a student in social work, in community work, and even in the store my activities had been group activities, rather than commercial. Some day I would find our children grown up, and I would be an old woman.

What would I think of life then?

I would not, like my mother, have a sublime faith that I had lived according to a vision, a vision greater than she could understand but unaltering and holy. I did not even believe that my work was faultless, that it was an ultimate answer to the social problems we met. Social work was simply a way of earning a living. As I continued in it, I knew more clearly, all the time, that we were simply putting patches on life, that the people who came to us for medical treatment, for group play and for advice in the difficulties of their lives were not really changed by what we did. They were, for that matter, only the smallest fraction of the very "neighborhood" in which we worked. We sent the sick mother away, to be healed of tuberculosis. But we could not change the conditions that gave her tuberculosis and which would, in turn, bring the disease to her children. We found a man work and so provided bread for his family, but we could not change the conditions that left him, untrained, sickly, unprepared to provide even for himself, and yet assuming the burden of a family: we could not give him vitality, education, a good heredity, a new youth with which to begin anew. We had classes and playgrounds for the children, but we could not give them proper homes and the birthright of childhood. We could not even provide a place in which youth was protected. We could just put patches on lives.

My mother lived simply. She lit her candles on Friday night, and she felt she served God in their lighting. She cooked the holiday meals and prepared them for honoring Him. She saved, denied herself even things she needed, to send her children to study Hebrew, that they might speak the language of her God. She gave, from her slender purse, to the poor and fed His children.

I gave my daily work, my life, to serving the poor, too. But I gave it as my job. There was no radiance in it. Fifteen years before, I had come as a young student to listen to a new gospel of service—social work. I had felt heartsick because rules and reasons were preached, instead of love and vision. Now I was grateful for rules that had been proven safe and tried, safe to use with the four thousand lives which we influenced from our offices. It is only in one's own life that one can dare to experiment.

Once I had thought of each person one would serve as a friend one would make, for how would one dare to enter into the plan of a whole life to change it in the least direction, unless one came with the one excuse of friendship? I had been appalled when first I saw "cases" discussed in charity organization staff meetings. But now I knew I could never do my work, unless it was done swiftly, impersonally, as a surgeon does his. Even in the groups we had coming every week, it was the group—and seldom the individuals in it—that was our interest. Perhaps the younger members of my staff, those doing the "case work" and the "club work" had friends among their people. I had not. I was there to see that each staff worker did her job, that the whole place "functioned." I was a mind with a special faculty in it stressed, a mind that planned our work and that had the gift of directing the work of others.

My work was, to me, a job to be done, with the greatest number of people helped by our two treasuries—"time" and "budget."

The men and women I knew spoke simply of their work as a matter in which the raising of money and "adequate staffing" were the essentials. Or perhaps sometimes it was the "lack of coöperation" of the sick and the poor, who would not do as the social worker told them to do. That wasted time and money.

I had learned now that it was not heartlessness that made this so, but the real desire to help, to bring results. One had so little with which to work, and so many came to be helped. One must be careful of money, of time, as a mother must stretch the income in her own small home, arrange her day in it, to allow her to do each essential task for all the children in it.

Only young students, not yet in the work, spoke of the "ideal" of it. Social work I had seen grow in fifteen years from an experiment in which anything (if only one wanted to "do good") was admitted as a qualification, to a profession with specialists, with experts. I did not think less of it for that. Its experts still were ill-paid, though now they gave more time to their training. Its workers were still sectarian, though now they met at conferences with various religious groups and denominations conferring.

Its workers did not speak of ideals, but there was one, limited by creed, race, background. Social workers now knew that their profession was not one to unite all mankind, except as a common search united them. But that search was definitely limited. There were also the boards to please.

But I knew ministers, too, were harassed by trustees. They submitted to their boards, expressed opinions or withheld them, because they must shield their children and hold their jobs. Their jobs, too, had become work for administrators, orators, young men who "understood how to interest the public" and who had to belong to a particular religious sect, in addition, of course.

They were trained for their work as they would have learned to do masonry—to receive a salary, not to preach the wonder and beauty of Jesus.

We social workers were trained for our work, too, to please the boards who paid our salaries—not to prove that mankind feels each of us is his brother's keeper.

I understood it all. And I understood it without bitterness.

For, after all, there were a hundred thousand cases treated each year by the agencies in our city. A hundred thousand lives were "helped"—in what degree one could not say. But they were made happier in some degree. What did it matter what limitations were found among the people who accomplished this—so long as the work was done?

My own board was a pleasant one. Elsa Harmon was my staunch friend on it. The one member with whom I worked most closely was friendly and amenable to suggestions. She was a Christian, but her husband had been a Jew and had left her his money. Her children were a strange medley of faiths: Protestant, Christian Science, Catholic. The daughters were "Scientists"; her elder son a Presbyterian, like his wife.

Their father had been an orthodox German Jew from Frankfort. He had lost his religion in this country, but he had not lost his discomfort with other faiths. In spite of their affection for each other, the difference in their faiths had clouded their lives. "Poor Felix," she always said, speaking of him.

Her youngest son owned a small stock company. It was because of him that there faced me on my calendar, the morning Miss Humphreys called, the phrase: "Pageant Tuesday?" He had worked indefatigably to put it across. He had quantities of vivacity and so much energy that it simply spilled over. He could not possibly have known how Hebraic he was with his bustling, noisy, cheerful manner, his neat little paunch protruding from under his single-button coat, where a great gold cross hung solidly.

It had been the wish of his mother to bring the Jewish and Polish groups together. We found it impossible, of course. If social workers divided themselves, choosing "their own religion" to work with, the groups we reached were as definite in their distinctions. They would not "mingle."

"But we must bring them together," my co-worker fretted. She could not see that the sympathetic union between diverse racial groups had not been accomplished in her own life, where love was the amalgam. She was spending $5,000 a year and a great part of her time, to do something which was impossible, which would only make unhappiness, if it were accomplished. She would not acknowledge that this interracial understanding is one for the individual to find. "We cannot do this," we told her. "The parents of the young people object to their coming together. The Jewish parents and the Polish alike."

"But that is rather nonsense," she said. She wanted to be home with her grandchildren, to read and to rest. But she spent hours at the settlement house, attended "Americanization meetings," got up "affairs"—to bring about a purpose which would have no social good. Races do not become friends by the will of others, but by their own, and not through groups, but through individuals in each group. Can one force friendships—even by money?

But she did not feel apologetic; she did not feel that she was accountable for the purpose to which she dedicated her time, her money or her sympathies. She was not being paid for the work she did. I was being paid. I was paid to do a job as my board wished. It was work with the poor, but it was their work I did.

For all that, I would not have chosen another; since I could not hope to earn my living by writing about people, I preferred to earn it by working with them. I did not think of myself as a brilliant success (I had no cause to), nor as a visionary idealist. But I was glad my job gave me the chance to help other people, and I knew that, even if others gave the money for social work, it was we, the workers, who made it possible. We gave our work at small salaries, living poorly, that it might be done. I knew that I could have earned $5,000 a year, if I had wished to leave social work. I knew it because I had been offered a post and had turned it down. Mrs. Carstairs, if she lost her money, would be left without a job. I had mine, waiting for me to take, whenever I chose to do it, in either of two fields. In each of them I could do my work not only as well as a woman who had no children, but as well as most men qualified for the positions I, too, could fill.

XXX

TO set the machinery of a hundred groups in motion, to keep them going, to oversee the seven-day activities which involved the lives of a thousand people, to plan with Mrs. Norton our medical work and with the play leader our recreational work, was a sufficient job. It had become increasingly hard to do, I was finding, if I were to have time enough at home.

That matter of giving more time to the children —how was I to settle it?

I was troubled—was I growing "stale" in my job? My husband spoke to me of taking a rest, of going away with him and the children for a "long summer" of three months. But that was impossible. It could not be done. I had stayed away when our youngest son was born, and it took months to get threads back into order, to unsnarl confusions that had arisen with the central authority gone.

Then I thought of a solution.

There was only one thing to do. I must find an exceptionally capable woman, an unusually qualified woman, qualified in background and in education and personality as well, to take charge of my home. She'd have to give my children that "time" which I was finding it almost beyond my strength, just now, to cut from my work.

I found her soon, a college woman with a little baby

son. Our home was large, roomy, sunny, and it had a big garden. It was just the place for a mother with a child, and she the very person for it. My husband, seeing her, thought her intelligent, but he hesitated: "She's not candid," he put it.

But she seemed, on the second interview, to be just sufficiently reticent. She had letters, introductions, from friends. She had been a high school teacher, had married late, was a widow now. She seemed just right.

It worked out as an ideal arrangement should. Our daughter was delighted with the new member of our home, never tired of hearing the woman tell about her college, about her dead husband. The baby was a plaything to Little Maid. She now had some one at home who had time to "make her feel she was important" in the home. I confess, sometimes I felt a little envy; I had not thought I would. I remembered my closeness to my own mother. I should have liked to have Little Maid tell me all the long stories she brought to my housekeeper. I should have liked to light in her eyes the laughter and the pleasure the nice woman with us called out. But that was absurd. It was on a par with the young mother in charge of our statistical department who mourned because her baby, when she came home in the evening, wept to go back to "Mama," the nurse who took care of him all day. I knew that, underneath all the changing friendships and allegiances, Little Maid was deeply mine.

Brother was no problem. He was busy and happy in his school.

Only our small son was solemn and quiet, as always. I knew it would take a bit to win him. The new housekeeper was charming enough to do so in time. I would not, I decided, speak to her, because it would be better if he won his way into her heart of his own shy accord.

One day I had been particularly busy. Mike Brown, one of our "boys," had gotten into trouble, and his mother came to us to ask our help. He'd broken into a store, and stolen some things, had been arrested and seemed to be in a pretty bad fix. We had to arrange to attend Mike's hearing, to send a worker up to "speak for him" and to promise to keep him under our eyes. Our milk station for the summer had just been opened and there was the usual rush of "strangers" who pushed "our own" mothers at the door. The little children were to be taken to the zoo that Saturday, and came with cards from their mothers, holding permission for the excursion.

In the afternoon we gave a historical pageant, with two hundred children taking part in it, the older boys and girls dressed in adult costumes, the littler ones in their own, and all in the dress of their native lands. How delighted the mothers were, when they came in, to see it! This was their own, and the "teachers" had thought so much of it that they had made a "whole show out of it," as one boy proudly expressed it.

That was what I wanted them to feel. I was pleased because the whole thing had been written and coached by two young students from the neighborhood, and the music had been taught the boys and girls by one of the men who lived near the House. I had taught the children of the people who came to us that their people had a voice, that they had something lovely to tell us here in America.

I came into the house earlier that afternoon than usual. I opened the door, and heard laughter, a hum of cooing. Through the window, I saw my daughter sitting with my housekeeper beside the baby's chair, playing with him. The child was adorable and rosy. It looked cuddly and sleepy, and my daughter was holding one slender forefinger for his wavering chubby hand to catch. I could not help smiling at the picture.

In order not to disturb them, before I re-dressed I went through the side door and into the study where I worked at home. There, in a corner, beside the chair where I sat, stood a tiny figure, forlorn, alone, very quiet in the first dusk. It was my little son, slight, fair, so fragile. He had one small grubby hand on the arm of my chair and was staring out of the window, alone.

Something clutched my heart, something intuitive and violent. I went out rapidly and came in upon that other group. My housekeeper rose, charming, amiable, as usual. She helped me with my hat, she laughed her pleasant, cheerful laugh. "So glad you could come home early!" she said. "We've been playing with baby!"

My little daughter looked at the baby, at my housekeeper, with adoration.

"Isn't Sonny well?" I asked, casually.

"Sonny?" repeated my daughter. "Oh, he's up in the library, somewhere. He hasn't been down here at all."

My housekeeper drew smooth brows together. "He's such a moody little fellow," she said, pleasantly. "I think they rather spoiled him at the kindergarten. He needs—well, discipline."

I sat with my hands in my lap. I have had children who were brought in to me psychoanalyzed, studied, and then I have helped plan their whole lives to be built as the doctor found for their best happiness.

"I don't think they spoiled him at the kindergarten," I replied. "I think, though, that he misses the friendly affection he used to have there," and I looked directly at her.

My housekeeper continued smiling. "Oh, it's not that," she replied. "Forgive me, but this one child of all your children seems to—well, Jewish—he seems to need a lot of petting, as Jewish children do. Now, this big girl, here, and Brother, do not crave it."

Little Maid was tall for her age. She looked very lovely in the dark light of evening, with her hair a halo about her head. She looked lovely and remote. Her glance went, now, not to me, but to the strange woman in my home. It went to her with understanding—and left out, not only me, but her brother. Little Maid was a stranger to me and to her brother. It was this woman, who was her friend, who was in the circle of her sympathy.

It startled me to realize it.

"I saw Son upstairs in my study," I said. "He was alone there. Does he often go off alone, and spend the afternoons there?"

My housekeeper frowned. "We ask him to stay here with us, and play, with baby and us," she said almost sharply. "But he will go off."

I nodded and changed the subject. But I stopped on my way up, and found my study empty. My little boy was in his room when I looked there, and there, alone again, he was playing with his toys very quietly.

Thereafter, I managed to come home at various times. I wanted to see what was happening to my baby. My daughter was close to my housekeeper and was receiving from her friendship and real leadership, valuable leadership, for she was a very intelligent woman. My elder boy was outdoors with the play group that was part of his school; he was cared for until he came home for supper, and even on Saturdays. Only my small son was always alone. He was as lonely as if he were an orphan, while the little orphan in our house received the affection and attention not alone of his mother—but of my daughter.

My other two children had fitted in, without a real flaw, with my plans. They required education, play, health, supervision—occasionally given to keep the machinery of their busy little lives smoothly running. All that I had been able to arrange for them. Even the companionship my daughter needed I had been able to buy for her, through my work.

Little Maid and Brother were average, usual, healthy children.

This baby of ours, though, seemed to need something more. He needed love. He was the "different child," just as I had been in my home, in my mother's life, and he had something besides, a real gift, perhaps, we sometimes thought, a genius. Whatever it was—small or little, this gift of his, evanescent, or with promise of growing into a treasure to which he could devote his life—this five-year-old of ours did not fit into the usual plans, the usual methods, which could be used for other children. At kindergarten he was absorbed, intense, about his work. But he played *by himself*. The one person to whom he seemed able to open that quiet little heart of his was—myself. I had been attending "child conferences," reading books on children, hearing "reports" and "cases." This was my own.

There are people, still, who believe that all children

come to be put through a common mold. Those who understand know better now. There are people who believe a child has no more personality than a bright mirror held up to the adults about him. But, of course, I knew better. I understood this small son of mine. He needed what my daughter had sought—time given to him individually.

I wanted to talk it over with my husband. But I felt shy. Suddenly, I felt constrained. We discussed the children's schooling, their health, the "mechanics" of their life, so to speak. But this?

Would he feel it my fault if I told him? Was it not my fault? It was well enough to speak of the equality of man and wife, in every way. But I knew that, in one thing, they were not equal, and that was in their responsibility to their children. Whichever way the burden was divided in every other respect, the weight of the children's lives *had* to be placed, always, on the mother's side, in addition. She could not have lived and been a woman, with things otherwise. Her "rights," her opportunities were not "equal rights," equal opportunities, but "additional ones," with the first that of assuming responsibility for her children.

Of course I did not tell that to my husband, nor would he admit it. But it is so. It was not he who left his office to see if our daughter's fever was lower when she was ill: it was I who always left mine. It was not he who was called up when our big, husky boy had his arm broken: it was my office that was called up. It was not he who had seen that hunger in our baby's eyes. This I did not ask for, when I set out to follow the profession for which my husband and I had been trained alike, and which we both practiced. This was my part, as the immemorial job of all mothers.

After dinner that evening, I tried to tell my husband of it: "Do you think Son is looking well?"

He looked quickly and apprehensively toward the little figure. "He's so quiet," he said at once.

"He's always quiet," replied our housekeeper.

Our small son came over, stood stood beside his father and said nothing.

"Are you well, old man?" asked his father, lifting him to his knee.

Two gray eyes were lifted to him, but no answer came. "He's so quiet," I fretted. I glanced quickly at the housekeeper; her level brows were drawn close together. She looked, what she was, capable, intelligent, and—I saw it—annoyed with the little boy who was demanding something that would destroy the studied routine of our home. He was not fitting into the skillfully run machine that she so effectively made of our home.

"Don't be a sissy, now," called out my older son. "Come on, Broth!"

A pale pink came to the little boy's cheek. He climbed down at once and went over to his brother's side. "It's intrusting," he said listlessly, watching the quick, absorbed movements of his brother, putting together a meccano.

"Would you like a meccano?" my husband asked, coming over to them.

The pale flush poured over the little face again. "I wisht I had one," he said. "Would you show me how to make a house, dad?"

My husband laughed ruefully: "Not for some time, little man. I'm going away for a month. Maybe Brother will?"

Our elder boy raised eyes as big and brilliant as

pansies. "Ah, dad, don't say that! Broth is such a baby—he's such a poke—always asking why!"

From the table came the voice of our housekeeper: "I'm afraid he should be asleep, Doctor." She lifted our little boy up and took him away. In the nursery there followed soon that familiar quiet; my small son was asleep. But from another room I heard giggles, cooing, a gurgle. My housekeeper was putting her child to sleep, they were having playtime together. "Oh, you cunningest—!" came my daughter's voice.

I could see the big gray eyes of my small son turned, as he had looked without speaking, at his father, the brief light, the color, that came when he asked, "Would you show me?" And then the obedient, utterly obedient little, "Good night, moth. Good night, dad," as he was put to bed—put away to bed.

I wanted to speak of this, now, to my husband. But a telephone call changed my plans. I had a meeting to attend.

"Will you come for me after the meeting?" I asked, hastily leaving. "We can walk home together."

We could talk then. He had made a brilliant success recently; he had not sent me clippings, but I had heard of it from friends. I had meant to speak to him of it, but it slipped my mind, somehow. I would speak to him of it when we walked home, I promised myself. I'd talk to him, and tell him why I was so worried about Sonny.

But when he came we walked along in silence. "Things going well?" he asked, drawing my arm closer. Things were not going well. My board wanted to cut the budget, to "reduce." I was worried about our summer camp. Mrs. Norton was leaving for the West, and I knew it would be hard to replace her. I was so tired. Was I, I wondered often now, really going stale?

I was silent, though. Why should I burden him with my difficulties?

Then I remembered his own good fortune. "I think it was splendid about that Carewe case," I said. "Why didn't you tell me?"

"Oh, that's just the day's job," he replied, dismissing it.

We walked on in silence again. His work took him away for weeks sometimes. Often, it would have been impossible for us even to tell each other what we did then. We seemed so far apart, miles apart. Sometimes, when I thought of him in his absence, it seemed he was near me, close at my side. But when we were together we seemed to be so far apart.

Then, suddenly, his hand went out, and mine, too. We walked hand in hand in the darkness. We walked miles, not home, but through the park, in the starlight. He took me in his arms and kissed me. We had not grown apart. Only life, work, busy years had come between us.

It will not be true to say it was my work alone that had done so. I have friends whose husbands must be away for long periods of time and who are close to their men despite absences. I know men who live with their wives day by day without separation, and they do not love one another.

We were becoming separated not by the fact that we worked apart, but by the press of life. Our outside interests were different. But when we came together, we were close, lovers as always; that which united us was vital as when first we disclosed our minds and our spirits to each other, as young man and wife.

Walking home, at last, I told him about my worry over Sonny. "He must be ill," he said. "He's such a quiet little chap one doesn't realize his unhappiness. He doesn't intrude even with that on any one. I wish he were more obstreperous!"

And then, with my hand in his, I said, "Couldn't you work at home more? Can't we arrange to have more time with the children, in our home, than we do? This isn't the way to live."

He stood waiting a moment in his characteristic attitude, and then he replied, "This business of each seeking his career whither it leadeth him is funny. Mine is pointing to New York. I've been asked to come there the first of October, if I decide to accept. I thought I might make it a part-time thing, spending part of each month here, part time in New York."

In the dark came to me the oval of my son's little face, the halo of curls about my daughter's head, the bright indifference of our older boy's glance as his brother stood beside him.

I thought of the time, eight years before, when I had seen a career opening to me in New York, in literature, and I had given it up without a question to go where my husband's work called. I thought of those dreary years that followed. How often I had remembered them and had told myself I would never do again what I did then—give up my opportunity for the sake of my husband. It was not for his best happiness, nor for mine, to do so.

But I had not Sonny to think of then.

"Take it," I said to my husband. "I'll go to New York, too."

"You'd give up your work here?" he asked.

I nodded. "One has to decide. I can't endure having Sonny hungry for love. He must have one of us —to live with him for a time. And, I guess, I must have you."

My resignation was sent in to take effect at the end of the summer, when a new worker could readily be found to succeed me.

But it was not until weeks later that my husband said, holding me close, "Suppose I had asked something of you, I wonder what you would have said?"

I waited, and he explained: "Suppose I had said I wanted our family moved to New York, even if you stayed here at your work. Had I not the right— equal with your own—to have our children with me, wherever I chose to be, just as you have that right? You would have done the communting then!"

I laughed. But in New York I was soon to find that there were women, working in the city, whose husbands kept the children with them, while the mothers did "commute" to their jobs. And the children were healthy, well and thoroughly happy. The normal child fitted in with anything that gave him play, food, care. It was only the unusual child that made a problem.

XXXI

NEW YORK was like a great jewel for me to hold, like a garden to enjoy. All my life before, there had been things to do. Now there was no need for me to do anything at all but give myself to my children and to rest, to play if I wished. That time I had thought of as incredibly far away was here. My husband's salary was modest, but it easily covered our needs and provided for the plans we made of our children. We learned what we had scorned to know before, and what rather embarrassed us to find out, that it is pleasant to be free of the immediate bondage to money. We could buy books, pictures in good reproductions. I came home one day, and there, in the corner where I always sat to read, stood that desk I had said we'd buy "if we could afford it some day."

My husband and I took one evening for ourselves, and we went on the Hudson, in one of the boats that made the trip up the river. All along the other shore lights were twinkling in houses in New Jersey. Great ships passed in peaceful majesty along the side of our own. The sounds of voices came to us like thin bells ringing. Young people on deck were sitting close together or dancing to the music. Presently the lights thinned; we were far up the Hudson now. The stars came out in a glory. My husband put out his hand and brushed back my hair from my forehead in the gesture I love. "Are you sorry you came here?" he asked.

"For the river trip?" I asked in return, willfully misunderstanding.

"To New York," he answered, and leaned forward to see my face.

"I love it here," I answered truly. I did, indeed, love New York, with Broadway like a long lane of laughter and Fifth Avenue stretching in solemn beauty beside the park. Before we had been so poor here; I had not even had time to look into the windows to see what was happening in the bright rooms beyond. Now the time was mine. "Just to be happy in—and to write," said my husband.

I shook my head. "Not yet," I answered. One must think out one's life before one can write. I did not want to think, but simply to be happy.

We did not speak as we sat there, but together watched the people passing to and fro, the glitter of the water beneath us. We sat in the crowning light of the big stars. And my husband's fingers closed over mine, as he said, "Little Boy, we've waited sixteen years—they've been—not easy. Thank you—for everything."

My eyes felt hot, stingingly hot, a moment. I lifted his hand to my cheek and could not answer. Had I not everything to thank him for? For love, for my children, for understanding, for that rarest thing of all, comradeship? I could not answer, but let my hand lie closer in his encircling fingers, as we looked at one another. One reads of the love of youth, of the dramatic crisis of marriage. The darkness of human tragedies make a "story." But the happy marriages have no chroniclers. They are not made up of high lights, of crashing climaxes. They grow like great trees, deep-rooted, year after year, quietly. There was no need for me to say anything to my husband. It was enough that, with our children growing up, with the new world calling to each of us, we still were to one another what we had first found we must be; friends for all life long, friends first, and then lovers, too.

The doctor in New York said that Sonny was well, but that he was starved for affection. He was like the children in the orphan asylums. They come to visitors and cling to skirts and fingers of kind-faced people. That is how Sonny clung to us that summer. I took my vacation early, my husband with me. We did not send the children to camp, but went away together.

I found a family. I had thought I knew them. They were, actually, strangers to me. My second son would never be close to me. His nature was developed into strength and utter independence. He was fond of me, adored me. But he was complete in himself; he did not require family ties.

For our small son I found a kindergarten for children of his type, "superior" children, they called it. Part of each day, for months, we were together. We became friends. We became chums. The strained look left his eyes, his face won color. His self-confidence grew. He became a little boy, and forgot he had been a frightened little phantom. My husband spent an hour a day with him, to win his belated confidence. We made it a part of our life to create a unity, a circle, of the family.

But there was so much time for me, with nothing to do! I had not known days were so long. Our maid did the housework in our apartment. The children were at school. In the afternoons, I had my small son, but as he became well, he ran off to play with the children in the park. He left me to sit, waiting until he came back, on the benches of the park, with the elderly, stout, well-dressed widows, the watchful nursemaids and old gentlemen leaning on their canes.

One day, my older son said to his brother, "Come on out with the fellows, Broth!"

Without waiting for permission, they were gone. They spent all that Saturday morning out-of-doors, while I sat, inside, with a book in my hands.

The next afternoon, my little son said to me, in his solemn, quaintly old manner, "I'm going out to play with Broth, momsie. Now, you sit right here, till I come back, momsie."

"You like me to sit here and wait for you?" I asked, catching him before he could disappear through the door into the corridor.

"Yes," he said. "I like you to sit right here, and wait for me until I come back!"

It made me laugh out loud. I laughed because of the fine, masculine confidence that my little boy had, that which made him believe so much in me and in himself, that he could leave me behind, and yet be certain I would not forget him, would not desert him. *That* I had done.

Since I was free to do nothing now, if I wished, free, for the first time in my life, to play, too, I might join the little clubs that some of our acquaintances found interest in having, go to lectures, see the incomparable art exhibits, hear musicians and visitors from foreign shores who were swarming into New York and to the lecture platform.

I AM A WOMAN—AND A JEW

My cousin Simeon came to us one afternoon, bringing a wife and a daughter. His wife was almost ethereally beautiful—so dainty, so exquisite, that simply to shake her very slender hand made one fear that injury would be done it. Simeon was no longer the morose, sullen, unhappy young man I had known when we were both students here. His shoulders had broadened, his hair was slightly gray. But he kept his waist trim and slender, his face was as meticulously immaculate as a woman's—as his wife's. They were the real New Yorkers.

Their home was on Central Park West; Riverside Drive was for the "Hester Street Jews." They paid "$6,000 a year in rent" alone. There were two cars for the use of the family. A half dozen servants took charge of the housekeeping, and of their little daughter, when she was not at school. The child was dressed in that most expensive of juvenile extravagances, the simple hand-made frocks brought from Paris to Fifth Avenue. She looked like a tiny angel, with her heavy bronze curls cut short about a wee, oval face, her eyes like dark stars. She curtsied when I spoke to her; she sat very quietly while we elders conversed. I could not repress speaking of her delicate, gentle remoteness.

Her mother smiled, brown eyes sparkling in a sudden, unexpected emotion. She had kept her lovely face entirely blank hitherto, carefully blank, as if to say, "See if you can read anything in my face."

"She has that from the nuns," she told me. "They teach the children that repose. I loved it there when I was a little girl."

Simeon's daughter was a student at a girls' convent, where the daughters of wealthy Jewish parents were taught manners, knowledge, and—what else? Surely not Christianity, for Simeon was intensely Jewish.

His father had died. The business was his. He was free now to do, to be, whatever he wished. He sent his daughter to a Catholic convent school. But the exclusive clubs to which he belonged had Jewish members only; the friends whom he met and whom he sought were Jews. His wife, it appeared, had been educated with and by Christians. There had been no restrictions laid upon her as a Jewess. But she had married a Jew, her friends were among her own people.

"You are a Zionist?" I asked, as we spoke of a great meeting being held in Carnegie Hall that night.

Simeon laughed. "Guess not," he said. "I can't become excited by the Jewish question. I had enough of it when I was a boy." His face darkened.

And yet, his whole life, in New York, in his home, was as Jewish as if he lived in an enclosed Jewish state. The Cathedral of St. John the Divine was discussed, and when one day, at our home, one of the men on the committee there spoke of the tremendous response of the whole city to the request for funds, Simeon turned his handsome graying head, and asked, "In London?" very courteously, as one asks a stranger about his faith.

"In New York!" answered our friend. "You have read the *Times?*"

"Oh—I saw the picture—an etching—in the *Times*, but I put it aside," murmured Simeon. I understood —he had not even thought to read what there was to be heard about it, for it was the house of worship of another people, strangers to himself. It was not in his world.

His wife was interested in two things, and they made

her whole life, for the child was away at school except for holidays.. Her interests were her incomparable, exquisite beauty and the "Monday Club" to which she belonged. To the former she gave four mornings a week. To the latter she gave all the afternoons she had free from the theater or concerts. All her intellectual life came through the club, whose lecturers, readers, "discussers," presented to her that part of the world which she saw outside her personal life. She was generous, giving much to charity (Jewish), but she never saw the door of a charitable institution. When the city held a drive, or when a national organization sent out an appeal, Simeon always forwarded a check.

Once every year he went to synagogue, the orthodox synagogue, and prayed for his father's soul, as a son should, according to his father's faith. His wife, however, went every Sunday morning, in her pretty coupé, to services, alone. She went to the Christian Science Church.

Half of the women in her Monday Club were members of that Church. They came of Jewish background —every one. They, in no way, had social contact with the non-Jewish members, if one may so describe them, of the church. They had no wish for that contact.

Sometimes I used to think of my husband's relative, Cynthia, whom I had known. Her group had been non-Jewish. It had not the advantages of education, wealth, culture, that Simeon's wife and her friends had. But their lives were so much alike, in the end.

There was a difference, however. For one day, across the front pages of the newspapers appeared the name of a Jew, as part of a scandal perpetrated. I had promised to come early to the Monday Club, to "lead the discussion" that afternoon. I arrived, planning to put down my notes in the quiet of the living room. But the room was half full. The pretty, delicate faces, exotic, exquisite, were clustered like a bunch of flowers about the reading table. There was a break in the circle as I came in, and it closed about me. I saw what lay under the light of the reading lamp. There was the story in the morning newspaper.

"It's a disgrace," said Marion Brown, the young bride of the group. "If it weren't a Jew, they'd have published a two or three-line item in the inner page, or perhaps none at all!"

Simeon's wife put a narrow, lovely hand on the table. "That isn't the point," she said with a thoughtfulness strange to her. "A Jew should feel responsible not to get into such ugly things as this. The Leopold-Loeb story is there—too—all over the newspapers."

This from a Christian Scientist.

The afternoon's program could not get started. There came a rush of memories, of stories. Stories remembered from friends, from childhood. "One's a Jew." One may join the Christian Science Church, but the Gollas of one's people lies, invisible, upon one's shoulders, heavy.

I might have been sitting in the sunny Sisterhood committee room at the Temple, or in the somber study where my father met his friends. But I was looking through a window curtained in costly lace and satin. I looked out upon Central Park and saw, far off, a white figure on the brown Drive; I turned my glance back to a dozen or so figures which might have been taken from a Parisian fashion salon. And yet the same undertone shadowed the speech of the people dwelling in these three utterly different settings—the dark shadow of anti-Semitism.

What had this group of women, educated in convent schools, without Jewish religious training, with all their ties made by pleasure and culture, with their ethical doctrine that of a New England mystic, to do with two young Jewish perverts in Chicago? But their pretty faces were shadowed and sad as they lifted. "Jews can't afford such things to happen," said one.

They had refused to be interested when a Jewish playwright made a success in New York; they barely read the books on "Jewish questions" which always arouse the eager interest of other Jews. But now that the shadow fell, they felt it on their shoulders, too.

It was strange, because these women so seldom chose to allow sorrow to reach them. Even death they brushed aside with the smooth sentences of Christian Science, like a soft cushion to lean upon. But not this.

My own mother could not have looked more troubled than they, because two stranger boys, Jewish boys, had committed a crime.

"What," asked Simeon's wife of me, "did—what did your husband think of it, Leah?"

"Of their being Jews?" I asked.

"Oh, no," and she flushed. "Does he think they're abnormal—?"

"Judge M—— called last evening," I remembered. "They discussed the case. Yes, they did think the boys were abnormal. Perverts."

The face of Simeon's wife looked more fragile, more delicate. "I wish—I wish they weren't Jews," she said.

"I wish they weren't so bright," another woman

added, her plump, lovely face looking like a pale rose.

They spoke of that now. It was sad enough when the ignorant Jew did things; there was so much to excuse him, though. But these two boys were like themselves, they came of fine homes, and admirable parents. They had education, culture, exquisite social graces.

They had committed a crime not only against society, but against their people, too. They had placed a dark mark on the name of Judaism.

I tried to think of the two boys, adolescent, pampered, neurotic, seeking to gratify abnormal appetites. There were many boys like them that I had seen in our social work. They were not any more Jewish than insanity is Jewish. The Jewish group was no more responsible for them than the Christian group is responsible for Edgar Allan Poe, the drunkard, or for Oscar Wilde, also a sexual pervert.

That was what I tried to express to the little group of women.

"I suppose he is," said Simeon's wife, her small face shadowed. "But that won't make it easier for my little girl. I'm thinking of her. . . ."

I wanted to smile. Her little daughter was just eight, and a student in a sheltered convent school. She was, in her religion, a Christian Scientist. "Oh, but our name is Jewish," said Simeon's wife. "And, even if it weren't, don't you think every one knows Gloria is Jewish? My own name was Brown before I was married, Sylvia Brown, and mamma belonged to Science since I was a tot. But when the Dreyfus case came up, I remember how worried mamma was until they took up his side."

Perhaps Sylvia might fear that her child must be held responsible for the faults of any Jew who took the public's reprobation. But, I knew, my children were different. They never so much as thought of themselves as Jews—as they did not think of themselves as Christians. They were just *people.* Every one of them, too, in that way.

It was all, it seemed to me, in the way you saw this thing yourself.

I was not interested in it as a Jewish problem. To me life was not Jewish or non-Jewish; it was universal. When, later that year, a social service worker told me of an opening in a Jewish agency, I protested, "But I'm not interested in doing sectarian work, and Jewish work must be that. I've always done non-Sectarian work."

"In New York it's almost impossible for a Jew to obtain an executive job outside Jewish work."

After fifteen years, the same story was told.

"Of course, your husband is non-Jewish, and perhaps you might fit in with some agency that does Jewish work, and would be glad to have a worker—"

"I think not," I said. "My work is not Jewish. It's just—work," and the secretary laughed with me. "I suppose that, by analogy, I might, if I knew how, get a job in a beauty parlor to manicure Jewish fingernails?"

"Precisely," she smiled.

It did not seem to me, because I happened to have been born a Jewess, to be necessary to have interest in just one sort of people. As a matter of fact, Jewish social work is largely tied up with the rabbis, it must work with the synagogue; it requires a respect for Jewish observance. Obviously, I did not even remotely belong to it.

Jewish social work I would not do; non-Jewish social work I could not do. But the days were so long!

XXXII

I WAS thirty-five. My children did not need me, my husband was earning an income big enough now for our needs. Our needs were simple. I had no hunger for luxuries, for costly foods and clothes, such as Simeon required. My brother Simeon, stopping over on his way back from a trip to Europe, arrived with a chauffeur and a car he had taken there. He felt that I had sacrificed myself by "marrying a—not marrying Myer." I had forgotten such a person as Myer existed. But it appeared Myer was enormously successful. He had a suite of offices. He was married: "Married a poor girl, and she has four maids now to wait on her," Simeon told me. Myer was still "an atheist," but he "stuck close to his people." He, like the people at the Temple, had not been able to break away from the Jewish social group, and to find friends outside Jewish friends. Simeon wished me to understand, I understood, that I could have been free in my religion, and yet enjoyed the blessings of wealth, if I had but married one of my own people. What had I now? Only a "professor," who could not even provide me with a Cadillac! To send our children to good schools, buy their "nice clothes" and keep our modest home open and friendly to our circle, was just within our means.

"You look peaked," said Simeon, with real concern then. "Thin."

He left each of my children a horribly expensive gift, and me a silk scarf, to wear with a gown that I could never afford to own. But after he left, I looked at myself in the mirror. Simeon was big, ruddy, bald, middle-aged. And I? I was middle-aged, too. I was not "peaked"; I was, though he did not recognize it—"older."

I was thirty-eight. More than half my life had been lived. And I was doing nothing. I was fretting at the long days, bored with the long evenings. There was nothing for me to do now.

I went to my desk, and there, like an old friend, stood my old typewriter. I had rented it for $5 for the first three months, and then for $12 a year. Finally I had bought it, in installments, for $20.

I had written three books, and perhaps twenty or so articles and stories on it. I could not use it as my secretary had used hers, as a machine which did her bidding. It was my friend, with which I communed by way of two fingers—both of us together speaking. Its infirmities I respected. Did I not recall how, once, when the letter M broke off, I wrote a whole story, cutting out as many M's as possible, because I had to put those in by pen? I knew the way its little bell rang—and meant nothing, like the barking of a friendly little dog that cannot really bite. The bell rang, but the old machine was unable to stop at the line's end, as it warned. It squeezed another word in when I wished.

I could write now, as my husband wished, write and "be happy" in cloistered, sheltered years to come.

Books cannot be written just because one wishes. Besides, I did not feel that I understood myself, my own mind, now. When I was younger there were definite things I said "I believe," or "I do not believe."

Now I did not know. I had thought I did not believe in my people; but there was my cousin Simeon's wife —I had been stirred and touched more deeply than I thought by her assumption of the burden of the Chicago trial. I could not forget the *unity* she had felt with her people. I did not dismiss it now. I had not believed, once, that a woman could, by any reason, be asked to leave her chosen work to go back to taking care of home and children; yet when our little son needed some one to give him immediate and intimate care, it was not my husband, but I, who had at once given up a work built up to give that care to him. I no longer said "I believe," but "I wonder if—" I was getting middle-aged.

But there were other things to write than books. In the library a perusal of the magazines disclosed that articles, stories and interviews were the principal contents. The articles did not appear to be particularly difficult to do: most of then were interviews. Ten years ago they had been analyses of civic conditions and municipal government. This style was simple. It was just writing the individual story of a striking personality.

One newspaper in New York had been particularly kind to all my books, in reviews. I thought I'd go there first.

The editor was young, handsome, and friendly. "You're new to New York?" he asked. I told him of my work, of my experience, my books.

"You wouldn't fit in newspaper work," he smiled. "There isn't a chance in a hundred for a woman, anyhow, here. But why don't you try magazine writing? It pays, and this doesn't."

"How does one do magazine writing?" I asked.

"Go around and see some of the editors," he advised. "Why not try the women's magazines?"

I shook my head. "I'm not interested in cooking, sewing, fashions, or in how to raise babies," I said. "If I write, I want it to be—well, just as a man would. I don't want to be committed to a 'feminine slant.'"

"Suppose you do a piece for me, some time," he said. He pointed out to me his three requirements: "News value, human interest—and brevity."

He discussed briefly what would interest them, and said, "Come in again." I wrote him the article we discussed, and he asked me for a second one. For two weeks' work I received $50, in each instance, from him.

I felt as if I had pushed a door open a little way. I did not know how to begin with the magazines. I wanted to know how "folks got their things into magazines." I had written before, as something outside daily living. The money I earned was, each time, a windfall.

My old editors were, I found, when I wrote to the three magazines I knew, gone. One was out West, one had left the magazine field, the other had gone into the moving picture business as a scenario editor. There were other things that one could do, then, besides writing!

But I did not know how to begin. I had gotten out of the quiet mood in which I could write before. I was not able to capture it again. I used to write gentle stories, from a girl's heart. I was a woman now. I sat down, wrote for two months, retyped my manuscript and sent it in a sealed envelope to one man who always remained apart from every editor I would ever know, my "first editor." In a week a letter came from him, preceded by a telegram. He could not use my story himself, but he told me who could, and I sent my story there. It was one of the "starred" stories of that year.

I went to a magazine editor and asked to see him. And, curiously, there was no red tape. It was easy to see magazine editors, where it had been like passing a rampart to get to the newspaper editors. We talked, and I found that all the years of my work were a mine on which I could draw, that I had been living through all these years, that I might build up a treasure from which I could draw my writing.

I received my first assignment, and another. I found other editors glad to have my work. At the end of the first year, I had earned three thousand dollars, as much as in the years I did social work. I earned it so easily! And it seemed criminal to have been so successful, for I was so happy in this work. I was happy in my work and in my home.

I had been living in a staid world where I did my duty. I made new friends, of an entirely new kind, in New York, through my writing.

Here was a new world where I did what was my pleasure, and it paid not only in terms of ordinary wages, but in a new color, a glamor, to life. I had thought of myself as—yes, definitely middle-aged. I had thought of myself as a woman whose life belonged to her children's future.

To my new friends I was not old. I was not staid and rather shy, but simply afraid to live, to taste life.

If anyone had told me, when I was nineteen, that at thirty-eight a man would—well, flirt with me, a married woman—I would have thought that person either insane or so insulting that I could not stop to listen. As I grow older, I read the novels of H. G. Wells, of

W. L. George, of the whole new school of English writers—and I smiled.

Of course, there were women who sought "the new freedom," in terms of sex. There had been my friend Cora. There was one girl on my staff who became the mistress of the fat little man who had sponsored our little theatre movement in my center.

But women like myself did not touch such aspects of life.

And I met young Harley, I shall call him. My husband and I met him together at a dinner to which we had gone, a very staid dinner given by a member of my husband's staff. Except to our host, Harley was a stranger there. He sat next to me. He hardly spoke all evening to my husband, and that embarrassed me, for I do not speak readily to strangers. I could only listen. My husband's blue eyes, meeting mine every now and then, lifted slightly in amusement. He saw I was embarrassed. This young man Harley spoke so vehemently. He spoke even violently. He drew the attention of the whole table to himself, and to me consequently. I could only blush.

As soon as we left the table, he followed me, cornered me, in fact. "Rum crowd," he said, looking around and sitting down.

I was too new to New York, and to my small success in it to feel it was a rum crowd. There was an editor there; there was the head of a social service organization; there were two extraordinarily pretty women, one of them an artist. There was my husband. I glanced at the group scattered, and my glance must have spoken for me, for Harley said, "Bunch of water-colors."

It developed he was an artist. Sometimes he wrote.

At present he was connected with a magazine. I told him that I was writing, too.

He frowned. "You write?" He looked as if he had tasted something acid.

"Lots," I answered, and because he waited, I told him. I had just come from across the continent, where I had been sent to get a "story." I was planning to go away again, on a real assignment, something that two men had wanted to do, but for which I had been chosen.

"You do that kind of truck?" asked Harley.

"Worse," I said, now really amused. I told him of a great financier with whom an interview of mine had been published, as a great scoop, under his own name. "I did that. I wrote it and he signed it."

"Shadow writing, eh?" he said, using a graphic phrase to describe it.

"I suppose you can write the financial page in a newspaper?" he asked.

"I have written financial articles," I said, hugely amused.

He leaned forward, and said, "Well, it's a damn shame. You're too pretty to do rot like that."

One may be thirty-eight, the mother of a nearly grown daughter and the acknowledged modern woman. But it is pleasant to be told one is "too pretty" to be whatever one is proud of doing. I laughed, but I was not unhappy. From across the room, my husband's eyes smiled to mine, and I felt like crying out to him, "Come here. Do come here and listen."

Harley took us home in his battered old automobile that looked more as if it belonged to a farmer in the country than to an editor in New York. "See you again," he said, as he tooted his horn and creaked away.

My husband lifted my chin and kissed me. "The artist is smitten," he said.

This was unusual, for we had become too staid for such interchanges, but I laughed with pleasure. It was pleasant to have my husband see me so.

Harley, however, kept his word. He came to see us within a week, and thereafter he came often. He had a curious sort of way that was familiar, and yet not impertinent. My husband liked him. "You're so dreadfully Biblical," he said to me. "A real Jewish wife!" I *was* startled!

His own crowd was made up of newspaper writers, a few editors of small magazines, some writers, one cartoonist who was a neighbor and a number of singers and actors. Many of these people were Jews. The old group which I had, long ago, met in the New York Bohemia seemed to be not only gone, but even forgotten by the new writers, dramatists, painters, who had succeeded. Even Frank Harris, whom once my Irish friend had taken me to see, was no longer the great god. Dreiser, who, I had heard, was his successor, was also in the twilight. Most of the people who were "doing things" were Jews. The larger number whom I saw were Jews of European parentage or birth. If New York was the intellectual and cultural center of the United States—as it was no doubt, just that—then the European Jew was the hub of that center. It was he who wrote the plays which the country saw, who produced them and who acted in them. He wrote the jazz music and played it. He conceived the books which thoughtful Americans read, and he published those books.

They were frankly Jewish. They had Jewish names, Jewish faces and the psychology of the Jew. Many times their work carried a distinct flavor, a definite color, from the particular Ghetto in which their parents had been born in Europe. But they were, themselves, as indissolubly part of New York as is Alfred A. Smith. They were not typical of the country; they were New Yorkers, and they were Jews. They would have been wretched elsewhere; New York was their natural land. They were the true cosmopolites. They married non-Jews from Kansas, Iowa or New England, or even Virginia—and, while remaining intensely Jewish, they never felt the slightest division, therefore, between their wives or husbands and themselves. That was because their whole lives were expressed in terms of art—and that is cosmopolitan.

It was only I, the daughter of a rabbinical background, seeking to discover a doctrine by which to live, who had needed an answer to the query—by what rule shall I live? They said, "Just live."

I had heard that New York was a Sodom and Gomorrah, a sink of iniquity. But I was too long a social worker to be carried away by the outer clothing of "sin." The same unconventionalities, infidelities, needs and lusts existed in the slums of little cities and in the outer (and even the inner, respectable) streets of small towns I had known. The women I met were younger, or older: they seemed to be more vivid than those I knew elsewhere. But one soon finds that in a great universe like New York that vividness is necessary if one is to be distinguished—as brilliant color is necessary in tropical richness. Part of my work was to "interview" writers, singers, statesmen, business men. It was an education in humanity.

I found that folks were pretty much the same. The only aspect which made New York striking was the accepted power of the Jew intellectually.

All along, the Jew had said that those who heaped hatred on him did so because there were only two kinds of Jew known—the one who made money and the one who needed it; that the intellectual Jew is the aristocrat. In New York the intellectual Jew made of the city his kingdom. Once, as I sat waiting for a chat with him while another writer showed his material for an article, an editor (a Jew) suddenly threw up his hands and said, in an exaggerated accent, "My stars, isn't there an honest-to-God Gentile we can quote once in this story?" Every one of the authorities quoted, it appeared, was a Jew. "But there aren't any men of the same standing—who aren't Jews," protested the writer. "Well, give them a boost—pick out some one who's a lesser star," advised the editor, folding the manuscript. "Bring a picture of that Gentile, too!"

After a performance in which a distinguished English actor had appeared, I went with my host "back stage" where he wished to speak to the leading lady; and we met there the producer of the play, a Russian Jew with a decided accent. He had resuscitated the medieval atmosphere of the Church for the stage, had spun out a lovely web of Christian faith and was just preparing to carry it to the Middle West. For the Jew in New York was not the intellectual king in his city alone: he made the thought of the country.

A young East Side Jew was the leading American humorist, succeeding Artemus Ward, I found. He wrote the dialect of the Jewish Ghetto in New York. A Middle Western Jew wrote the sophisticated comedies for the stage. An elderly New York Jew was writing the most highly spiced sex plays. In moving pictures the Jew was almost the one power.

These Jews did not feel it necessary to do what, long ago, my teacher of English had said I ought to do, if ever I became a writer: utter the thought and voice of the Jewish people. They spoke as artists. They were conscious of themselves as artists first, Jews after that.

I admired them. Even Harley, who could paint delicate pastels that looked like dream memories, was a Jew, it developed. "Hurvitz," he said, introducing his brother. "Called myself Harley," he explained, "when I went into advertising." In advertising and in business, in New York, the Jew fared badly, it appeared. But as an artist, a teacher, a writer, he held leadership. "Because Americans don't know how yet," said Harley. "Wait until they learn!"

"Are you so Semitic?" I asked, for he was usually so gay and thoughtless that he seemed like thistledown blowing, and the Jew is somber, even as a jester. He is, at the most, a jester with eyes holding tears.

"I'm not," said Harley. "But the other folks are anti-Semitic."

"Oh, not in New York!" I answered. "Not among writers and educators."

"You'll see," he said.

But I only laughed at this odd turn in him. Had I not seen for myself? That spring I received a most lovely letter from a school near by, telling me that one of my articles had been used as "text" in the class, that one of my books was now being read, and asking me to speak to the students. The girls were intelligent —evidently coming from good homes—intelligent and not wealth-proud.

I AM A WOMAN—AND A JEW

When, late that summer, my husband and I decided that we wished our daughter to spend a year at a boarding school, I wrote to the school, which I had liked for its quiet simplicity, and the gentle scholarly dean in charge. A most charming letter came from the dean, in which she not only told us how glad she would be to have her, but added that she knew my name from some of my "published materials," and that she was delighted to have my daughter.

"You're getting famous," said my husband. But I liked it! I knew I was not "getting famous," but my work was good, it was not work of which I would be ashamed later. Even the newspaper articles were written with meticulous care, and my magazine stories I worked over as carefully as if they were to go into a book. Did not one do that with work one loved?

I went with Little Maid to register her. And as we sat in the office of the pleasant schoolhouse I learned something I had not known before.

The dean was as charming to meet again as she had been in her letter. She questioned my daughter and was obviously pleased with her. She gave me, presently, the application blank to fill out. I wrote her name, birth date and then paused at a space after "Religious affiliation?" We belonged to no church, and so I wrote: "Father, Gentile; Mother, Jewess."

Our daughter was not admitted to the college. There was a "quota" of Jews allowed, and the quota had been filled the June before, it appeared.

I was bewildered and angry. But I would not have had my daughter live only as the daughter of her father. That Jewish heritage I bring her must be hers, too. She must know it and realize it, I told myself, as I rose, bowed and went out.

I remembered something then, as if it had come from a long way back: "But this is impossible." I could hear Father John's voice saying it, and then my father's. But surely this was impossible.

Outdoors, the sunshine on the bright grass seemed suddenly to blur into a sparkling blanket of separate, crystal-topped blades. There were, I was ashamed to realize, tears in my eyes.

I forced them back and walked beside my daughter to our taxicab.

She spoke to me of it, on our way back home, in the taxi.

"You were angry, momsie," she began.

I was too angry to speak. But I recalled the whole interview, the friendliness of the registrar, the politeness of the dean, the pleasant chat in the office and then this query.

"The name?"

My daughter has for her middle name my grandmother's name. "Biblical," she smiled in appreciation.

"She is named after my mother," I answered.

I liked the quiet of the school, its simplicity of outlook, its sound scholastic training, given with respect for the young woman's personality. I looked at my daughter, sweet and thoughtful in her tailored suit, her eyes wide under her straw hat. She did not look like her father, but like my people, and yet she did not "look Jewish." Why I could not tell.

"You'll fill out the registration slip?" And then I saw the query, "Religious affiliations?"

"We have none," I answered.

The dean smiled. Most of the young people who came here were of "liberal" parents; it was only a matter of form, of routine. I wrote, "Father, Gentile;

Mother Jewess." How strange the classification appeared after my name! If I had written, "Mother, dark-eyed; mother, social worker; mother, professional woman; mother, writer; mother, professional executive," I would have recognized myself. That was how I had thought of myself now. But—Jewess. I had forgotten I was a Jewess. In a vivid sort of flash, I saw my mother's eyes, radiant and lovely, lifted to my father as he stood before the Sabbath loaves, invoking the blessing. I had not seen my mother for almost two years. Even there, my contact had so thinned.

"Jewess?" repeated the dean.

I smiled. "My father was a cantor and a rabbinical assistant. I had really forgotten about it! But, by birth, of course, I'm a Jewess."

The dean was smiling awkwardly, flushing. She stammered. "This is most unfortunate—er—most unfortunate—. Er—perhaps Dr. Ellison—"

Dr. Ellison was president of the institution. But what had he to do here? My daughter had passed with really admirable grades. She was not a brilliant student, but she had all the qualities I knew this school wanted—health, cleanliness of outlook, a cultivated home background and sound all-round athletic and intellectual abilities.

"We have so few Jews," said the dean at last. "Oh, we do have them!" she interrupted, hastily. "Some of our finest girls—most clever, most clever—are Jewish girls. We do have Hebrew students! But—er—we have been speaking of this—we have more now than we had planned—we cannot—if you please, do let me call in Dr. Ellison—"

They had a quota here, a quota of Jewish students, just as they did in Russia. My great-uncle had been a physician, but he had been the one Jewish student in the whole province admitted to the college. My daughter, almost a whole century later, in the United States of America, came with the name of a Gentile father, and because her mother was a Jewess, she, too, was to be allowed in, or squeezed out—by a quota that decided how many "Jews" could receive an education.

It was funny.

I lifted up the blank, tore it in two and put the pieces in my purse.

"Do come to call on us," I reminded the dean, as we went to go. "We shall be happy to have you." I could hardly keep my lips firm, but I was proud to have been able to say that.

In the taxi, though, I did not feel so firm. I looked into the gray eyes of my daughter.

"Did it make you unhappy?" I asked her, as quietly as I could.

"The Jewish part?" she said. "Why, no, momsie. You see, some of the girls at school before knew I was partly Jewish, too. If it mattered to them, I just dropped them, that's all."

"There were some it mattered to?" I asked, with a fierceness I could not hold back. Had she been made unhappy, even while in prep school?

Little Maid laughed. "Oh, not the kind I cared about," she answered. "I didn't care about making the sororities, and my crowd just thought it was sort of romantic that, well, that I had a Jewish mother, momsie."

Our eyes met. I wanted to smile, but there was a lump in my throat. "*I* am the 'romantic Jewish strain,'" I said to myself. The real blood, the daily strain—that was the Gentile. Was I already being put into the dimmer halo of the past when I would be described: "We had a Jewish grandmother . . ." by my children's children?

My daughter's children would say it to their children with a sort of pride in the exotic strain.

But she would not do it, I told myself, with a sweep of feeling I had not expected to feel before.

She would not brush aside the Jewish strain—as if it were stranger to her. My children were Jewish, as well as Gentile. They were mine. They belonged to my people.

The word struck me. "My people."

But, of course.

They shall not be ashamed of my people. They shall know the glory and the pride of being a Jew. They may know the misery and the handicaps, too. That was part of it. They shall not be ashamed of my people and deny them.

I entered Little Maid in a school where, before she came, she was described as "of part Jewish ancestry," and that was explained and made definite by my parenthetical explanation: "mother a Jewess." My husband laughed as I wrote it, and said, "Do you think it is necessary? Why say it, if they do not care to know?" He put his hand on my hair and brushed it back. "Is it because you want Little Maid to know?" he added. And, of course, that was why I had done it.

And my son, what did he think? He was as old now as I when first I met my friend Rose, and we discussed the differences of Christianity and Judaism. I called him to me one day, and we took one of the long hikes he loves, "alone together," just he and I. We tramped over the rocky paths of the Palisades, stopped to drink soda water and to buy pretzels and nut-nougat in sticky paper wrappings, talked to the man who had the little booth, my boy discussing with him the merits of fishing tackle and the qualities that singled out Babe Ruth for particular worship. "But he's practically a dumb-bell, anyhow, I bet," said my son, the intellectual snob, nodding his bright brown head. "Our teacher said he wasn't much more than a moron. The idea is to do this ball-playing yourself." I wanted to smile, and repressed my mirth by an effort. Just so gravely would I, too, have discussed the gods of my time and cast them down for my authorities, when I was the "little Polak."

"Ruth a dumb-bell?" asked the soda-water man, appalled. "Why, he hit twenty balls in one—"

My son and he discoursed upon the subject, while I, a mere female, stood respectfully by. Had I not learned, when I was a girl, to listen silently while men spoke?

But, coming back, the topic was reopened for me. "Our teacher—he's the man that was quarter-back at Dartmouth, momsie, he told us Babe Ruth is all right, he's a good batter, but that's not what a fellow wants to be, he wants to bat with his—his arms—I mean his bat, but there's his brains—." My son looked at me beseechingly, and said, "He's not a sissy, momsie," bespeaking my understanding for the teacher who had taught him that character and mind counted more than skill, even in sports. "He's six feet one, momsie." I gravely acknowledged that I understood.

He spoke, then, to me of the friends he had at school, answering my queries about those I knew through acquaintanceship made in our home. "And Don, where's he?" I asked.

Brother's eyes, as big and brilliant as pansies,

seemed to withdraw from me. "Oh, he's around the school."

Don and he had been so thick that I felt the undescribed break the short sentence expressed, and I asked, "Did you have a quarrel, Brother?"

My son shook his head. But I asked further, "What was the quarrel about?" My boy was so sunny and so happy that a serious quarrel with his closest chum seemed improbable. I knew that, sometimes, these boyish breaks can be healed by a wise move made by "momsie," who invited the lost friend to lunch, or to matinée, with her own boy. Brother had always accepted my assistance loftily, almost as if pained, but he and Don had both been overjoyed to have me intervene. Sometimes, it was Don's mother who intervened. Don's mother was the wife of a merchant, living in a suburb near our city, a fine, intelligent and gentle woman of forty-five, who adored her baby, the one boy among six children. She and I had both been glad to have the boys make friends because their temperaments—her boy slow and thoughtful, mine vivid, passionate—blended and supplemented one another.

Brother looked aside now, though, and did not reply. "What happened?" I asked. "Was it a real, never-to-be-forgiven insult?" I smiled then.

"It was nothing much," my boy answered. "Just that he said—we're reading Ivanhoe—he said the Jews are such rotters, it was a good thing Rowena got the best of it." He stared out over the Palisades, his square little shoulders straight. "He said it in class, and I got up and said I thought Rowena was a kind of a dub, she was a dumb-bell, and Rebecca, she was—she's—well, our teacher even said she's great."

I felt the strangest hurt. Suddenly, over my years,

I heard my father's voice saying, in another tongue, "This is my people—"

"Was it because you're—because I'm a Jewess—that you think that?"

My son's face colored. He looked up quickly, and said, speaking with a curious intensity, "Oh, I'm not a Jew, momsie! My gosh, I'm not a Jew, only I can't let the fellows say anything about them, now can I?"

I wanted to laugh, to put my hand on his shoulders. But I did not. I said, instead, very quietly, "Do any of the fellows—what do they think you are? Do they ask you?"

He looked at me directly, as he answered, "Oh, a lot of them go to church, you know, all the kinds there are, I guess. Some of the—Jews," and the color came to his face again, "they go to Ethical Culture. Now, we don't go to anything—"

"What do you say you are when they ask you?" I asked then. "Do they ask you?" I did not say, Did Don ask you? But I understood now.

"Oh, they're not fellows like that!" he answered. "But I, well, I tell them by race I'm French and English and Russian, I'm kind of mixup—"

I lifted his chin, then, and said, "And aren't you Jewish, too?"

His big eyes grew stormy; they became dark, as they do when he is angry. "Not much," he answered. "I'm not—that way, momsie. I know the Jewish fellows in the school. I'm not—I'm different."

"Yes, perhaps," I answered. "Different. But you belong to them, too, just as you do to the French and the English—and not to the Russian. My people," and I wondered as the words came so, "lived in Russia, but they are not Russian. I can look back five generations and name each man and woman who stood behind me—and you, my son—and they were Jews. Why should you—why would you want to deny that? You're going on to big manhood soon—if you were a Jew, you'd have taken the oath of allegience—confirmation they call it—to my people this coming year. You would have pledged yourself to the Jewish people, to be one of them—"

"Momsie," said my son then, his voice curiously frightened, "please don't talk that way!"

I looked at him, his rosy face, his clear eyes. They were my mother's eyes, big, brilliant, full of vivid dreams. They were frightened, because I was pointing out to him my part in his heritage. A strange hurt stabbed me.

"You must not feel that it's a disgrace to have the Jewish part of you," I said, trying to speak carefully, so that he would not be offended, driven into inimical misunderstanding. "There have been such great men who were Jews—Disraeli, Mendelssohn, Lord Palgrave (the man that put together the Golden Treasury, he's a Jew, son), they're all Jews, or partly Jews—"

From across many years, came to me a memory, and I wanted to smile, I would have smiled at myself, if my lips had not been trying so hard to seem quiet and natural in their even speech. For had I, I myself, not always laughed at the Jew who asked honor from the Jews of the past, those who had brought honor to the name of our people?

But now I knew that what they had done, what every Jew is and does, is something which must, indeed, belong to his people; that no other people living have our peculiar quality, which is not individual, but racial, and which gives to each of us who accomplishes with genius, the ability to express through himself only the accumulated genius of his race, so that every Jewish writer, statesman, actor, is not only himself, but the mirror of his people, the voice of his people.

I did not feel part of the Jewish State. I did not need it. But the Jewish nation does not need the boundaries of a land, it does not require the frontier of a physical country. Each of us carries the boundaries, the acknowledgment of its sovereignty, in our hearts, in our blood. The way our eyes see life, our minds thought, we discover through our Jewishness. Those who spoke with genius and who came from us—spoke for us. We may, in truth, point to them with pride, with intimate possession.

My own self I gave to my husband in marriage, and it meant happiness to me. But within me was something that I could give to no one—that belonged to my people. It was not traditional patriotism; that went to my country. It was not piety; that I had not. It did not ask for a place in my heart: it lived there. It was myself, Jewess. It was what I had passed on to my children. That I wanted them to know, and to find a glory in knowing.

My country I have often seen wrong, yet I have followed her in her mistakes, followed her mistaken leaders. That was because I am a citizen, and so one of the great family of her sons and daughters, who must stand by the mother land whether she be right or wrong. As a Jewess, I had found a creed not mine to believe, and I had put it aside, but I had not been able to put my Jewishness aside. That was because of the essential differences between the American citizen and the Jew, both of which met in me. The citizen chose his country, with reason, with love. But the Jew in me could, by no choice, no reasoning, elect to be anything but a Jew: that was part of the life which poured through my veins; it had come to me in my mother's womb, before I had thought, before I had being.

And that was what all we, who are Jews, "part Jews" or "all Jews," share. We can be, in American life, try as we will, not Austrians, not Galicians, not Spaniards, amalgamated into the product that makes "American"—not anything but Jews. For all these racial strata in the United States are different from one another, but we Jews are alike. We have the same intensities, the sensitiveness, poetry, bitterness, sorrow, the same humor, the same memories. The memories are not those we can bring forth from our minds: they are centuries old and are written in our features, in the cells of our brain.

I had found that the Jew met handicaps in business, in professions. I had discovered that, even in the education of his children, he is held apart. In my love, alone, there is no marking line of Jew and Gentile, in my love and in my children. But my children did mark that line—they marked it and were preparing to stand on the strangers' side. I meant to see that they shall feel glad, proud and glad, to stand on my side.

Yes, as my father said, "with our people." My husband is tenderly amused; he is an individualist and feels one is not, ever, part of a group. One is one's self. But not when one is a Jew. Did he not love in me that which was Jewish in me, has not all that he finds in me come from my people? "Rebecca and the student," he once said, gently to me, describing us, and I did not wish it to be so. But now I know it was true. He loved the Jewess, I the scholar and the student.

Our children must honor his gift to them—but mine, too. I made that resolution.

I wanted my children to know they belong to my people. Thereafter, I meant to send the children to my folks for part of each summer, if only a week. I meant that they should read the history of the Jews and know it. I meant, too, that they should know the literature of the Jews.

I did not mean to make them Jews. I have not sent them to a Jewish synagogue. Their creed must be their own, just as their work, their love later, is to be their own, and not their father's or mine. I do not plan that they should feel that they are forced into the narrowed circle of Jewish people. They are attending schools where their friends find in common with them the play life and the study life of children. But at home, with me, they know that the Jew exists as a definite part of the world—past, and present, too.

Their father has put up a spruce tree for them each Christmas, as a remembrance of his childhood. They have Easter eggs to color each spring. But now they are taught, too, the story of Judas Maccabeus, and they see the candles lighted. They come with me to the Day of Atonement and hear the sacred songs; they spent one Passover with Simeon to see the solemn service observed.

I do not believe ritual makes any religion. I do not teach my children a religion. But the rituals of a creed like ours are the glamorous shrouds of its history, its psychology. That I wish my children to understand—and to realize as part of the poetry, the meaning, of their own lives.

Their lives are their own to direct, to make, of course. But I should be proud, yes, to have it said, "This man and this woman, children of Leah Morton, were great among men, and their mother was a Jewess."

I am a Jewess, though I do not belong to any church, nor have my world enclosed among my people. The divisions are in my memories, in my heart.

Last winter I sat at the table of a famous governor, discussing with him a national crisis that I was sent to write about.

We touched, unexpectedly, an international angle of it and I said, "Do you think that will be hard on us Jews?"

He told me startled, he had not thought me a Jewess. I answered, "*I* know I am." I am that before everything. Perhaps not in my work or in my daily life. But in that inner self that cannot change, I belong to my people. My life is only a tiny atom of their long history.

THE END